D0571157

Collect **British** *Stamps*

A Stanley Gibbons checklist
of the stamps of Great Britain

Collect **British** *Stamps*

62nd Edition
2011

Stanley Gibbons Limited
London and Ringwood

By Appointment to Her Majesty The Queen
Stanley Gibbons Ltd, London
Philatelists

Published by Stanley Gibbons Ltd
Editorial, Publications Sales Offices
and Distribution Centre:
7 Parkside, Christchurch Road, Ringwood,
Hants BH24 3SH

© Stanley Gibbons Ltd 2011

Copyright Notice

The contents of this Catalogue, including
the numbering system and illustrations, are
fully protected by copyright. No part of this
publication may be reproduced, stored in a
retrieval system, or transmitted in any form
or by any means, electronic, mechanical,
photocopying, recording or otherwise, without
the prior permission of Stanley Gibbons
Limited. Requests for such permission should
be addressed to the Catalogue Editor. This
Catalogue is sold on condition that it is not,
by way of trade or otherwise, lent, re-sold,
hired out, circulated or otherwise disposed
of other than in its complete, original and
unaltered form and without a similar condition
including this condition being imposed on the
subsequent purchaser.

British Library Cataloguing in
Publication Data.
A catalogue record for this book is available
from the British Library.

Errors and omissions excepted. The colour
reproduction of stamps is only as accurate as
the printing process will allow.

ISBN-10: 0-85259-781-9
ISBN-13: 978-0-85259-781-1

Item No. R0289-11

Printed by Sterling, England

Contents

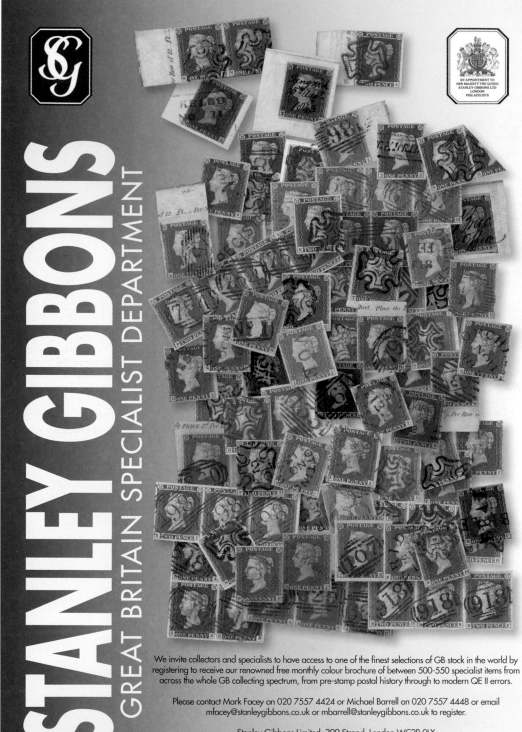

STANLEY GIBBONS

GREAT BRITAIN SPECIALIST DEPARTMENT

We invite collectors and specialists to have access to one of the finest selections of GB stock in the world by registering to receive our renowned free monthly colour brochure of between 500-550 specialist items from across the whole GB collecting spectrum, from pre-stamp postal history through to modern QE II errors.

Please contact Mark Facey on 020 7557 4424 or Michael Barrell on 020 7557 4448 or email mfacey@stanleygibbons.co.uk or mbarrell@stanleygibbons.co.uk to register.

Stanley Gibbons Limited, 399 Strand, London WC2R 0LX
Tel: 020 7836 8444   Fax: 020 7836 7342
To view all our stock 24 hours a day visit www.stanleygibbons.com

The 2011 Edition

COLLECT BRITISH STAMPS has been the standard guide for collectors of Great Britain ever since the first edition was published in September 1967.

It provides a straightforward, easy-to-use work of reference, with every stamp design illustrated in colour and clear, uncomplicated listings ideally suited to the newer collector, while at the same time providing a handy checklist for the more advanced philatelist – small wonder that over four million copies have been sold to collectors around the world.

Collect British Stamps appears in the autumn of each year: for a more detailed listing, the *Great Britain Concise Catalogue* is published in the spring incorporating many additional features and is ideal for the collector who needs more information about GB stamps. An at-a-glance guide to the Stanley Gibbons' Catalogues can be found on page xlvi.

Scope. Collect British Stamps comprises:

- All stamps with different watermark (wmk) or perforation (perf).
- Visible plate numbers on the Victorian issues.
- Graphite-lined and phosphor issues, including variations in the numbers of phosphor bands.
- First Day Covers for Definitives from 1936, Regionals and all Special Issues.
- Presentation, Gift and Souvenir Packs.
- Post Office Yearbooks.
- Regional issues and War Occupation stamps of Guernsey and Jersey.
- Postage Due and Official Stamps.
- Post Office Picture Cards (PHQ cards).
- Commemorative gutter pairs and 'Traffic Light' gutter pairs listed as mint sets.
- Royal Mail Postage Labels priced as sets and on P.O. First Day Cover.
- The introduction includes a full design index for commemorative issues, a Great Britain collector's glossary and articles giving helpful advice on a range of collecting topics

Stamps of the independent postal administrations of Guernsey, Isle of Man and Jersey are contained in *Collect Channel Islands and Isle of Man Stamps*.

New for this edition

- A thorough review of all prices has been carried out, with a number of increases since the 2010 edition
- Issues for 2011 have been added and the listings of earlier issues carefully checked and updated
- An article by Frank Brench, previously published in *Gibbons Stamp Monthly* in 1986, introduces the stamps of King George V. All *Gibbons Stamp Monthly* articles, from 1890 to 2009, are now available to collectors in the *Gibbons Stamp Monthly Archive*, available from Stanley Gibbons.

Layout

Stamps are set out chronologically by date of issue. In the catalogue lists the first numeral is the Stanley Gibbons catalogue number; the black (boldface) numeral alongside is the type number referring to the respective illustration. A blank in this column implies that the number immediately above is repeated. The denomination and colour of the stamp are then shown. Before February 1971 British currency was:

£1 = 20s   One pound = twenty shillings and

1s = 12d   One shilling = twelve pence.

Upon decimalisation this became:

£1 = 100p   One pound = one hundred (new) pence.

The catalogue list then shows two price columns. The left-hand is for unused stamps and the right-hand for used. Corresponding small boxes are provided in which collectors may wish to check off the items in their collection. Our method of indicating prices is: Numerals for pence, e.g. 10 denotes 10p (10 pence). Numerals for pounds and pence, e.g. 4·25 denotes £4·25 (4 pounds and 25 pence). For £100 and above, prices are in whole pounds and so include the £ sign and omit the zeros for pence.

Colour illustrations

The colour illustrations of stamps are intended as a guide only; they may differ in shade from the originals.

Size of illustrations

To comply with Post Office regulations stamp illustrations are three-quarters linear size. Separate illustrations of surcharges, overprints and watermarks are actual size.

Prices

Prices quoted in this catalogue are our selling prices at the time the book went to press. They are for stamps in fine condition; in issues where condition varies we may ask more for the superb and less for the sub-standard. The unused prices for stamps of Queen Victoria to King George V are for lightly hinged examples. Unused prices for King Edward VIII to Queen Elizabeth II are for unmounted mint (though when not available unmounted, mounted stamps are often supplied at a lower price). Prices for used stamps refer to fine postally used copies. All prices are subject to change without prior notice and we give no guarantee to supply all stamps priced, since it is not possible to keep every catalogued item in stock. Individual low value stamps sold at 399, Strand are liable to an additional handling charge. Commemorative issues may only be available in complete sets.

In the price columns:

† = Does not exist.

(—) or blank = Exists, or may exist, but price cannot be quoted.

* = Not normally issued (the so-called 'Abnormals' of 1862–80).

Perforations

The 'perforation' is the number of holes in a length of 2 cm, as measured by the Gibbons Instanta gauge. The stamp is viewed against a dark background with the transparent gauge put on top of it. Perforations are quoted to the nearest half. Stamps without perforation are termed 'imperforate'. From 1992 certain stamps occur with a large elliptical (oval) hole inserted in each line of vertical perforations. The £10 definitive, No. 1658, is unique in having two such holes in the horizontal perforations.

Elliptical perforations

Se-tenant combinations

Se-tenant means 'joined together'. Some sets include stamps of different design arranged se-tenant as blocks or strips and these are often collected unsevered as issued. Where such combinations exist the stamps are priced both mint and used, as singles or complete sets. The set price refers to the unsevered combination plus singles of any other values in the set.

First day covers

Prices for first day covers are for complete sets used on plain covers (Nos. 430/8, 453/60, 462/78b, 485/90, and 503/12) or on special covers (Nos. 461, 479/84, 491/502 and 513 onwards), the stamps of which are cancelled with ordinary operational postmarks (1924–1962) or by the standard 'First Day of Issue' postmarks (1963 onwards). The British Post Office did not provide 'First Day' treatment for every definitive issued after 1963. Where the stamps in a set were issued on different days, prices are for a cover from each day.

Presentation Packs

Special packs comprising slip-in cards with printed information inside a protective covering, were introduced for the 1964 Shakespeare issue. Collectors packs, containing commemoratives from the preceding twelve months, were issued from 1967. Some packs with text in German from 1968–69, exist as does a Japanese version of the pack for Nos. 916/17. Yearbooks, hardbound and illustrated in colour within a slip cover, joined the product range in 1984.

PHQ cards

Since 1973 the Post Office has produced a series of picture cards, which can be sent through the post as postcards. Each card shows an enlarged colour reproduction of a current British stamp, either of one or more values from a set or of all values. Cards are priced here in fine mint condition for sets complete as issued. The Post Office gives each card a 'PHQ' serial number, hence the term. The cards are usually on sale shortly before the date of issue of the stamps, but there is no officially designated 'first day'. Used prices are for cards franked with the stamp depicted, on the obverse or reverse; the stamp being cancelled with an official postmark for first day of issue. For 1973–76 issues cards with stamps on the obverse are worth about 25% more than the prices quoted.

Gutter pair

Gutter pairs

Almost all modern Great Britain commemoratives are produced in sheets containing two panes of stamps separated by a blank horizontal or vertical margin known as a gutter. This feature first made its appearance on some supplies of the 1972 Royal Silver Wedding 3p, and marked the introduction of Harrison & Sons' new 'Jumelle' stamp-printing press. There are advantages for both the printer and the Post Office in such a layout which has now been used for almost all commemorative issues since 1974. The term 'gutter pair' is used for a pair of stamps separated by part of the blank gutter margin. We do not list gutter pairs for self-adhesive stamps since, although the production format is the same, the stamps are separated by die-cutting.

Most printers include some form of colour check device on the sheet margins, in addition to the cylinder or plate numbers. Harrison & Sons used round 'dabs' or spots of colour, resembling traffic lights. For the period from the 1972 Royal Silver Wedding until the end of 1979 these colour dabs appeared in the gutter margin. Gutter pairs showing these 'traffic lights' are worth considerably more than the normal version. From the 2004 Entente Cordiale set, Walsall reintroduced traffic lights in the gutters of certain sets. Where these extend over more than one section of gutter margin on any stamp they are priced as blocks rather than pairs.

Traffic light gutter pair

Catalogue numbers used

This checklist uses the same catalogue numbers as other current Stanley Gibbons catalogues.

Latest issue date for stamps recorded in this edition is 2 November 2010.

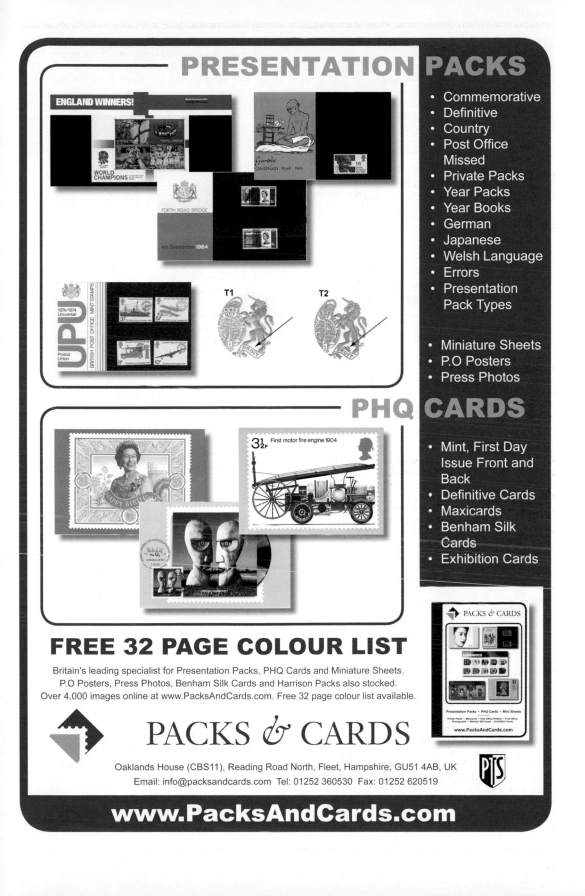

PRESENTATION PACKS

- Commemorative
- Definitive
- Country
- Post Office Missed
- Private Packs
- Year Packs
- Year Books
- German
- Japanese
- Welsh Language
- Errors
- Presentation Pack Types

- Miniature Sheets
- P.O Posters
- Press Photos

PHQ CARDS

- Mint, First Day Issue Front and Back
- Definitive Cards
- Maxicards
- Benham Silk Cards
- Exhibition Cards

FREE 32 PAGE COLOUR LIST

Britain's leading specialist for Presentation Packs, PHQ Cards and Miniature Sheets.
P.O Posters, Press Photos, Benham Silk Cards and Harrison Packs also stocked.
Over 4,000 images online at www.PacksAndCards.com. Free 32 page colour list available.

PACKS & CARDS

Oaklands House (CBS11), Reading Road North, Fleet, Hampshire, GU51 4AB, UK
Email: info@packsandcards.com Tel: 01252 360530 Fax: 01252 620519

www.PacksAndCards.com

DO YOU COLLECT GREAT BRITAIN?

OUR MONTHLY RETAIL PRICE LIST

Covers all issues from SG No. 1. Queen Victoria through to Queen Elizabeth II. At any one time, we expect to have in stock most of the stamps listed in this catalogue, so if you want to fill those blank spaces, we cordially invite you to...
SEND FOR A FREE COPY OF OUR LATEST LIST!!

PRIVATE TREATY CATALOGUES

Aimed at the more serious collector, **these profusely illustrated listings** are extremely popular and are issued twice monthly; they contain a wide selection of **better Singles, Rarities, Proofs, Colour Trials, High Values, Multiples and much specialised material.**
Seldom offered elsewhere!!

FREE

May we send you a copy of our latest catalogue so that you can see for yourself what you are missing. please write, fax, phone or email us at sales@gbstamps.co.uk for your free copy

Why not visit our very easy to use website,
www.gbstamps.co.uk
where we have up to £1 million of Great Britian stamps for you to browse

NEW bargain basement section on website, 1000's of discounted offers

Arthur Ryan & Co.
OF RICHMOND
(DEPT CBS)

MAIL ORDER ONLY

2 THE SQUARE, THE QUADRANT, RICHMOND, SURREY, TW9 1DY.
TELEPHONE:- 020 8940 7777   FAX:- 020 8940 7755

Commemorative Design Index

HOW MUCH?

YOUR PRICE IS OUR PRICE!

Buying at auction means buying at source.
It's where dealers buy to re-sell later at a profit.

REGULAR EXHIBITORS AT STAMPEX & PHILATEX

Auctions are open to everyone, yourself included. Singles, sets, covers, complete collections – everything, worldwide, all periods, mint and used. Lots from £1-£1000's. Never again pay more than you want to!

Our full colour catalogues are free and all purchases are covered by our 'Return for any reason' full and immediate refund guarantee.

What have you got to lose?

Tip – your bid isn't **WHAT** you'll pay; it's the **MOST** you'll pay.
Simply bid no more than the cheapest offer elsewhere, and you cannot lose!

APEX PHILATELIC AUCTIONS

11 Adelphi Terrace, London WC2N 6BJ

Contact Rick Warren or Tim Francis on:
Tel: +44 (0) 1342 833413 Fax: +44 (0) 1342 833892
email: sales@apexstamps.com

See us on-line at www.apexstamps.com

A Noble Investments (UK) PLC Company

Reply today and we'll give you £100* off.
* 5 credit notes for £20, each valid when £50 or more spent in any one sale New customers only

Name_____
Address _____
_____
_____
e-mail:_____

Please send me your next 5 auction catalogues free of charge and my £100 introductory vouchers

CBS11

Struggling to keep up with all the new issues these days?

Then below is one of the cheapest and fun ways of doing so for as little as a tenth of a penny per stamp

GENUINE GB CHARITY: Fed up with sifting through GB Charity mixture that appears to have been picked through before, that is old and unexciting? We now recieve GB Charity sent to us direct from the donator by bypassing the charity and any other dealer and can supply you still in its sealed envelopes unopened by anybody and therefore unpicked by any charity worker or dealer. You could be sifting through stamps that have been collected by offices, schools, banks as recently as last week and therefore should be up-to-date. Tried and tested and extremely popular as our customers have expressed the excitement of sorting through GB charity that nobody has been through before!

5kg Box £65.00 9kg Box £115.00. Not suitable for overseas customers unless full postage is paid.

SPECIAL OFFER: Buy 1lb Gb Commems, 1lb GB H.V Defins, 21lbs GB Regionals & 18 kgs GB Defins for the dicounted price of £106.00

GB COMMEMS NO XMAS. A wide ranging on paper mixture with many recent hard to find issues and high values. ½lb £13.00, 1lb £25.00

GB HIGH VALUE DEFINS On paper. Excellent variety, a clean mixture ½lb £13.00, 1lb £25.00

GB REGIONALS. On paper. A wealth of variety from all four regions, find those elusive band/perf varieties very cheaply. Over 7000-8000 stamps/2lbs. 1lb £8.00, 2lb £15.00

GREAT BRITAIN DEFINITIVES: An 18kg sack of On paper which is bound to contain much post-mark interest, possible Regionals, High Values, much Phosphor, paper and perf varieties. Sorted and delivered only by charitable institutions. (Delivered to your door, post paid inland). Only £40

Stamp Collections at Trade Prices!!! All collections are off paper, all stamps different.

GREAT BRITAIN Off paper mixture. The tedious washing of this modern mixture has been done for you already by charity supporters! There are nearly 500 basic machins to collect. One of each in good nick can cost over £150.00 to collect. We can't guarantee all in there but you'll have great fun sorting, includes commems, h.v commems etc. Guaranteed totally unpicked and all genuine postally used. At least 10,000 stamps. **1lb £16.50, 2lbs £30.00.**

GREAT BRITAIN
500 differnt. List price £9.00. Trade price £7.00
1000 different. List price £32.00. Trade price £27.00
1500 different. List price £85.00. Trade Price £60.00
2000 different. List price £115.00. Trade price £85.00

GREAT BRITAIN COMMEMS ONLY
500 different. List price £21.00. Trade price £17.00
1000 different. List price £99.00. Trade price £75.00

GREAT BRITAIN H. VALUE COMMEMS ONLY
100 different. List price £12.00 Trade price £8.00
300 different. List price £49.00 Trade price £42.00
500 different. List price £95.00 Trade price £80.00
700 different. List price £220.00. Trade price £160.00

COURT PHILATELICS: DEPARTMENT GB, P.O. BOX 6198, LEIGHTON BUZZARD, BEDS LU7 9XT
Tel: 01296 662420, Fax. 01296 668328. Email: courtphilatelics@aol.com, Website: www.stampmixtures.co.uk

All prices include P & P inland. We accept personal cheques, postal orders and all major credit/debit cards - please advise expiry date and security code.

Great Britain illustrated Price List 1840 – 2008

Phone or write for your **free copy** of our latest 56 page list or visit

www.britishstamps.com

Swan Stamps   PO Box 501 Torquay Devon   TQ1 9FE

Telephone 01803 290619   email steve@britishstamps.com

399 Strand

Our world famous stamp shop is a collector's paradise, with all of our latest catalogues, albums and accessories and, of course, our unrivalled stockholding of postage stamps.
www.stanleygibbons.com
shop@stanleygibbons.co.uk
+44 (0)20 7836 8444

Specialist Stamp Sales

For the collector that appreciates the value of collecting the highest quality examples, Stanley Gibbons is the only choice. Our extensive range is unrivalled in terms of quality and quantity, with specialist stamps available from all over the world.
www.stanleygibbons.com/stamps
shop@stanleygibbons.co.uk
+44 (0)20 7836 8444

Stanley Gibbons Auctions and Valuations

Sell your collection or individual rare items through our prestigious public auctions or our regular postal auctions and benefit from the excellent prices being realised at auction currently. We also provide an unparalleled valuation service.
www.stanleygibbons.com/auctions
auctions@stanleygibbons.co.uk
+44 (0)20 7836 8444

Stanley Gibbons Publications

The world's first stamp catalogue was printed by Stanley Gibbons in 1865 and we haven't looked back since! Our catalogues are trusted worldwide as the industry standard and we print countless titles each year. We also publish consumer and trade magazines, Gibbons Stamp Monthly and Philatelic Exporter to bring you news, views and insights into all things philatelic. Never miss an issue by subscribing today and benefit from exclusive subscriber offers each month.
www.stanleygibbons.com/shop
orders@stanleygibbons.co.uk
+44 (0)1425 472 363

Stanley Gibbons Investments

The Stanley Gibbons Investment Department offers a unique range of investment propositions that have consistently outperformed more traditional forms of investment, from guaranteed minimum return products with unlimited upside to portfolios made up of the world's rarest stamps and autographs.
www.stanleygibbons.com/investment
investment@stanleygibbons.co.uk
+44 (0)1481 708 270

Fraser's Autographs

Autographs, manuscripts and memorabilia from Henry VIII to current day. We have over 60,000 items in stock, including movie stars, musicians, sport stars, historical figures and royalty. Fraser's is the UK's market leading autograph dealer and has been dealing in high quality autographed material since 1978.
www.frasersautographs.com
sales@frasersautographs.co.uk
+44 (0)20 7557 4404

stanleygibbons.com

Our website offers the complete philatelic service. Whether you are looking to buy stamps, invest, read news articles, browse our online stamp catalogue or find new issues, you are just one click away from anything you desire in the world of stamp collecting at stanleygibbons.com. Happy browsing!
www.stanleygibbons.com

Collecting Stamps – the Basics

It seems reasonable to assume, since you are reading this, that you already collect British stamps – but of course there are many ways of building on any collection and, if you are relatively new to it, I hope that the following will be of some guidance.

Traditionally, stamp collectors were introduced to the hobby with a quantity of world stamps, some still on envelopes and cards, which were then sorted and mounted in an album. In due course, many would decide to concentrate on a single country or group of countries and "specialisation" would begin, based on the experience built up as a "world collector".

More recently, an alternative route has become prevalent, in which, often as a gift, collection may be built on a "standing order" from a philatelic bureau, with stamps or covers arriving automatically, as they are issued, to be mounted in an album or stockbook. Albums are conveniently designed to meet the needs of this type of collection, with an illustrated space in which to mount every stamp.

This type of collection has much to recommend it – but one big disadvantage – it will be exactly the same as thousands of others, built up in the same way.

For this reason, many collectors are now returning to the delights of general collecting while maintaining their existing collections, and finding that the fun they had as children is very easy to recapture!

If you came to the hobby via "the standing order" route and would like to start a second "general collection", here are a few tips and suggestions.

Obtaining your stamps

Children were encouraged to buy – or persuade their parents to buy – the largest packet of stamps they could, as just sorting them into countries would prove enormously useful and interesting. Unfortunately large packets of world stamps are not as easy to obtain as they used to be, but you can still buy existing collections of all sorts at stamp fairs, shops or at auction, prices to suit every pocket. Just sorting and remounting such a collection will prove tremendously exciting.

Sooner or later, of course, you will identify gaps in your collection that you want to fill. It is useful to keep a note of these in a book that you can take with you when you visit a stamp shop or stamp fair – no one can remember everything and it is always annoying to discover that you have just bought a stamp you didn't need!

It is vitally important of course that you keep your "wants" book up-to-date and cross out items as you acquire them.

As well as visiting stamp fairs, you can check out the advertisements in the press; establish a good relationship with a dealer you like and, he will be happy to receive a "wants list" from you. He will then supply you with any items

on it he has currently in stock and keep a record of anything else so that he can send it on to you if he gets one. All such items are usually "on approval", so that if you have found them somewhere else, you are not obliged to purchase them.

More expensive items can be purchased at auction. Many of the larger auction houses do not like to sell items of lower value and therefore, in the main, offer more expensive single stamps and covers or complete collections and accumulations.

Other auctions offer single items of lower value and these can be a great way of picking up items you need. Stanley Gibbons Postbid auctions fall into this category, but there are many others and, once again, it is good to identify an auction house which regularly offers the type of material you are looking for and provides a reliable service.

Another method of buying stamps is "kiloware". These are stamps sold by weight and generally assumed to be "unsorted" i.e. no one has been through them before and picked the good ones out. Many collectors enjoy this approach to stamp collecting and they will tell you of the wonderful "finds" they have made – but inevitably you will be left with a vast majority of stamps that you do not want because they duplicate items already in your collection. Charity shops will always be happy to receive them – and they will eventually finish up in someone else's "genuinely unsorted kiloware" – so once again, if this is your kind of collecting, establish a good relationship with a reliable supplier.

"Kiloware" is generally supplied in the form of stamps on paper, torn or cut from envelopes – so this is probably a good point at which to discuss one of the real basics of stamp collecting – soaking stamps off paper.

It is helpful to carry out some rudimentary sorting before you start. Soaking stamps is quite a time-consuming process, so you do not want to waste time on stamps you don't need or don't want, maybe because they are damaged.

Once you have sorted out the stamps you want to soak off, pour some clean water (warm but *not* hot) into a bowl; then float each stamp (face uppermost) on the surface of the water. You can float as many stamps at one time as you have room for.

Leave the stamps for 15 minutes or so to give the water time to soak the gum that is sticking the stamp to the paper. Most stamps can then be gently peeled away. If they do not come away easily do not try to tear them off the paper. Leave them for another five minutes or so and try again.

Providing your hands are clean it's better to handle the stamps with your fingers when peeling off the envelope paper. The paper of stamps is weakened when it is damp and picking them up with tweezers may damage them.

When you have peeled the stamps off the envelope there will probably be some damp gum still on the back of them. Use a soft brush dipped in water to remove this, a paint brush is ideal. Alternatively let the stamp float on the water for a few minutes – the gum will dissolve away. However, do not immerse the stamp in water. For most stamps this would be safe enough but for some it would be dangerous as the ink may run.

Then shake off any excess water and place the stamps face upwards on a sheet of clean kitchen paper towel. This is why it is so important to clean all the gum off. If you do not, your stamps will stick to the paper and you will have to float them off all over again. When all the stamps are laid out cover them with more paper towel then make a kind of sandwich by putting a few sheets of ordinary paper on top.

Place a heavy book on this sandwich. This will flatten the stamps as they dry. After half an hour open up the sandwich and carefully remove the stamps. Spread them out on another piece of clean paper and leave to dry in the air for a little while. When completely dry they are ready for mounting in your album.

Or you can just lay the stamps face down on paper towel and allow them to dry out in the air. If you use this method do not try to speed up the drying by putting the stamps in the sun or close to a hot radiator as they will curl up and you may damage them when you flatten them out to put them in your album.

There are two things which you must be very careful about when floating stamps. Firstly, many old stamps were printed in special inks which run, change colour, or even disappear completely in water. Fewer modern stamps are affected in this way but even so it is best to be safe, so avoid letting water get on the surface of the stamp when you are floating-off. Be careful when floating stamps to keep separate stamps affixed to white and coloured envelopes. Take out any stamp which are stuck to bits of coloured paper and float these separately. Floating can easily make the ink run and so damage your stamps by staining them with unwanted colours.

These days, many countries produce "self-adhesive" stamps and these may not come away from their backing paper at all. If you believe that a stamp may be "self-adhesive", it would be better to leave it on the paper, carefully trimming round it with scissors, making sure you do not cut into the stamp.

Finally, always think twice before tearing a stamp off an envelope. Most old stamps and some modern ones too, if they have interesting postmarks, will be more valuable if left on the envelope. If in doubt always try to ask a more experienced collector's advice.

Choosing an Album and Mounting your stamps

These are two different topics but really need to be considered together, as the way you mount your stamps will depend on the album you choose and your choice of album may depend on the way you wish to mount your stamps. Here are some of the options:

Printed Albums

You may be used to an album printed with a space for every stamp, and these may be obtained for larger groups of countries, such as the Stanley Gibbons New Imperial Album, with spaces for all Commonwealth and Empire stamps up to 1936. If this is the sort of collection you hope to build they are fine albums – but as they have a space for every stamp, filling one would be a time-consuming and expensive business!

New Imperial album

Blank albums

These are made up of blank pages, printed with a faint "quadrille" (tiny squares) which help you lay your stamps out neatly. These give you freedom to lay your collection out as you wish, leaving spaces for stamps you are hoping to obtain, or a neat display of the stamps you have. The former option may mean that you have a lot of gaps on the page, the latter may mean fairly regular rearrangement of your collection – the choice is yours.

Blank albums come in a wide range of prices and binding types, from inexpensive ring binders, through traditional "springbacks" to high quality "peg-fitting" types. Again, the choice is yours.

Stockbooks

In the past, collectors used stockbooks to hold duplicates and stamps awaiting mounting in the main album, but due to their convenience and cost, many collectors are now using stockbooks to house their main collections.

They certainly make it easy to "mount" your stamps – you just slip them into the strips on the pages and you can move them around easily to accommodate new acquisitions too! You can even write notes regarding different stamps or sets and slip those into the strips.

Stock albums

These are loose-leaf stockbooks, which have the added benefit of being able to insert extra pages in the book. Also, because the strips come in a number of formats, they look better than a stockbook layout which is a bit restricting and does not show larger items, such as covers, blocks and miniature sheets, very well.

Mounting your stamps

Before we come on to cover albums, let's return to the matter of mounting your stamps. If you have chosen either the stockbook or stock album option, this is not really an issue as you can just slip your stamps into the strips on the page. If you have opted for a printed or blank album, on the other hand, the question of mounting is important.

The traditional stamp hinge is generally the preferred option for used stamps. Instructions for their use are generally given on the packet, so I will not repeat them here, but I must stress that the key points are to *lightly* moisten the hinge before attaching it to the stamp or album page and *not to try to remove it* until it's dry or you may damage the page – or even more important, the stamp.

For unused stamps that have been previously mounted, stamp hinges are also perfectly acceptable, but for stamps which still have "full original gum" and show no evidence of having been previously hinged, most collectors now favour "hingeless mounts", which allow you to attach the stamp to the page without disturbing the gum (keeping the stamp "unmounted").

For most of the most frequently encountered stamp sizes, cut-to-size mounts are available for immediate use. Less common sizes will have to be cut from bigger strips, but even large blocks and miniature sheets cab be mounted in this way.

Although hingeless mounts are gummed, ready for use, many collectors prefer to use hinges to attach them to the album page as this makes them easier to move around when new stamps are added.

Covers

Many collectors like to include covers in their collections – either "first day" or "souvenir" covers or simply envelopes that show examples of the stamps in use. This is especially desirable of early covers, which might show unusual postmarks or other features.

Universal album

Covers can be mounted on blank pages using gummed photograph corners, but may also be accommodated in

purpose-built cover albums. There are even albums, such as the Stanley Gibbons Universal, which are designed to hold stamp and cover pages together (and booklet pages too!).

What else?

So, that's covered the choice of album and the mounting of stamps: What else do you need? This comes under two headings: equipment and information.

Information

You can manage without background information, but it would be a bit like setting out on a journey to somewhere you've never been without a map.

The first thing is a catalogue to tell you what exists and will help you to identify what you have. The Stanley Gibbons catalogue range includes something for every collector from the beginner to the specialist. The features of each title are given elsewhere in this checklist (see page xlvi).

Beyond that there are specialist handbooks on just about everything, but many are printed in quite small numbers and, once sold, are unlikely to be reprinted. However, specialist dealers and auction houses can be a useful source of out-of-print literature.

> You should also try to keep up with what is going on in the philatelic world and, again, Stanley Gibbons is able to help, via its monthly magazine, *Gibbons Stamp Monthly*, recently described as "the best magazine for stamp collectors published anywhere". For a free sample copy and subscription details, please write to Stanley Gibbons Publications, *(the address is at the front of this checklist)*.

Of course, as with everything else, much information may also be found on the internet and you will almost certainly find it worth joining the local society in your area, other stamp collectors are always happy to help a newcomer.

Equipment

Again, what you need in the way of equipment will depend largely on what you are collecting, the degree of specialisation you intend to achieve and the type of album you use.

We have already discussed albums and stamp mounts, the only other item every stamp collector must have is a pair of tweezers. All stamps should be handled with tweezers; they ensure that the natural oils in our fingers do not get on to the stamps and, after a bit of practice, they are easier to use than fingers as well. They come in different lengths, with different points and made from different materials (generally stainless steel or gold-plated). Find a style that suits you and stick with it.

From then on the equipment you need is up to you. Most collectors like to have a magnifying glass so they can look at their stamps more closely. Again, they come in a wide range, from the fairly basic, offering 2 or 3× magnification, to pocket microscopes giving 30× magnification, and a digital microscope that you can attach to your computer for really detailed examination of your stamps. If this appeals to you, a demonstration of its use can be found on the Stanley Gibbons website – look for the Zoom Digital Microscope.

Another useful type of magnifier is one that incorporates a millimetre scale – ideal for measuring overprints and other features.

Even a quick look in any catalogue will show that differences in perforation, watermark and colour can make an enormous difference to the price of a stamp. So most collectors like to have the necessary equipment to measure perforations, view watermarks and identify colours and shades.

Fortunately, as far as perforations are concerned, the perforation gauge used by most of the world's top collectors and dealers is accessible to all – it's the Stanley Gibbons Instanta – which measures perforations to a decimal point and is easy to use. There is an electronic perforation measurer which is even easier to use – but it is a bit more expensive than the Instanta.

Watermark detectors also come in a variety of types and a wide range of prices, all of which are effective in their different ways. If you are collecting older stamps, watermarks are generally clearer and can be identified simply by placing the stamps face down on a dark background or watermark tray and, if necessary, adding a few drops of lighter fluid or watermark fluid. The Morley Bright products are an excellent alternative if you do not like using fluids, which many collectors do not.

More modern stamps, especially mint ones are more difficult to sort and for these one of the electric watermark detectors will probably be the answer. The Stanley Gibbons Detectamark and other similar products take a bit of practice to get used to, but are very effective. Their drawback is that they can only handle single stamps and cannot accommodate blocks or sheets. If you are able to, visit a shop where you can see the different products demonstrated and make your choice.

Happily, the standard colour guide for stamp collectors, the Stanley Gibbons colour key, is another relatively inexpensive item which will provide years of use. It features 200 different colours and will allow you to tell the difference between "mauve", "purple", "lilac" and "violet" with ease.

Finally and especially if you are collecting the modern stamps of Great Britain at a more specialised level, you will probably want an ultraviolet lamp to identify different papers and phosphor types. Again, these come in a range of designs at different prices, so it is useful to seek the advice of an experienced collector before deciding on the one to buy. If you collect Great Britain stamps, you really need a "short wave" lamp to identify different phosphors, but some lamps incorporate both "long" and "short" wave bulbs, which give them wider potential use.

A lamp with a "hood" is generally to be recommended, firstly because direct exposure to prolonged ultraviolet light is damaging to the eyes, so you should avoid lamps which cause you to see the bulb itself while you are using it. Also, such lamps are more effective in the dark, so anything which shields the stamp being examined from other light sources, including daylight, will improve the effectiveness of the lamp. Ideally, you should use an ultraviolet lamp in a completely darkened room – but this is not practical at a stamp fair!

Philatelic accessories of all types are available from Stanley Gibbons Publications in Ringwood or at the SG shop in London. The current product guide is available on request. Alternatively, a host of useful information can be found here: www.stanleygibbons.com

Stanley Gibbons Numbers

When Stanley Gibbons published his first stamp catalogue in 1865 the stamps in it were simply listed by country and description. It was not long, however, before there were just too many stamps to be listed in this way and in order to simplify the way in which stamps could be ordered by customers, each was given its unique and individual number.

Nowadays, as each stamp is added to the catalogue in the supplement published in *Gibbons Stamp Monthly,* it is assigned its number; sets being listed according to the date on which they were issued and then by face value within that set. If several stamps of the same value belong to one set, usually issued in the form of a sheet or sheetlet, the numbering starts at the top left-hand stamp and runs down to the stamp at bottom right.

Long definitive series are listed together for the convenience of collectors so this often involves adding new numbers to an existing series. It can also happen that a stamp or set of stamps are discovered which were unknown at the time of issue – these also have to be inserted in their correct chronological sequence.

Easy identification

The Stanley Gibbons number appears in the left-hand column of the stamp listing and should not be confused with the bold number that often appears to its right and refers to its illustration. So, by using the country name and catalogue number, every stamp can be easily identified and, rather than having to order Great Britain 1924 10d. turquoise-blue on Block Cypher watermarked paper, all you have to do is order a Great Britain SG428 and state whether you want it used or unused.

In order to render them immediately identifiable, certain types of stamps are given a prefix to their catalogue number thus a number prefixed with a "D" is a postage due stamp, while an "O" means it's an official stamp. Some countries' stamps also have a prefix to allow them to be easily identified. Thus, in this catalogue, Scotland stamp numbers are prefixed with an "S" and those for Wales with a "W".

Changes

Once a number has been assigned it is not changed unless absolutely necessary. The reason, for this is that collectors often maintain their 'wants lists' using SG numbers, while auction houses around the world quote them in their descriptions, as do books and articles in the philatelic press.

Expertising bodies, including the expert committee of the Royal Philatelic Society London and the British Philatelic Association also quote SG numbers in their certificates, which generally identify scarcer or more valuable stamps, so regular changing of those numbers would render such certificates out-of-date.

Nevertheless, sometimes complete sections of the catalogue, occasionally even complete countries, have to be reoganised, and under such circumstances renumbering does take place – but this is infrequent.

Usually, new stamps added into the middle of listings have a letter suffix. This can occur in two forms. If the stamp is listable in its own right the suffix forms a part of the "main" number in the left-hand column of the listing. Thus, when the Wilding 4½d. and 5d. values with phosphor bands appeared, in 1961 and 1967 respectively, but the 4d. and 6d., both issued in 1960, had already been given the numbers 616 and 617, the 4½d. became 616a and the 5d. was listed as 616b.

Varieties of such "main" stamps, such as errors, booklet panes and watermark varieties are given letter suffixes in a different way, so that the phosphor version of the 1963 6d. Paris Postal Conference stamp (SG 636) has a "p" suffix which appears in the listing itself, to differentiate it from the normal, non-phosphor stamp – so to order one, all you need to ask for is SG 636p.

Sometimes, of course, so many stamps are subsequently added to a listing that the use of suffix letters would just become too complicated and, so far as Great Britain is concerned, this has happened with the decimal Machin series, which are prefixed "X" for the conventionally perforated series, first issued in 1971, and "Y" for the series with elliptical perforations at each side, first issued in 1993.

Adding new numbers

Thus when new stamps are added to such series – and several are appearing each year – adding new numbers does not have to mean changing those of subsequently issued commemorative issues.

Within the "Y" series, new "main" values are initially added with a suffix letter, so the numbers of previously issued stamps do not have to be adjusted with each new catalogue, but every four or five years the complete listing is updated to eliminate the suffix letters and maintain a "clean" listing of numbers. When ordering stamps from these series it is as well to mention which edition of the catalogue you are using as, if your dealer is using a different one, you may not receive what you expect!

> The Stanley Gibbons numbering system represents an easy-to-use and universally recognised system of stamp identification.

Collectors all over the world use it to keep their collections in order and dealers sort and classify their stocks by it, so its use makes life easier for everyone.

Stanley Gibbons numbers are fully protected by copyright and, while their use is encouraged, they may not be reproduced without the prior permission of Stanley Gibbons Limited.

The Stanley Gibbons Guide to Stamp Pricing

Catalogue editor and lifelong collector, Hugh Jefferies, offers a few tips.

It is a common fallacy that the prices in this catalogue show what a stamp is 'worth', should you wish to sell it.

They are, instead, the price at which Stanley Gibbons will sell a fine example of the stamp in question, but that price includes a lot of other factors, as well as the inherent 'value' of the stamp itself. There are costs in running any business and these are built into the price of any stamp shown in the catalogue, although the proportion of the price that relates to the stamp and that which relates to 'business overheads' will vary from stamp to stamp.

What is true is that the prices shown in this catalogue represent an accurate 'guide' to the value of the stamps listed in it. Stanley Gibbons are now the only major philatelic publisher whose stamp catalogue is also their price list. Naturally, if the prices are set too high, no one will buy our stamps, if they are too low, we will have difficulty replacing our stocks. It is therefore vitally important to the future of the company that the prices in this catalogue are set as accurately as possible. As a result, a great deal of care is taken over those prices – which is why they are held in such authority by collectors, dealers and stamp auction houses throughout the world.

A very accurate picture

Each year, every price in our annual catalogues is checked and amended if necessary, having regard to the prices being achieved at auction as well as the demands of our customers at 399 Strand and orders coming in via the post, email and our website. Prices are held, increased or reduced according to those factors, giving a very accurate picture of the state of the market for each and every stamp.

Can stamps be purchased for less than the prices quoted in this catalogue? Of course they can. Stanley Gibbons themselves will frequently have stamps in stock at prices lower than 'full catalogue'. Every business offers discounts and makes 'special offers' from time to time and Stanley Gibbons is no different. That apart, however, it should always be remembered that the prices quoted in this catalogue are for stamps in fine condition. Stamps with minor defects, heavy postmarks, slight fading and other flaws will frequently be offered at lower prices, both by Stanley Gibbons and by other dealers and auction houses.

Checking condition

It is very important that, when you are thinking of buying a stamp for your collection, you carefully consider the condition of the item in question. Does it match up to the Stanley Gibbons definition of 'Fine'? If it doesn't, is the price at which it is being offered too high? If you believe that the price is higher that it should be, leave it alone – or if you are really desperate, haggle for a better deal.

The knowledge as to what is 'fine' and therefore worthy of 'full catalogue' is one that you will gain with experience and will vary from stamp to stamp. Any stamp less than 100 years old should really be perfect in every way, but one can be more forgiving with older issues.

Briefly, here are a few of the things to consider.

- **Gum** – for unused stamps issued after 1936 prices are for unmounted mint – stamps never previously hinged. Modern stamps with hinge marks should be substantially discounted. For earlier stamps, heavy mounts and multiple hinges will also detract from the value, while unused stamps with the gum removed are worth considerably less.

- **Margins** – for imperforate stamps these should be clear on all sides – the design should not be cut into or even touching the edge of the stamp.

- **Perforations** – check that these are complete, that none are missing or short, especially at the stamp corners. Ideally the margin between the stamp design and the perforations should be even and well balanced – known as 'well-centred'.

- **Paper** – Check that there are no tears or thins to the paper – on the front as well as the back – and that there are no bends or creases. Again, the greater the damage the further away from 'full catalogue' the stamp is worth.

- **Postmarks** – these should be clear, clean and should not disfigure the stamp. The prices for all British stamps issued after 1880 assume used stamps to be cancelled with a clean, clear circular datestamp. Heavy parcel, wavy line or slogan cancellations reduce stamp values significantly. On the other hand, very lightly cancelled stamps should sometimes be viewed with suspicion. There needs to be enough of the postmark showing to prove that the stamp has really been used!

If the above notes seem complicated, don't worry. You will soon become adept at viewing every stamp in the light of its condition and deciding what proportion of catalogue you are prepared to pay. If you are not certain, ask the dealer for a guarantee that he will refund your money if you're not happy with your purchase. All good dealers will be happy to provide this.

So, buy carefully – but, above all, have fun!

> It should always be remembered that the prices quoted in this catalogue are for stamps in fine condition.

SEE FIRST – PAY LATER
with our *at home* selections

All periods available, both mint and used – no obligation to purchase

All stamps in our selections are shown with:
Price (before discount) •
SG catalogue number •
SG catalogue value •

The stamp you see is • the stamp you buy

PRICE £ ....
S.G. No. ....
CAT. VAL. ....

FREE FOR YOU

So sure are we that our service will delight you, that we are offering these two complete fine used sets, catalogue value over £15.00 FREE to all applicants – yours to keep whether you buy anything or not!

Victoria – line engraved, embossed, surface printed, all issues up to £5, sound, collectable examples frequently with **massive discounts** from catalogue value, up to superb examples with cds cancels.

Edward VII & George V – all issues, incl. perf changes and watermarks, Downey Heads, photogravure, Seahorses and commems to £1

George VI – all issues commems and defins to top values, in both sets or single values.

QEII – everything, from first Wildings to latest Machins, normal & elliptical perfs, different printers, phosphor, graphite and watermark variations, vals to £10, commems incl phosphor and perf types – from one of the country's most expensive and comprehensive stock of 21st century issues – yes, the latest issues in **used** condition also!

Back of the book – with Officials and Post Dues. The cheapest and the rarest – we handle it all.

Channel Islands (and other countries) – extensive stocks held of most British Commonwealth and mainstream foreign.

Discounts too!
Up to **25%** reduction when you spend as little as **£15**!

Plus extra bonus discount with our unrivalled loyalty Connoisseur Points scheme.

• **Inspect** • **Consider** • **Choose** Pick the best for *your* collection

No two stamp collections are the same. That's why our *at home* **stamp selections are individually tailored to your requirements**

My interests are / I collect:
Mark as appropriate

Great Britain CI / IOM ☐   All World ☐   All BE ☐

OTHER (please state) _____

QV / GV ☐   GVI ☐   QEII - 1970 ☐   QEII mod ☐

Mint & Used ☐   Mint Only ☐   Used Only ☐

YES. Please send me at home selections. I claim my free offer. I am under no obligation and may cancel at any time.

Name: _____
Address: _____
_____
_____

email: _____

CBS 11

All approved selections governed by our Standard Terms & Conditions. A copy sent with each selection.

MasterCard   VISA

at home selections 11 Adelphi Terrace, London WC2N 6BJ Contact Rick Warren or Tim Francis on: Tel: +44 (0) 1342 833413
Fax: +44 (0) 1342 833892 email: sales@apexstamps.com   **See us on-line at www.apexstamps.com**
A Noble Investments (UK) PLC Company

An introduction to the stamps of King George V

This article by Frank Brench. first published in Gibbons Stamp Monthly in January 1986, takes a personal look at the British stamps of King George V and explains why they provide such an interesting collecting field.

2010 Has seen widespread philatelic celebrations linked to the centenary of the accession of King George V – the 'Philatelist King'.

His reign of just over 25 years was hugely important from the perspective of international relations, social development and the postal service; with the arrival, amongst other factors of the first airmails and the first British commemorative stamps.

The first postage stamp that I can remember seeing was in 1924 at the British Empire Exhibition held at Wembley Park, London. As a special treat I had been taken to the great show to visit my father who was representing the company with whom he was employed making chocolate. The stamp in question was coloured red and affixed to a picture postcard depicting the 'Australian Pavilion', one of the exhibits. Included in the design of the stamp was an illustration of a lion, an animal about which I had recently learned from a child's picture book. Also on the stamp was a portrait of a benign old gentleman with a beard, whom I called, 'the king'. This landmark in my life was reached at the age of three years and eight months. The picture card belonged to my father who was showing it to some colleagues at the exhibition centre. It is at this point that my memory fails me.

A few years were to pass before I saw the picture again. It had spent the intervening time in a 'secret' drawer of an antique secretaire belonging to my parents, and the day I discovered it, memories of the first occasion on which I had seen it, together with a hazy recollection of the Wembley visit were rekindled. The benign gentleman was now known to me as King George V whose impending silver jubilee as the reigning monarch was soon to be celebrated in St Paul's Cathedral and throughout the Commonwealth. The postcard was posted at Wembley during the early days of the exhibition, but alas, not on the first day of issue of the special stamps. However, at the time of the discovery of the card, I was not aware of, or familiar with the term, 'first day of issue', but my interest in postage stamps had been aroused.

I began looking around the house for any other picture cards, envelopes and birthday cards of which there were many, kept by my parents. Most bore the familiar Id. or ½d. postage stamps of King George V. From this time my interest in stamp collecting was confirmed, and in particular, those bearing the portrait of the 'benign old gentleman'. This reference to the King, by the way, is not really mine but that coined by a school chum, himself a keen stamp collector and subsequently my philatelic mentor. Needless to say the phrase became part of my vocabulary and has remained so ever since.

The King's silver jubilee was fast approaching, the preparations for it were well under way and I learned that the Post Office would issue a special set of postage stamps commemorating the great event, and for the first time I found myself buying, out of my limited pocket money, stamps which would not be used for postage, but put away and admired in the luxury of my first stamp album.

The Accession of George V — end of the Victorian epoch

Why then do I find the stamps issued during the reign of King George V so interesting and attractive? There are many reasons. I was born just a few years after the new king came to the throne. As a very young schoolboy it was easier and cheaper to buy King George V stamps, and one soon identified with them. Today, I do not have the same regard for the stamp issues of the previous reigns, attractive as they may be. When the King's father, Edward VII, died in May of 1910, the brief 'Edwardian' period came to an end, and the door on the monumental 'Vicorian epoch' was finally closed. Fresh air blew over the country activating people's minds and getting rid of cobwebs which had hung around far too long. New postage stamps were necessary with new designs to accompany the new reign and this was to prove difficult. King George V had no time for modern art but had definite ideas about design. It was not surprising, therefore, that in the choice of designs for the stamps, he was not easily satisfied. After all, it was his royal prerogative to approve or disapprove of postage stamps bearing his portrait surrounded by complex embellishments, no matter how appropriate they may seem.

It was agreed finally that the new stamps should include a three-quarter profile of the King's head, and the brief presented to the selected designers stipulated that at least one of the designs should include a lion, couchant, at the base of the stamp. The Id. stamp of 1911 illustrates this feature together with a laurel wreath encircling the head, all of which is worthy of study because to me the concept more than reflects Britain's power and prestige in the world at that time. The only other denomination in this new series, the ½d., is a little more subdued graphically, depicting dolphins swimming into the stamp from the left and right-hand bottom corners.

New — but not successful

The duration of this new issue of postage stamps was short. The King was not happy with his likeness which was based on a photograph taken by the court photographers, W and D Downey. The public was not used to a three-quarter profile of its monarch and expressed its disapproval vehemently. The printing by the typographic process was not completely successful, the beard in particular presented problems. At first it was too dark and muddy looking, and had to be re-etched to make it appear lighter with more detail. After only 18 months the series was discontinued and replaced by another design deemed to be more appropriate and befitting a king whose subjects numbered 446 million of the world's population. It

2011
Call for Annual List

Andrew Vaughan
Philatelics Limited

Great Britain
1840 to Date

Annual List 2010

Special Offer Discounts
Spend £50 or more for a 5% reduction or £500 or more for a 10% reduction
Maximum £250 per item or set to receive discount
Interest free credit available on all orders over £300. See inside cover for terms and conditions.

P|T|S Andrew Vaughan
Philatelics Limted

- Full Mail Order Service
- Major Stamp Shows Attended
- Illustrated Monthly List
  On Request

Andrew Vaughan Philatelics Limited
PO Box 6051

Tamworth Staffs B78 3JB England

E: sales@stampsgb.co.uk

TEL: 01827 63367
FAX: 01827 67579

www.stampsgb.co.uk

Embassy Philatelists
Est. 28 years

RARE GB BOUGHT & SOLD DAILY

FREE RETAIL
BROCHURES

AVAILABLE
ON REQUEST

P.O. Box 161, Chichester, West Sussex PO19 3SU
Tel: 023 9241 2512
E-mail: info@embassystamps.co.uk web: www.embassystamps.co.uk

is a great pity that the first stamps of the new reign were so unsuccessful, certainly they were a new departure from those produced for the previous reigns. Nevertheless I found them, as did my contemporaries, highly collectable and full of interest.

The new profile head issues were introduced in October 1912, and the royal portrait was finally settled. The head, based on the 'coinage' profile head by Bertram Mackennal, remained as the focal point of all the British stamps issued during the remainder of the reign. As it became necessary to print more and more stamps over the years, variations abounded. My new-found hobby had no boundaries and I delighted in collecting and exchanging the postage stamps I was gathering about me. The year was 1930 and I started collecting in earnest.

The Wembley Issue and the land fit for heroes

Prompted by the discovery of the picture card posted at Wembley, and the recently acquired knowledge that the 1924 British Empire Exhibition stamps were unique in that they were the first commemorative or special stamps to be issued by the Post Office, I decided that there was much more to collecting stamps than sticking them in an album. Why for instance was a stamp issued anyway, other than representing a receipt for prepayment for postage?

When the First World War came to an end in 1918, the land fit for heroes promised by the politicians of the day, failed to materialise. The new post-war economy could not provide the jobs or income demanded by our soldiers and sailors who were fortunate to return home. In an effort to strengthen our trade and industry at home and abroad, the British Empire Exhibition of 1924-5 was conceived and held at Wembley. The show opened in April and certainly attracted huge crowds, particularly from overseas, but whether it attracted more business for our ailing economy is debateable. The exhibition closed in October 1924 after a period of six months for general refurbishment, and re-opened its doors again in May, closing them finally in October. Like all outdoor events held in this country, its success or failure depended so much on the weather. Regrettably 1925 proved to be a particulary bad year weather-wise, and it came as no surprise that attendance figures slumped considerably and fewer stamps were sold during the second year, especially at Wembley itself.

The 1930s — a good time to start stamp collecting

Finding the 1925 stamps, used or unused, during the early 1930s was difficult and challenging. The great philatelic points of study in the school stamp club during those days were not the 'penny

blacks' or 'penny reds' but the BEE stamps of 1924-5. For me it was a good time to start collecting stamps.

Basking in the sunshine of my hobby, I was intrigued when my philatelic mentor showed me four stamps, bearing the now familiar King George V effigy, but different in design from any of those in my possession up to that time. They were very 'modern' I thought; austere would have been more appropriate perhaps, but in those far off days I did not appreciate design, and was intrigued by the difference between them and the familiar King George V definitive stamps decorating my album pages. What was the reason for these stamps? The answer, in part, was incorporated in the design with the message, 'Postal Union Congress 1929', appearing loud and clear on each stamp. The ninth 'Congress' of member nations was due to be held in London during that year, and the Post Office, because of its active participation and strong support of the Universal Postal Union, marked the occasion with the issue of its second set of commemorative stamps, close on the heels of the 'Wembleys' of 1924-5. I acquired these as quickly as I could; the difference between them and the general definitives I thought was considerable.

However I was soon to suffer my first philatelic shock. The local stamp dealer, from whom I bought the stamps, said 'What about the £1 stamp to complete the set?' and produced the most beautiful stamp that I had ever seen, and arguably the most beautiful British stamp ever. The price he quoted caused the school boy philatelist to gulp. Where on earth would I find such a sum of money to buy a stamp, and for the first time I doubted the viability of my hobby and bade the dealer good day. Many years were to pass before it was possible for me to acquire an example of this superb stamp, designed by Harold Nelson who was responsible for the design of the Wembley stamps.

After close inspection of this stamp and the 'Wembleys' it is not difficult to appreciate that both are by the hand of the same designer. So different from the sombre approach of the Victorian and Edwardian designs. The King was well pleased with this one.

My Introduction to the Seahorses

It was at about this time, the early 1930s, that I was introduced to a stamp catalogue in the reference library section of the local public library. It was indeed a great occasion I thought, and so did a lot of people from my locality, young folk as well as adults, all trying to find their way through the various philatelic publications. The silence in the reading rooms had to be experienced to be believed.

I decided to study the £1 PUC, which I was convinced then would never be part of my collection, but after a preliminary flick through the pages I found information about four other postage stamps as awesome as the £1 PUC, and three of them still obtainable — in mint condition — at post offices for 2s. 6d., 5s., and 10s. What could one possibly post for these vast sums of money I wondered.

Bertram Mackennal's designs for the 'Seahorse' high value stamps epitomised the 'art nouveau' thinking of young designers expressing themselves through their artisistic skills when King George V ascended the throne. The theme conveyed, quite simply, was that of Britannia ruling the waves, a national sentiment engendered in the minds of the populace through the size and strength of the Royal Navy. They are superb stamps demonstrating the expertise of the engraver, J.A.C. Harrison, and continue to be enthusiatically sought after.

1934 — an Important year

1934 is probably the most important year for the collectors of my generation. Since 1840 British postage stamps had been printed by line-engraved, or surface-printed (letterpress/typographic) processes, which meant that a design in whatever form was made up of varying lengths, thicknesses, shapes and sizes. This is easily appreciated in a pre-1934 stamp is viewed through an enlarging lens. Because Harrison and Sons, the printers, had pioneered in this country the photogravure process, they gained the Post Office contract for printing the low value postage stamps by this method. The principal advantage of this process is greater production at lower costs, so important when more letters and parcels were being posted throughout the land. However there is

yet another advantage which the photogravure printing process offers, it is that of light and shade-gradation — particularly in portraiture. Highlights are softer, detail in the shadow areas is increased; black and white gives way to halftones. And so in 1934 commencement began on the reprinting of the low value definitive stamps which were to appear brighter and cleaner than those previously printed.

Jubilee year

Without doubt the peak of my philatelic collecting, at that time, came with the introduction of the stamps produced to commemorate the silver jubilee of the King in 1935. The nation was to celebrate the occasion on a scale never seen before in the United Kingdom. King George V had not had an easy reign: he ascended the throne in 1910 during the constitutional crisis over the 'People's Budget'. During the First World War he received an injury while visiting the troops at the front; an injury from which he never fully recovered. When the war was over his reign was to last for another 17 years, highlighted by innumerable crises and problems to overcome, including growing unemployment in the country, and it would be true to say that the majority of his subjects were more than a little fed up: the celebrations were to help lift the veil of despondency. The cities, towns and villages were bedecked with decorations of red, white and blue, attracting visitors to overflowing. In London they lined the processional route from Buckingham Palace to St Paul's Cathedral, where His Majesty, accompanied by his Consort Queen Mary, gave thanks for 25 years constitutional rule; the date was 6 May 1935.

The Post Office was asked to consider the part it could play in the celebrations and after due deliberation proposed a special issue of four stamps to be issued on 7 May, and a new precedent was established. Twelve artists were briefed and the most successful designs, in the opinion of the experts, were those submitted by Barnett Freedman a brilliant young graphic designer. The King warmly approved of the designs, about which there was much to learn. They were printed by the now established photogravure process, the first time a British commemorative stamp had been so printed. They were to be in the horizontal format, another first for such an event. Again the Mackennal head was used,

prominently arranged in the centre of each design completing a set of postage stamps worthy of majesty. There had never been anything quite so inspiring for the young stamp collector. One of the best known errors in British stamps occurred when some sheets of the 2½d. value printed in Prussian blue instead of ultramarine were accidentally put on sale.

George V Issues —Three philatelic firsts

King George V died on 20 January 1936. As well as carrying his kingly duties with consummate skill and wise counsel, he was an ardent philatelist. During his busy reign many events occurred which will always be remembered philatelically: a different concept of portraiture introduced at the beginning of his reign, albeit unsuccessfully (but paving the way for the later success of the Wildings); the introduction of commemorative stamps to mark national events and the introduction of new designs and printing methods. And let us not forget the first official airmail service to take place in the United Kingdom, between London and Windsor on 9 September 1911. All this, for me, makes collecting King George V more than worthwhile.

Selling your stamp collection?

Warwick and Warwick have an expanding requirement for world collections, single country collections, single items, covers, proof material and specialised collections, with GB material being particularly in demand. Our customer base is increasing dramatically and we need an ever larger supply of quality material to keep pace with demand. The market has never been stronger and if you are considering the sale of your collection, now is the time to act.

FREE VALUATIONS

We will provide a free, professional valuation of your collection, without obligation on your part to proceed. Either we will make you a fair, binding private treaty offer, or we will recommend inclusion of your property in our next public auction.

FREE TRANSPORTATION

We can arrange insured transportation of your collection to our Warwick offices completely free of charge. If you decline our offer, we ask you to cover the return carriage costs only.

FREE VISITS

Visits by our valuers are possible anywhere in the country or abroad, usually within 48 hours, in order to value larger collections. Please phone for details.

VALUATION DAYS

We are staging a series of valuation days across the country. Please visit our website or telephone for further details.

EXCELLENT PRICES

Because of the strength of our customer base we are in a position to offer prices that we feel sure will exceed your expectaions.

ACT NOW

Telephone or email Ian Hunter today with details of your property.

Get the experts on your side!

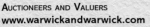

Warwick & Warwick

AUCTIONEERS AND VALUERS

www.warwickandwarwick.com

Warwick & Warwick Ltd.
Chalon House, Scar Bank, Millers Road
Warwick CV34 5DB England
Tel: (01926) 499031 • Fax: (01926) 491906
Email: ian.hunter@warwickandwarwick.com

Leading Buyers

Est. **40** Years

and
Recognised Valuers

Serious professional buyers of all things philatelic

Corbitts would welcome the opportunity to discuss the sale of your collection
by your preferred method.

PUBLIC AUCTION ⚜ OUTRIGHT PURCHASE ⚜ PRIVATE TREATY

We need all types of Philatelic material from general ranges and accumulations
to specialised studies, good singles and covers. We buy it all.

So if you are considering selling part or all of your collection - I urge you to call now
and discuss the many advantages of selling through Corbitts.

For a friendly and personal service, call Freephone 0800 525804
and ask for David McMonagle or Richard Vincent.

CORBITTS

5 Mosley Street, Newcastle upon Tyne NE1 1YE
Tel: 0191 232 7268 Fax: 0191 261 4130
Email: info@corbitts.com Website: www.corbitts.com

PLEASE CONTACT US FOR
A COMPLIMENTARY CATALOGUE

Members of Philatelic Traders Society > American Stamp Dealers Association > American Philatelic Society

Great Britain stamp collector's glossary

Adhesive A gummed stamp

Albino A design impression without colour

Aniline A fugitive (water soluble) ink or dye

Bisect Part of a stamp that has been cut in two for separate use; usually during a shortage of stamps

Blind perforation A perforation which has not been punched out

Block A group of four or more unseparated stamps

Bogus A spurious, pretend stamp

Booklet A small book containing 'panes' of stamps

Booklet pane A leaf or page of stamps from a booklet

Cachet A commemorative marking, usually applied by rubber stamp

Cancellation Any authorised defacing mark on a stamp

Centre The position of a stamp design within its perforations, e.g. 'well-centred' or 'off-centre'

Chalk-surfaced paper Stamp paper coated with a chalky solution for security purposes. Attempted removal of the postmark damages the surface of the stamp

Charity stamp One bearing a premium or surcharge for charitable purposes

Classic A country's early stamp issues, mostly up to about 1875; a choice stamp

Coil stamp One from a roll of stamps used in vending machines

Coil join A tab uniting two sections of a roll of stamps

Commemorative A stamp issued to mark a special anniversary or event

Country stamp See Regional

Cover A postally used envelope, letter-sheet or wrapper

Cylinder number Letters/numerals in sheet margins identifying printing cylinders. Normally collected in 'Cylinder block' of six stamps. Also see 'Plate number'

Die An engraved plate for impressing design etc. on softer metal

Doctor blade A steel blade which removes surplus ink from the printing cylinder in the press – faulty wiping by this blade will cause a 'Doctor blade' flaw

Embossing A form of printing in relief, now rarely used

Error A mistake in stamp design, printing or production

Essay A trial stamp design, sometimes differing from the

issued stamps

Face value The denomination of a stamp, expressed on its face

Fake A genuine stamp doctored in some way to deceive collectors

First Day Cover A cover bearing stamps postmarked on their day of issue

Flaw A fortuitous blemish on a stamp; a printing fault

Forgery A fraudulent copy of a genuine postage stamp, overprint or postmark

Frama stamps See Machine label

Graphite lines Black vertical lines printed on the back of GB definitives, 1957–1959, for use with automatic letter-sorting equipment. Also see 'Phosphor' stamps

Greetings stamp Stamp intended for use on birthday or other greetings mail

Gum Mucilage on the back of adhesive stamps. Not 'glue'

Gutter The narrow space between stamps in the sheet permitting perforation

Gutter margin The blank margins dividing a sheet of stamps into panes

Handstamp A postmark or overprint applied by hand

Imperforate Stamps printed and issued without perforations, deliberately or in error

Imprint The name of the printer or issuing authority inscribed on the stamps or in the sheet margins

Imprinted stamps Stamps other than adhesives, printed direct on postal stationery items (postcards, envelopes, etc)

Jubilee line Coloured line found in the sheet margin of British stamps

'Local' A stamp with geographical limits of postal use and validity. These are not normally listed in the Stanley Gibbons catalogues

'Machin' The name given to GB definitives, first issued in 1967, bearing the Queen's head designed by Arnold Machin

Machine label Postage stamp produced by a micro-processor machine after the insertion of coins of the required value, popularly known as Frama stamps

Maltese cross Name given to the cross-shaped cancellation used on the first British stamps

Margin The unprinted edging surrounding or dividing a sheet of stamps. See also 'Gutter margin'

Maximum card A picture postcard bearing a stamp and cancellation relevant to the picture on the card

Miniature sheet A small sheet of one or several stamps, usually with decorative margins, issued as a souvenir for collectors

Mint A stamp in its original pristine state, with full gum (if so issued), when it is said to have its 'original gum' ('O.G.'). 'Unmounted mint' stamps have not been hinged. Also see 'Unused'

Mulready Envelopes and letter sheets issued by Britain in 1840 with a pictorial motif designed by William Mulready

Non Value Indicator stamp (NVI) A stamp which bears no monetary inscription, but shows the class of postage (1st, 2nd) instead

Obsolete A stamp no longer sold by a post office though it may still be valid for postage

Overprint A printed addition to a stamp. Also see 'Surcharge'

Pair Two unseparated stamps, joined as originally issued

Pane A formation or group of stamps within the sheet. Also see 'Booklet pane'

Perforations Holes punched between stamps in sheets to enable easy separation

Personalised stamp Stamp with an attached non-postal label bearing an image taken from a personal photograph

Phosphor stamps Stamps overprinted or coated with phosphorescent materials recognised by high technology letter sorting machinery

Plate number Letters/numerals in sheet margins identifying printing plates. Also see 'Cylinder number'

Postmark Any mark, such as a cancellation, connected with the postal service and found on items transmitted by post

Presentation pack A philatelic souvenir containing a set of stamps and descriptive text

Prestige booklet Stamp booklet devoted to a particular subject or event and containing special panes of stamps with descriptive text printed alongside

Proof A trial impression taken from an original die or printing plate

Regional Name given by collectors to stamps issued by Royal Mail (who term them Country stamps) for use in England, Scotland, Wales or Northern Ireland. Issues were also made for Guensey and Jersey (until 1969) and the Isle of Man (until 1973)

Seahorse Name given to the high value definitive stamps of King George V

Self-adhesive Gummed stamps (with protective backing) which do not require moistening

Se-tenant Stamps of different design or face value that are joined together

Specimen Sample stamp usually with 'specimen' overprinted or perforated on it

Strip Three or more stamps joined in a row

Tête-bêche A stamp inverted in relation to the adjoining stamp in a pair

Traffic lights Collectors' term for the colour check dots found in sheet margins

Unused An uncancelled stamp, not necessarily 'mint'

Used A stamp which has been postally used and appropriately postmarked

Used abroad Stamps of one country used and postmarked in another

Used on piece Stamp kept on part of the original cover to preserve the complete postmark

Variety A stamp differing in some detail from the normal issue

Watermark A distinctive device or emblem in stamps, formed by 'thinning' of the paper during production. A watermark is normally viewed through the front of the stamp

'Wilding' The name given to British definitive stamps, first issued in 1952, bearing the Queen's head from a photographic portrait by Dorothy Wilding

Wing margin Wide margin on one side of a stamp caused by central perforation of the sheet gutter margin

For other and fuller definitions, see the Stanley Gibbons book *Philatelic Terms Illustrated* by James Mackay.

GREAT BRITAIN 1840 TO DATE

To browse one of the biggest and easiest to use GB websites on the net please visit:

www.british-stamps.com

You will find 1000's of items pictured ranging from basic commemorative sets and single stamps to rare Victorian issues. Also shown are FDC's, Packs and Cards plus Machins, Regionals and Booklets etc etc. There is even a Postal History section with both sides of the cover shown! The site features a secure server so you can "order online" if you wish. Items are added almost daily.

For my Commonwealth stock visit: **www.commonwealth-stamps.com**
For my Foreign stock visit: **www.foreign-stamps.com**
For my USA stock visit: **www.usa-stamps.com**

SG 131 light mounted mint

ROWAN S BAKER

PO BOX 65814, London, EC1P 1NR

email: rowanbaker@btopenworld.com
www.british-stamps.com

Telephone: 0207 812 1030
10.30am to 7.30pm Monday – Friday

"32 years in full time dealing"

How can Stanley Gibbons help you to build your collection?

Our History

Stanley Gibbons started trading in 1856 and we have been at the forefront of stamp collecting for more than 150 years, making us the world's oldest philatelic company. We can help you build your collection in a wide variety of ways – all with the backing of our unrivalled expertise.

When building a collection it helps to know what you have. You can use *Collect British Stamps* as a checklist to highlight all the items you currently own. You can then easily see where the gaps are that you need to fill.

Visit 399 Strand, London, UK

Our world famous stamp shop is a collector's paradise which aims to keep a full range of stock to sell at current catalogue price - so if there are any changes via a different catalogue, then prices will be adjusted accordingly. As well as stamps, the shop stocks albums, accessories and specialist philatelic books. Plan a visit now!

GB Specialist Department

When purchasing high value items you should definitely contact our specialist department for advice and guarantees on the items purchased. You need to make sure you consult the experts to ensure they help you make the right purchase. With Stanley Gibbons this comes with over 150 years of experience. For example, when buying early Victorian stamps our specialists will guide you through the prices – so a penny red SG 43 has many plate numbers which vary in value. We can explain what to look for and where, and help you plan your future collection.

Auctions and Valuations

You might find other ways of buying material to go into your collection, such as through auction – buying at auction can be great fun. You can buy collections and merge them with your own - not forgetting to check your *Collect British Stamps* checklist for gaps. Once again, you do need to make sure the condition of the collection you are buying is comparable to your own.

Stanley Gibbons Auctions have been running since the 1900's. They offer a range of auctions to suit all levels of collectors and dealers. You can of course also sell your collection or individual rare items through our public auctions and regular postal auctions. You can check out charges with the auction department directly (see contact details below).

Stanley Gibbons Publications

Our catalogues are trusted worldwide as the industry standard (see page xlvi for more details).

To keep up to date with new issues you can follow the additions to this listing in our magazine *Gibbons Stamp Monthly*. This is a must-read for all collectors and dealers. It contains news, views and insights into all things philatelic, from beginner to specialist.

Completing the set

When is it cheaper to complete your collection by buying a whole set rather than item by item? You can use the prices in *Collect British Stamps*, which lists single item values and a complete set value, to check if it is better to buy the odd items missing, or a complete set. Some of the definitive sets can be built up over time. The current definitive set is augmented by the Post Office regularly.

Condition

Condition can make a big difference on the price you can pay for an item (see '*The Stanley Gibbons Guide to Stamp Pricing* on p xxxi). The prices in this catalogue are for items undamaged. When building your collection you do need to keep condition in mind and always buy the best condition you can find and afford. Collectors are reminded that for issues from 1936 to date, prices in the unused column are for unmounted mint. This means that the condition of the gum is the same as issued from the Post Office. If the gum is disturbed or has had an adhesion it can be classed as mounted. When buying issues prior to 1936 you should always look for the least amount of disturbance and adhesion. You do have to keep in mind the age of the issue when looking at the condition.

When buying philatelic items listed you need to make sure they are in the same condition as issued by the Post Office. This applies to Presentation packs, were the stamps are issued on a stock card with an information card and held together in a plastic wallet and also to Year Books, which should be in a slip case with a stock card of stamps. The prices quoted are for a complete item in good condition so make sure you check this – and of course that they are complete. You will find some items may appear in different format (e.g. language, different bindings, etc) which will be listed under the normal listing within this catalogue.

Ask the Experts

While you are building your collection, if you need help or guidance, you are welcome to come along to Stanley Gibbons in the Strand and ask for assistance. If you would like to have your collection appraised, you can arrange for a verbal evaluation Monday to Friday 9.00am – 4.30pm. We also provide insurance valuations should you require. Of course this up-to-date catalogue listing can assist with the valuation and may be presented to an insurance agent or company.

See the Stanley Gibbons Contact details: on page xxv.

Features Listing

An at-a-glace guide to what's in the Stanley Gibbons catalogues

Area	Feature	Collect British Stamps	Stamps of the World	Thematic Catalogues	Comprehensive Catalogue, Parts 1-22 (including Commonwealth and British Empire Stamps and country catalogues)	Great Britain Concise	Specialised catalogues
General	SG number	√	√	√	√	√	√
General	Specialised Catalogue number						√
General	Year of issue of first stamp in design	√	√	√	√	√	√
General	Exact date of issue of each design				√	√	√
General	Face value information	√	√	√	√	√	√
General	Historical and geographical information	√	√	√	√	√	√
General	General currency information, including dates used	√	√	√	√	√	√
General	Country name	√	√	√	√	√	√
General	Booklet panes				√	√	√
General	Coil stamps				√		√
General	First Day Covers	√				√	√
General	Brief footnotes on key areas of note	√	√	√	√	√	√
General	Detailed footnotes on key areas of note				√	√	√
General	Extra background information				√	√	√
General	Miniature sheet information (including size in mm)	√	√	√	√	√	√
General	Sheetlets				√		
General	Stamp booklets				√	√	√
General	Perkins Bacon "Cancelled"				√		
General	PHQ Cards	√				√	√
General	Post Office Label Sheets					√	
General	Post Office Yearbooks	√				√	√
General	Presentation and Souvenir Packs	√				√	√
General	*Se-tenant* pairs	√			√		
General	Watermark details - errors, varieties, positions				√	√	√
General	Watermark illustrations	√			√	√	√
General	Watermark types	√			√	√	√
General	Forgeries noted				√		√
General	Surcharges and overprint information	√	√	√	√	√	√
Design and Description	Colour description, simplified		√	√			
Design and Description	Colour description, extended	√			√	√	√
Design and Description	Set design summary information	√	√	√	√	√	√
Design and Description	Designer name				√	√	√
Design and Description	Short design description	√	√	√	√	√	√

Area	Feature	Collect British Stamps	Stamps of the World	Thematic Catalogues	Comprehensive Catalogue, Parts 1-22 (including Commonwealth and British Empire Stamps and country catalogues)	Great Britain Concise	Specialised catalogues
Design and Description	Shade varieties				√	√	√
Design and Description	Type number	√	√		√	√	√
Illustrations	Multiple stamps from set illustrated	√			√	√	√
Illustrations	A Stamp from each set illustrated in full colour (where possible, otherwise mono)	√	√	√	√	√	√
Price	Catalogue used price	√	√	√	√	√	√
Price	Catalogue unused price	√	√	√	√	√	√
Price	Price - booklet panes				√	√	√
Price	Price - shade varieties				√	√	√
Price	On cover and on piece price				√	√	√
Price	Detailed GB pricing breakdown	√			√	√	
Print and Paper	Basic printing process information	√	√	√	√	√	√
Print and Paper	Detailed printing process information, e.g. Mill sheets				√		√
Print and Paper	Paper information				√		√
Print and Paper	Detailed perforation information	√			√	√	√
Print and Paper	Details of research findings relating to printing processes and history						√
Print and Paper	Paper colour	√	√		√	√	√
Print and Paper	Paper description to aid identification					√	√
Print and Paper	Paper type				√	√	√
Print and Paper	Ordinary or chalk-surfaced paper				√	√	
Print and Paper	Embossing omitted note						√
Print and Paper	Essays, Die Proofs, Plate Descriptions and Proofs, Colour Trials information						√
Print and Paper	Glazed paper				√	√	
Print and Paper	Gum details				√		√
Print and Paper	Luminescence/Phosphor bands - general coverage	√			√	√	√
Print and Paper	Luminescence/Phosphor bands - specialised coverage						√
Print and Paper	Overprints and surcharges - including colour information	√	√	√	√	√	√
Print and Paper	Perforation/Imperforate Information	√	√		√	√	√
Print and Paper	Perforation errors and varieties				√	√	√
Print and Paper	Print quantities				√		√
Print and Paper	Printing errors				√	√	√
Print and Paper	Printing flaws				√		√
Print and Paper	Printing varieties				√	√	√
Print and Paper	Punctured stamps - where official				√		
Print and Paper	Sheet positions				√	√	√
Print and Paper	Specialised plate number information						√
Print and Paper	Specimen overprints (only for Commonwealth & GB)				√	√	√
Print and Paper	Underprints					√	√
Print and Paper	Visible Plate numbers	√			√	√	√
Print and Paper	Yellow and Green paper listings				√		√
Index	Design index	√			√	√	

Stanley Gibbons Publications

1 Commonwealth & British Empire Stamps 1840–1970

Commonwealth Country Catalogues
Australia and Dependencies (6th edition, 2010)
Bangladesh, Pakistan & Sri Lanka
(1st edition, 2004)
Belize, Guyana, Trinidad & Tobago
(1st edition, 2009)
Brunei, Malaysia & Singapore
(3rd edition, 2009)
Canada (3rd edition, 2008)
Central Africa (2nd edition, 2008)
Cyprus, Gibraltar & Malta (2nd edition, 2008)
East Africa with Egypt and Sudan
(2nd edition, 2010)
Eastern Pacific (1st edition, 2007)
Falkland Islands (4th edition, 2010)
Hong Kong (3rd edition, 2010)
India (including Convention and Feudatory States)
(3rd edition, 2009)
Indian Ocean (1st edition, 2006)
Ireland (4th edition, 2008)
Leeward Islands (1st edition, 2007)
New Zealand (4th edition, 2010)
Northern Caribbean, Bahamas & Bermuda
(2nd edition, 2009)
St. Helena & Dependencies (3rd edition, 2007)
Southern Africa (2nd edition, 2007)
West Africa (1st edition, 2009)
Western Pacific (2nd edition, 2009)
Windward Islands and Barbados
(1st edition, 2007)

Foreign Countries
2 **Austria & Hungary** (7th edition, 2009)
3 **Balkans** (5th edition, 2009)
4 **Benelux** (6th edition, 2010)
5 **Czechoslovakia & Poland** (6th edition, 2002)
6 **France** (7th edition, 2010)
7 **Germany** (8th edition, 2007)
8 **Italy & Switzerland** (7th edition, 2010)
9 **Portugal & Spain** (5th edition, 2004)
10 **Russia** (6th edition, 2008)
11 **Scandinavia** (6th edition, 2008)
12 **Africa since Independence A-E** (2nd edition, 1983)
13 **Africa since Independence F-M** (1st edition, 1981)
14 **Africa since Independence N-Z** (1st edition, 1981)
15 **Central America** (3rd edition, 2007)
16 **Central Asia** (4th edition, 2006)

17 **China** (7th edition, 2006)
18 **Japan & Korea** (5th edition, 2008)
19 **Middle East** (7th edition, 2009)
20 **South America** (4th edition, 2008)
21 **South-East Asia** (4th edition, 2004)
22 **United States** (7th edition, 2010)

Great Britain Specialised Catalogues
Volume 1   **Queen Victoria** (15th edition, 2008)
Volume 2   **King Edward VII to King George VI**
(13th edition, 2009)
Volume 3   **Queen Elizabeth II Pre-decimal issues**
(11th edition, 2006)
Volume 4   **Queen Elizabeth II Decimal Definitive**
Issues – Part 1 (10th edition, 2008)
Part 2 (2010)
Volume 5   **Queen Elizabeth II Decimal Special**
Issues (3rd edition, 1998 with 1998-99 and
2000/1 Supplements)

Thematic Catalogues
Stanley Gibbons Catalogues for use with **Stamps of the
World.**
Collect Aircraft on Stamps (2nd edition, 2009)
Collect Birds on Stamps (5th edition, 2003)
Collect Chess on Stamps (2nd edition, 1999)
Collect Fish on Stamps (1st edition, 1999)
Collect Motor Vehicles on Stamps
(1st edition 2004)

Other Publications
Philatelic Terms Illustrated (4th edition, 2003)
Collect British Stamps (61st edition, 2010)
Great Britain Concise Stamp Catalogue
(25th edition, 2010)
How to Identify Stamps (4th edition, 2007)
Collect Channel Islands and Isle of Man Stamps
(26th edition, 2010)
Great Britain Numbers Issued (3rd edition, 2008)
Enjoy Stamp Collecting (7th edition, 2006)

For other titles, and further details on the above, please
see *www.stanleygibbons.com*

STANLEY GIBBONS

GREAT BRITAIN SPECIALIST DEPARTMENT

BY APPOINTMENT TO
HER MAJESTY THE QUEEN
STANLEY GIBBONS LTD
LONDON
PHILATELISTS

We invite collectors and specialists to have access to one of the finest selections of GB stock in the world by registering to receive our renowned free monthly colour brochure of between 500-550 specialist items from across the whole GB collecting spectrum, from pre-stamp postal history through to modern QE II errors.

Please contact Mark Facey on 020 7557 4424 or Michael Barrell on 020 7557 4448 or email mfacey@stanleygibbons.co.uk or mbarrell@stanleygibbons.co.uk to register.

Stanley Gibbons Limited, 399 Strand, London WC2R 0LX
Tel: 020 7836 8444   Fax: 020 7836 7342
To view all our stock 24 hours a day visit www.stanleygibbons.com

Guide to Entries

A **Accession to the Throne**

B **Illustration** – Generally all stamps illustrated. To comply with Post Office regulations illustrations are reduced to 75%, with overprints shown actual size.

C **Illustration or Type Number** – These numbers are used to help identify stamps, in the type column.

D **Date of Issue** – When a set of definitive stamps have been issued over several years the Year Date given is for the earliest issue, commemorative sets are set in chronological order.

E **Phosphor Description** – Phosphorised paper is activated by ultraviolet light.

F **Perforations** – The 'perforation' is the number of holes in a length of 2cm, as measured by the Stanley Gibbons *Instanta* gauge. From 1992 certain stamps occur with a large elliptical (oval) hole inserted in each line of vertical perforations. From 2009 certain stamps have U-shaped die-cut slits.

G **Stanley Gibbons Catalogue Number** – This is a unique number for each stamp to help the collector identify stamps, in the listing. The Stanley Gibbons numbering system is universally recognized as definitive, where insufficient numbers have been left to provide for additional stamps listings, some stamps will have a suffix letter after the catalogue number.

H **Catalogue Value** – Mint/Unused. Prices quoted for pre-1945 stamps are for lightly hinged examples. Prices quoted of unused King Edward VIII to Queen Elizabeth issues are for unmounted mint.

I **Catalogue Value** – Used. Prices generally refer to fine postally used examples.

Prices

Before February 1971 British currency was:

£1 = 20s One pound = twenty shillings *and*
1s = 12d One Shilling = 12 pence

Under decimalisation this became:

£1 = 100p One pound = one hundred (new) pence

Shown in Catalogue as	Explanation
10	10 pence
1.75	£1.75
15.00	£15
£150	£150
£2300	£2300

J **Face Value** – This refers to the value of the stamp and is sold at the Post Office when issued. Some modern stamps do not have their values in figures but instead shown as a letter.

K **Type Number** – Indicates a design type on which stamp is based. These are bold figures found below each illustration. The type numbers are also given in bold in the second column of figures alongside the stamp description to indicate the design of each stamp.

L **Colour** – Colour of stamps (if fewer than four colours, otherwise noted as 'multicoloured').

M **Sets of Stamps** – Two or more stamps with a common theme or subject.

N **First Day Covers** – Prices for first day covers are for complete sets used on plain covers or on special covers.

O **Presentation Packs** – Special packs consisting of the issue and slip-in cards with printed information inside a protective covering.

P **PHQ Cards** – Each card shows a large reproduction of a current British stamp.

Q **Sets of Gutters** – The term is used for a pair of stamps separated by part of the blank gutter margin or with Traffic Lights on the gutter margin.

R **Footnote** – Further information on background or key facts on issues.

S **Other Types of Stamps** – Postage Dues, Officials and Regional Issues

T **Number Prefix** – Stamps other than definitives and commemoratives have a prefix letter before the catalogue number.

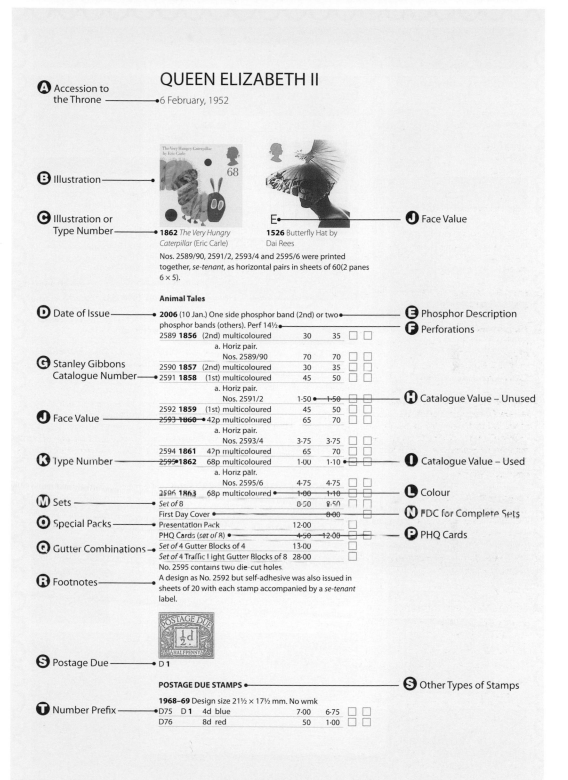

QUEEN ELIZABETH II

A Accession to the Throne — 6 February, 1952

B Illustration —

C Illustration or Type Number — **1862** *The Very Hungry Caterpillar* (Eric Carle)

E — **1526** Butterfly Hat by Dai Rees

J Face Value

Nos. 2589/90, 2591/2, 2593/4 and 2595/6 were printed together, *se-tenant*, as horizontal pairs in sheets of 60(2 panes 6 × 5).

Animal Tales

D Date of Issue — **2006** (10 Jan.) One side phosphor band (2nd) or two phosphor bands (others). Perf 14½

E Phosphor Description
F Perforations

2589 **1856**	(2nd) multicoloured	30	35	☐	☐
	a. Horiz pair. Nos. 2589/90	70	70	☐	☐
2590 **1857**	(2nd) multicoloured	30	35	☐	☐
2591 **1858**	(1st) multicoloured	45	50	☐	☐
	a. Horiz pair. Nos. 2591/2	1·50	1·50	☐	☐
2592 **1859**	(1st) multicoloured	45	50	☐	☐
2593 **1860**	42p multicoloured	65	70	☐	☐
	a. Horiz pair. Nos. 2593/4	3·75	3·75	☐	☐
2594 **1861**	42p multicoloured	65	70	☐	☐
2595 **1862**	68p multicoloured	1·00	1·10	☐	☐
	a. Horiz pair. Nos. 2595/6	4·75	4·75	☐	☐
2596 **1863**	68p multicoloured	1·00	1·10	☐	☐
Set of 8		8·50	8·50	☐	
First Day Cover			8·00		
Presentation Pack		12·00		☐	
PHQ Cards (*set of 8*)		4·50	12·00	☐	☐
Set of 4 Gutter Blocks of 4		13·00		☐	
Set of 4 Traffic Light Gutter Blocks of 8		28·00		☐	

G Stanley Gibbons Catalogue Number

J Face Value

K Type Number

H Catalogue Value – Unused

I Catalogue Value – Used

L Colour

N FDC for Complete Sets

P PHQ Cards

M Sets

O Special Packs

Q Gutter Combinations

R Footnotes — No. 2595 contains two die-cut holes. A design as No. 2592 but self-adhesive was also issued in sheets of 20 with each stamp accompanied by a *se-tenant* label.

S Postage Due — D **1**

S Other Types of Stamps — **POSTAGE DUE STAMPS**

1968–69 Design size 21½ × 17½ mm. No wmk

T Number Prefix —

D75	D **1**	4d blue	7·00	6·75	☐	☐
D76		8d red	50	1·00	☐	☐

Quite Exceptional Offers
Just compare and save at Rushstamps

GERMAN EDWARD VII TRIALS

Produced in 1913 in Blue with "zig zag" watermark.
Imperf single at just **£120.00**

WOULD YOU PAY £15 FOR THIS STAMP?

Ask for the latest list of Commemoratives, including Complete Year Units at the very best prices **COMPARE AND SAVE!**

1000 MINT GREAT BRITAIN!

All issued before 1971 in singles, blocks and multiples to include Commoratives Definitives and Regionals. The face value alone is over £30.
SPECIAL "CBS" OFFER £19.50

DO YOU COLLECT GB ERRORS/VARIETIES

Ask for photocopies (please state your interests)

2010 LONDON 'SPECIAL' OPD MINIATURE SHEET

On Sale for 8 days only.....**Contact us for a very special price**

CHANNEL ISLANDS AND IOM SOUVENIR FDC'S

100 Different Souvenir FDC's, Superb Selection.......... **£25.00**

1929 £1 PUC OFFICIAL ROYAL MAIL REPRINT

ONLY **£5.00**

STARTER COLLECTION OF QUEEN VICTORIA AND EDWARD VII USED OFFICIALS

10 stamps * **AT ONLY** **£6.95**

2000 £1 CORONATION

On Official Royal mail card with Westminster Abbey cancellation
SG MS2147.................... **£3.95**

1897 DIAMOND JUBILEE 'PHANTOMS

½d., 1d. 2d and 3d.
Normally £11 Only **£3.50**

WORLDWIDE KILOWARE

A really good assortment accumulated from various sources, mainly on paper, including some older material, plenty of smaller countries and higher and unusual values
Lots of sorting! Per ½ Kilo (approx. 2,500 stamps) .... **£22.00** (UK post paid)

*Ask for full details of contents which will really surprise you.

FDC EXTRA SPECIAL

100 different G.B. commemoratives, definitives & regional souvenir first day covers. To good to miss.
ONLY **£24.00**
150 different **£49.00**

G.B. HI-VAL COLLECTION

All Used, 1883 to 1993 £10 Britannia 42 different stamps * Normally cat over £1000 'One of our best sellers'.
ONLY **£84.50**

SMILERS SHEETLETS

Compare and Save Special 35% Discount Offer Compare and Save! Ask for listing.

MACHIN 1999 20p. Imperforated Pair Error SG Y1681a Unmounted mint Contact us for a very special price to tempt you

BUMPER G.B. ONLY, FOREIGN OR WORLDWIDE ONLY BONUS MIXED LOTS

A real pot-pouri – a wonderful selection on album pages, stock leaves, packets, loose etc. with little duplication – great value. Satisfaction or refund
Lots at ....£25, £50 and £100 (Please state which required)

CAN YOU REFUSE THIS OFFER? Send us £2 (coins, stamps, P.O or cheque) and we will forward our latest 144 page G.B. RushExpress, together with a special **"Mystery Free Gift"** and a **"£5 Credit Note"** to be used against your first order over £10! Too good to miss! Mention CBS please. You will not be disappointed.

YES - WE ALSO BUY - GB also

British Commonwealth & Foreign. Top prices – Prompt Payment. Send for offer or write with details. Complimentary Courier Collection Service available for faraway / bulky lots.

We accept Mastercard and Visa credit/debit cards. UK orders post paid

Visit our website at
www.rushstamps.co.uk

RUSHSTAMPS (RETAIL) LTD.
P.O BOX ONE, LYNDHURST, HAMPSHIRE, ENGLAND SO43 7PP
TEL: (023) 8028 2044, FAX: (023) 8028 2981

E-mail: enquiries@rushstamps.co.uk

QUEEN VICTORIA

1837 (20 June)–1901 (22 Jan.)

5 **8** **6**

9 Watermark extending over three stamps

IDENTIFICATION. In this checklist Victorian stamps are classified firstly according to which printing method was used –line-engraving, embossing or surface-printing.

Corner letters. Numerous stamps also have letters in all four, or just the lower corners. These were an anti-forgery device and the letters differ from stamp to stamp. If present in all four corners the upper pair are the reverse of the lower. Note the importance of these corner letters in the way the checklist is arranged.

Watermarks. Further classification depends on watermarks: these are illustrated in normal position, with stamps priced accordingly.

1 Line-engraved Issues

1

1a

1b

3 White lines added above and below head

2 Small Crown watermark

4 Large Crown watermark

Letters in lower corners

1840 Wmk Small Crown Type 2 Imperforate

2	**i**	1d black	£10000	£275	☐	☐
5	**1a**	2d blue	£30000	£675	☐	☐

1841

8	**1b**	1d red brown	£500	25·00	☐	☐
14	**3**	2d blue	£4250	75·00	☐	☐

1854–57 (i) Wmk Small Crown Type 2 Perf 16

17	**1b**	1d red-brown	£300	25·00	☐	☐
19	**3**	2d blue	£3750	90·00	☐	☐

(ii) Wmk Small Crown Type 2 Perf 14

24	**1b**	1d red-brown	£600	60·00	☐	☐
23	**3**	2d blue	£7750	£200	☐	☐

(iii) Wmk Large Crown Type 4 Perf 16

26	**1b**	1d red	£1800	£110	☐	☐
27	**3**	2d blue	£12000	£375	☐	☐

(iv) Wmk Large Crown Type 4 Perf 14

40	**1b**	1d red	45·00	10·00	☐	☐
34	**3**	2d blue	£2250	60·00	☐	☐

7

Letters in all four corners

Plate numbers. Stamps included a 'plate number' in their design and this affects valuation. The cheapest plates are priced here; see complete list of plate numbers overleaf.

1858–70 (i) Wmk Type 9 Perf 14

48	**7**	½d red		90·00	18·00	☐ ☐

(ii) Wmk Large Crown Type 4 Perf 14

43	**5**	1d red		18·00	2·50	☐ ☐
51	**8**	1½d red		£400	60·00	☐ ☐
45	**6**	2d blue		£300	12·00	☐ ☐

Plate numbers on stamps 1858-70 having letters in all four corners

Positions of Plate Numbers

Shows Plate 9 (½d)   Shows Plate 170 (1d, 2d)   Shows Plate 3 (1½d)

HALFPENNY VALUE (SG 48)

48	*Plate 1*	£275	75·00	☐ ☐
48	*Plate 3*	£200	40·00	☐ ☐
48	*Plate 4*	£130	30·00	☐ ☐
48	*Plate 5*	90·00	18·00	☐ ☐
48	*Plate 6*	£100	18·00	☐ ☐
48	*Plate 8*	£500	£100	☐ ☐
48	*Plate 9*	£5500	£700	☐ ☐
48	*Plate 10*	£110	18·00	☐ ☐
48	*Plate 11*	£100	18·00	☐ ☐
48	*Plate 12*	£100	18·00	☐ ☐
48	*Plate 13*	£100	18·00	☐ ☐
48	*Plate 14*	£100	18·00	☐ ☐
48	*Plate 15*	£150	40·00	☐ ☐
48	*Plate 19*	£250	55·00	☐ ☐
48	*Plate 20*	£300	75·00	☐ ☐

PENNY VALUE (SG 43)

43	*Plate 71*	45·00	3·50	☐ ☐
43	*Plate 72*	50·00	4·50	☐ ☐
43	*Plate 73*	50·00	3·50	☐ ☐
43	*Plate 74*	50·00	2·50	☐ ☐
43	*Plate 76*	40·00	2·50	☐ ☐

43	Plate 77	—		☐	☐	43	Plate 145	35·00	2·75	☐	☐
43	Plate 78	£110	2·50	☐	☐	43	Plate 146	45·00	6·50	☐	☐
43	Plate 79	38·00	2·50	☐	☐	43	Plate 147	55·00	3·50	☐	☐
43	Plate 80	55·00	2·50	☐	☐	43	Plate 148	45·00	3·50	☐	☐
43	Plate 81	55·00	2·75	☐	☐	43	Plate 149	45·00	6·50	☐	☐
43	Plate 82	£110	4·50	☐	☐	43	Plate 150	18·00	2·50	☐	☐
43	Plate 83	£140	8·00	☐	☐	43	Plate 151	65·00	10·00	☐	☐
43	Plate 84	70·00	2·75	☐	☐	43	Plate 152	65·00	6·00	☐	☐
43	Plate 85	50·00	3·75	☐	☐	43	Plate 153	£110	10·00	☐	☐
43	Plate 86	60·00	4·50	☐	☐	43	Plate 154	55·00	2·50	☐	☐
43	Plate 87	38·00	2·50	☐	☐	43	Plate 155	55·00	2·75	☐	☐
43	Plate 88	£170	8·50	☐	☐	43	Plate 156	50·00	2·50	☐	☐
43	Plate 89	50·00	2·50	☐	☐	43	Plate 157	55·00	2·50	☐	☐
43	Plate 90	50·00	2·50	☐	☐	43	Plate 158	35·00	2·50	☐	☐
43	Plate 91	60·00	6·50	☐	☐	43	Plate 159	35·00	2·50	☐	☐
43	Plate 92	40·00	2·50	☐	☐	43	Plate 160	35·00	2·50	☐	☐
43	Plate 93	55·00	2·50	☐	☐	43	Plate 161	65·00	8·00	☐	☐
43	Plate 94	50·00	5·50	☐	☐	43	Plate 162	55·00	8·00	☐	☐
43	Plate 95	45·00	2·50	☐	☐	43	Plate 163	55·00	3·50	☐	☐
43	Plate 96	50·00	2·50	☐	☐	43	Plate 164	55·00	3·50	☐	☐
43	Plate 97	45·00	4·00	☐	☐	43	Plate 165	50·00	2·50	☐	☐
43	Plate 98	55·00	6·50	☐	☐	43	Plate 166	50·00	6·50	☐	☐
43	Plate 99	60·00	5·50	☐	☐	43	Plate 167	50·00	2·50	☐	☐
43	Plate 100	65·00	2·75	☐	☐	43	Plate 168	55·00	9·00	☐	☐
43	Plate 101	65·00	10·00	☐	☐	43	Plate 169	65·00	8·00	☐	☐
43	Plate 102	50·00	2·50	☐	☐	43	Plate 170	40·00	2·50	☐	☐
43	Plate 103	55·00	4·00	☐	☐	43	Plate 171	18·00	2·50	☐	☐
43	Plate 104	80·00	5·50	☐	☐	43	Plate 172	35·00	2·50	☐	☐
43	Plate 105	£110	8·00	☐	☐	43	Plate 173	75·00	10·00	☐	☐
43	Plate 106	60·00	2·50	☐	☐	43	Plate 174	35·00	2·50	☐	☐
43	Plate 107	65·00	8·00	☐	☐	43	Plate 175	65·00	4·00	☐	☐
43	Plate 108	85·00	2·75	☐	☐	43	Plate 176	65·00	2·75	☐	☐
43	Plate 109	90·00	4·00	☐	☐	43	Plate 177	45·00	2·50	☐	☐
43	Plate 110	65·00	10·00	☐	☐	43	Plate 178	65·00	4·00	☐	☐
43	Plate 111	55·00	2·75	☐	☐	43	Plate 179	55·00	2·75	☐	☐
43	Plate 112	75·00	2·75	☐	☐	43	Plate 180	65·00	5·50	☐	☐
43	Plate 113	55·00	14·00	☐	☐	43	Plate 181	50·00	2·50	☐	☐
43	Plate 114	£290	14·00	☐	☐	43	Plate 182	£100	5·50	☐	☐
43	Plate 115	£110	2·75	☐	☐	43	Plate 183	60·00	3·50	☐	☐
43	Plate 116	80·00	10·00	☐	☐	43	Plate 184	35·00	2·75	☐	☐
43	Plate 117	50·00	2·50	☐	☐	43	Plate 185	55·00	3·50	☐	☐
43	Plate 118	55·00	2·50	☐	☐	43	Plate 186	70·00	2·75	☐	☐
43	Plate 119	50·00	2·50	☐	☐	43	Plate 187	55·00	2·50	☐	☐
43	Plate 120	18·00	2·50	☐	☐	43	Plate 188	75·00	11·00	☐	☐
43	Plate 121	45·00	10·00	☐	☐	43	Plate 189	75·00	7·50	☐	☐
43	Plate 122	18·00	2·50	☐	☐	43	Plate 190	55·00	6·50	☐	☐
43	Plate 123	45·00	2·50	☐	☐	43	Plate 191	35·00	8·00	☐	☐
43	Plate 124	32·00	2·50	☐	☐	43	Plate 192	55·00	2·50	☐	☐
43	Plate 125	45·00	2·50	☐	☐	43	Plate 193	35·00	2·50	☐	☐
43	Plate 127	60·00	2·75	☐	☐	43	Plate 194	55·00	9·00	☐	☐
43	Plate 129	45·00	9·00	☐	☐	43	Plate 195	55·00	9·00	☐	☐
43	Plate 130	60·00	2·75	☐	☐	43	Plate 196	55·00	5·50	☐	☐
43	Plate 131	70·00	18·00	☐	☐	43	Plate 197	60·00	10·00	☐	☐
43	Plate 132	£150	25·00	☐	☐	43	Plate 198	45·00	6·50	☐	☐
43	Plate 133	£125	10·00	☐	☐	43	Plate 199	60·00	6·50	☐	☐
43	Plate 134	18·00	2·50	☐	☐	43	Plate 200	65·00	2·50	☐	☐
43	Plate 135	£100	28·00	☐	☐	43	Plate 201	35·00	5·50	☐	☐
43	Plate 136	£100	22·00	☐	☐	43	Plate 202	65·00	9·00	☐	☐
43	Plate 137	32·00	2·75	☐	☐	43	Plate 203	35·00	18·00	☐	☐
43	Plate 138	22·00	2·50	☐	☐	43	Plate 204	60·00	2·75	☐	☐
43	Plate 139	65·00	18·00	☐	☐	43	Plate 205	60·00	3·50	☐	☐
43	Plate 140	22·00	2·50	☐	☐	43	Plate 206	60·00	10·00	☐	☐
43	Plate 141	£125	10·00	☐	☐	43	Plate 207	65·00	10·00	☐	☐
43	Plate 142	75·00	28·00	☐	☐	43	Plate 208	60·00	18·00	☐	☐
43	Plate 143	65·00	16·00	☐	☐	43	Plate 209	55·00	10·00	☐	☐
43	Plate 144	£100	22·00	☐	☐	43	Plate 210	70·00	13·00	☐	☐

43	Plate 211	75·00	22·00	☐ ☐
43	Plate 212	65·00	12·00	☐ ☐
43	Plate 213	65·00	12·00	☐ ☐
43	Plate 214	70·00	20·00	☐ ☐
43	Plate 215	70·00	20·00	☐ ☐
43	Plate 216	75·00	20·00	☐ ☐
43	Plate 217	75·00	8·00	☐ ☐
43	Plate 218	70·00	9·00	☐ ☐
43	Plate 219	£100	75·00	☐ ☐
43	Plate 220	45·00	8·00	☐ ☐
43	Plate 221	75·00	18·00	☐ ☐
43	Plate 222	85·00	45·00	☐ ☐
43	Plate 223	£120	65·00	☐ ☐
43	Plate 224	£150	55·00	☐ ☐
43	Plate 225	£3000	£700	☐ ☐

Plates 69, 70, 75, 77, 126 and 128 were prepared but rejected. No stamps therefore exist, except for a very few from Plate 77 which somehow reached the public. Plate 177 stamps, by accident or design, are sometimes passed off as the rare Plate 77.

THREE-HALFPENNY VALUE (S.G. 52)

52	Plate (1)	£600	80·00	☐ ☐
52	Plate 3	£400	60·00	☐ ☐

Plate 1 did not have the plate number in the design. Plate 2 was not completed and no stamps exist.

TWOPENNY VALUE (S.G. 45)

45	Plate 7	£1400	50·00	☐ ☐
45	Plate 8	£1300	35·00	☐ ☐
45	Plate 9	£300	12·00	☐ ☐
45	Plate 12	£2200	£120	☐ ☐
45	Plate 13	£325	22·00	☐ ☐
45	Plate 14	£425	30·00	☐ ☐
45	Plate 15	£400	30·00	☐ ☐

Plates 10 and 11 were prepared but rejected.

2 Embossed Issues

Prices are for stamps cut square and with average to fine embossing. Stamps with exceptionally clear embossing are worth more.

12

11

10

13

1847–54 Wmk 13 (6d), no wmk (others) Imperforate

59	**12**	6d lilac	£13000	£900	☐ ☐
57	**11**	10d brown	£8000	£1200	☐ ☐
54	**10**	1s green	£16000	£850	☐ ☐

3 Surface-printed Issues

IDENTIFICATION. Check first whether the design includes corner letters or not, as mentioned for 'Line-engraved Issues'. The checklist is divided up according to whether any letters are small or large, also whether they are white (uncoloured) or printed in the colour of the stamp. Further identification then depends on watermark.

PERFORATION. Except for Nos. 126/9 all the following issues of Queen Victoria are perf 14.

14

15   **16**   **17**

18   **19**   **20** Emblems

No corner letters

1855–57 (i) Wmk Small Garter Type 15

62	**14**	4d red	£7000	£375	☐ ☐

(ii) Wmk Medium Garter Type 16

65	**14**	4d red	£7500	£375	☐ ☐

(iii) Wmk Large Garter Type 17

66a	**14**	4d red	£1350	£110	☐ ☐

(iv) Wmk Emblems Type 20

70	**18**	6d lilac	£1100	95·00	☐ ☐
72	**19**	1s green	£2500	£260	☐ ☐

Plate numbers. Stamps Nos. 90/163 should be checked for the 'plate numbers' indicated, as this affects valuation (the cheapest plates are priced here). The mark 'Pl.' shows that several numbers exist, priced in separate list overleaf.

Plate numbers are the small numerals appearing in duplicate in some part of the frame design or adjacent to the lower corner letters (in the 5s value a single numeral above the lower inscription).

21   **22**   **23**

24   **25**

Small white corner letters

1862–64 Wmk Emblems Type 20, except 4d (Large Garter Type 17)

76	**21**	3d red	£2000	£250	☐ ☐
80	**22**	4d red	£1500	90·00	☐ ☐
84	**23**	6d lilac	£1700	90·00	☐ ☐
87	**24**	9d bistre	£3500	£350	☐ ☐
90	**25**	1s green Pl.	£2500	£200	☐ ☐

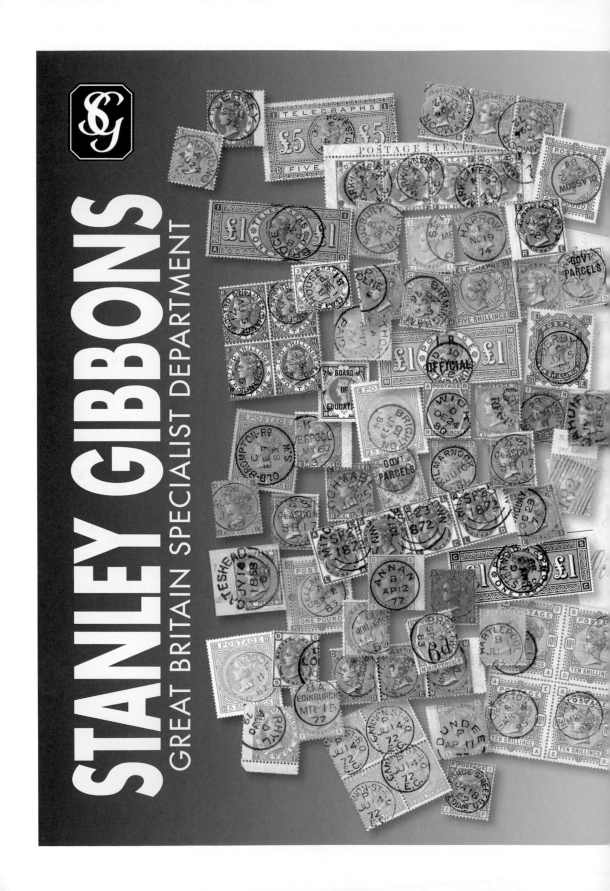

STANLEY GIBBONS

GREAT BRITAIN SPECIALIST DEPARTMENT

We invite collectors and specialists to have access to one of the finest selections of GB stock in the world by registering to receive our renowned free monthly colour brochure of between 500-550 specialist items from across the whole GB collecting spectrum, from pre-stamp postal history through to modern QE II errors.

Please contact Mark Facey on 020 7557 4424 or Michael Barrell on 020 7557 4448 or email mfacey@stanleygibbons.co.uk or mbarrell@stanleygibbons.co.uk to register.

Stanley Gibbons Limited, 399 Strand, London WC2R 0LX
Tel: 020 7836 8444   Fax: 020 7836 7342
To view all our stock 24 hours a day visit www.stanleygibbons.com

26   **27**   **28** Hyphen in SIX-PENCE

29   **30**   **31**

Large white corner letters

1865–67 Wmk Emblems Type 20 except 4d (Large Garter Type 17)

92	**26**	3d red (Plate 4)	£1900	£180	☐	☐
94	**27**	4d vermilion Pl.	£450	55·00	☐	☐
97	**28**	6d lilac Pl.	£900	80·00	☐	☐
98	**29**	9d straw Pl.	£4250	£500	☐	☐
99	**30**	10d brown (Plate 1)	*	£42000	☐	☐
101	**31**	1s green (Plate 4)	£2200	£200	☐	☐

32   **33** Spray of Rose   **34**

1867–80 Wmk Spray of Rose Type 33

103	**26**	3d red Pl.	£450	55·00	☐	☐
105	**28**	6d lilac (with hyphen) (Plate 6)	£1500	80·00	☐	☐
109		6d mauve (without hyphen) Pl.	£550	80·00	☐	☐
110	**29**	9d straw (Plate 4)	£2000	£275	☐	☐
112	**30**	10d brown Pl.	£2800	£300	☐	☐
117	**31**	1s green Pl.	£650	35·00	☐	☐
118	**32**	2s blue Pl.	£3250	£175	☐	☐
121		2s brown (Plate 1)	£20000	£3250	☐	☐

1872–73 Wmk Spray of Rose Type 33

122b	**34**	6d brown Pl.	£575	50·00	☐	☐
125		6d grey (Plate 12)	£1600	£225	☐	☐

PLATE NUMBERS ON STAMPS OF 1862–83
Small White Corner Letters (1862–64)

90	*Plate 2*	1s green	£2500	£200	☐	☐
90	*Plate 3*		£32000		☐	☐

Plate 2 is actually numbered as '1' and Plate 3 as '2' on the stamps.

Large White Corner Letters (1865–83)

103	*Plate 4*	3d red	£1500	£250	☐	☐
103	*Plate 5*		£450	55·00	☐	☐
103	*Plate 6*		£475	55·00	☐	☐
103	*Plate 7*		£550	60·00	☐	☐
103	*Plate 8*		£525	55·00	☐	☐
103	*Plate 9*		£525	60·00	☐	☐
103	*Plate 10*		£775	£120	☐	☐
94	*Plate 7*	4d verm	£600	£100	☐	☐
94	*Plate 8*		£500	60·00	☐	☐
94	*Plate 9*		£500	60·00	☐	☐

94	*Plate 10*		£700	£130	☐	☐
94	*Plate 11*		£500	60·00	☐	☐
94	*Plate 12*		£475	55·00	☐	☐
94	*Plate 13*		£550	55·00	☐	☐
94	*Plate 14*		£600	85·00	☐	☐
97	*Plate 5*	6d lilac	£900	80·00	☐	☐
97	*Plate 6*		£3000	£150	☐	☐
109	*Plate 8*	6d mauve	£600	£120	☐	☐
109	*Plate 9*		£550	80·00	☐	☐
109	*Plate 10*		*	£30000	☐	☐
123	*Plate 11*	6d buff	£800	£100	☐	☐
123	*Plate 12*		£3000	£280	☐	☐
98	*Plate 4*	9d straw	£4250	£500	☐	☐
98	*Plate 5*		£18000		☐	☐
114	*Plate 1*	10d brown	£2800	£300	☐	☐
114	*Plate 2*		£45000	£14000	☐	☐
117	*Plate 4*	1s green	£1200	60·00	☐	☐
117	*Plate 5*		£650	35·00	☐	☐
117	*Plate 6*		£1000	35·00	☐	☐
117	*Plate 7*		£1200	70·00	☐	☐
119	*Plate 1*	2s blue	£3250	£175	☐	☐
119	*Plate 3*		*	£12000	☐	☐
127	*Plate 1*	5s red	£8250	£600	☐	☐
127	*Plate 2*		£12500	£1200	☐	☐

Large Coloured Corner Letters (1873–83)

139	*Plate 1*	2½d mauve	£525	80·00	☐	☐
139	*Plate 2*		£525	80·00	☐	☐
139	*Plate 3*		£800	£120	☐	☐
141	*Plate 3*	2½d mauve	£1100	£110	☐	☐
141	*Plate 4*		£425	50·00	☐	☐
141	*Plate 5*		£425	50·00	☐	☐
141	*Plate 6*		£425	50·00	☐	☐
141	*Plate 7*		£425	50·00	☐	☐
141	*Plate 8*		£425	50·00	☐	☐
141	*Plate 9*		£425	50·00	☐	☐
141	*Plate 10*		£475	65·00	☐	☐
141	*Plate 11*		£425	50·00	☐	☐
141	*Plate 12*		£425	50·00	☐	☐
141	*Plate 13*		£425	50·00	☐	☐
141	*Plate 14*		£425	50·00	☐	☐
141	*Plate 15*		£425	50·00	☐	☐
141	*Plate 16*		£425	50·00	☐	☐
141	*Plate 17*		£1400	£275	☐	☐
142	*Plate 17*	2½d blue	£475	55·00	☐	☐
142	*Plate 18*		£475	40·00	☐	☐
142	*Plate 19*		£475	40·00	☐	☐
142	*Plate 20*		£475	40·00	☐	☐
157	*Plate 21*	2½d blue	£400	35·00	☐	☐
157	*Plate 22*		£350	35·00	☐	☐
157	*Plate 23*		£350	28·00	☐	☐
144	*Plate 11*	3d red	£350	45·00	☐	☐
144	*Plate 12*		£400	45·00	☐	☐
144	*Plate 14*		£425	45·00	☐	☐
144	*Plate 15*		£350	45·00	☐	☐
144	*Plate 16*		£350	45·00	☐	☐
144	*Plate 17*		£400	45·00	☐	☐
144	*Plate 18*		£400	45·00	☐	☐
144	*Plate 19*		£350	45·00	☐	☐
144	*Plate 20*		£650	£100	☐	☐
158	*Plate 20*	3d red	£775	£140	☐	☐
158	*Plate 21*		£400	80·00	☐	☐
152	*Plate 15*	4d verm	£2400	£425	☐	☐
152	*Plate 16*		*	£30000	☐	☐
153	*Plate 15*	4d green	£1100	£275	☐	☐
153	*Plate 16*		£1000	£250	☐	☐

153	*Plate 17*		*	£17500		
160	*Plate 17*	4d brown	£350	60·00		
160	*Plate 18*		£350	60·00		
147	*Plate 13*	6d grey	£400	60·00		
147	*Plate 14*		£400	60·00		
147	*Plate 15*		£400	60·00		
147	*Plate 16*		£400	60·00		
147	*Plate 17*		£750	£140		
161	*Plate 17*	6d grey	£400	65·00		
161	*Plate 18*		£350	65·00		
150	*Plate 8*	1s green	£650	£120		
150	*Plate 9*		£650	£120		
150	*Plate 10*		£600	£140		
150	*Plate 11*		£600	£120		
150	*Plate 12*		£500	£100		
150	*Plate 13*		£500	£100		
150	*Plate 14*		*	£35000		
163	*Plate 13*	1s brown	£675	£140		
163	*Plate 14*		£550	£140		

35   **36**   **37**

38

39 Maltese Cross

40 Large Anchor

1867–83 (i) Wmk Maltese Cross Type 39 Perf 15½ × 15

126	**35**	5s red Pl.	£8250	£600		
128	**36**	10s grey (Plate 1)	£50000	£2800		
129	**37**	£1 brown (Plate 1)	£80000	£4000		

(ii) Wmk Large Anchor Type 40 Perf 14

134	**35**	5s red (Plate 4)	£27000	£3250		
131	**36**	10s grey (Plate 1)	£120000	£4800		
132	**37**	£1 brown (Plate 1)	£135000	£9000		
137	**38**	£5 orange (Plate 1)	£12500	£4500		

41   **42**   **43**

44   **45**   **46**

47 Small anchor   **48** Orb   **49** Imperial Crown

Large coloured corner letters

1873–80 (i) Wmk Small Anchor Type 47

139	**41**	2½d mauve Pl.	£525	80·00		

(ii) Wmk Orb Type 48

141	**41**	2½d mauve Pl.	£425	50·00		
142		2½d blue Pl.	£475	40·00		

(iii) Wmk Spray of Rose Type 33

143	**42**	3d red Pl.	£350	45·00		
145	**43**	6d pale buff (Plate 13)	*	£20000		
147		6d grey Pl.	£400	60·00		
150	**44**	1s green Pl.	£500	£100		
151		1s brown (Plate 13)	£4000	£600		

(iv) Wmk Large Garter Type 17

152	**45**	4d vermilion Pl.	£2400	£425		
153		4d green Pl.	£1000	£275		
154		4d brown (Plate 17)	£2400	£475		
156	**46**	8d orange (Plate 1)	£1500	£300		

3d   6d

(50)   **(51)**

Surcharges in red

1880–83 Wmk Imperial Crown Type 49

157	**41**	2½d blue Pl.	£350	28·00		
158	**42**	3d red Pl.	£400	80·00		
159		3d on 3d lilac (surch Type 50)	£500	£130		
160	**45**	4d brown Pl.	£350	60·00		
161	**43**	6d grey Pl.	£350	65·00		
162		6d on 6d lilac (surch Type 51)	£550	£130		
163	**44**	1s brown Pl.	£550	£140		

52   **53**   **54**

55   **56**

1880–81 Wmk Imperial Crown Type 49

164	**52**	½d green	45·00	12·00		
166	**53**	1d brown	22·00	12·00		
167	**54**	1½d brown	£200	45·00		
168	**55**	2d red	£275	90·00		

| 169 | **56** | 5d indigo | £675 | £110 | ☐ ☐ |

57   Die I   Die II

1881 Wmk Imperial Crown Type 49
(a) 14 dots in each corner, Die I

| 171 | **57** | 1d lilac | £200 | 30·00 | ☐ ☐ |

(b) 16 dots in each corner, Die II

| 174 | **57** | 1d mauve | 2·50 | 1·50 | ☐ ☐ |

58   **59**

60

Coloured letters in the corners

1883–84 Wmk Anchor Type 40

178	**58**	2s 6d lilac	£500	£140	☐ ☐
181	**59**	5s red	£850	£200	☐ ☐
183	**60**	10s blue	£2000	£475	☐ ☐

61

1884 Wmk 3 Imperial Crowns Type 49

| 185 | **61** | £1 brown | £30000 | £2500 | ☐ ☐ |

1888 Wmk 3 Orbs Type 48

| 186 | **61** | £1 brown | £65000 | £4000 | ☐ ☐ |

1891 Wmk 3 Imperial Crowns Type 49

| 212 | **61** | £1 green | £3600 | £750 | ☐ ☐ |

62   **63**   **64**

65   **66**

1883–84 Wmk Imperial Crown Type 49 (sideways on horiz designs)

187	**52**	½d blue	25·00	8·00	☐ ☐
188	**62**	1½d lilac	£110	38·00	☐ ☐
189	**63**	2d lilac	£175	70·00	☐ ☐
190	**64**	2½d lilac	75·00	15·00	☐ ☐
191	**65**	3d lilac	£225	90·00	☐ ☐
192	**66**	4d dull green	£450	£185	☐ ☐
193	**62**	5d dull green	£450	£185	☐ ☐
194	**63**	6d dull green	£475	£200	☐ ☐
195	**64**	9d dull green	£950	£400	☐ ☐
196	**65**	1s dull green	£1100	£250	☐ ☐

The above prices are for stamps in the true dull green colour. Stamps which have been soaked, causing the colour to run are virtually worthless.

71   **72**   **73**

74   **75**   **76**

77   **78**   **79**

80   **81**   **82**

'Jubilee' Issue

1887–1900 The bicoloured stamps have the value tablets, or the frames including the value tablets, in the second colour. Wmk Imperial Crown Type 49

197	**71**	½d vermilion	1·50	1·00	☐ ☐
213		½d green*	1·75	2·00	☐ ☐
198	**72**	1½d purple and green	15·00	7·00	☐ ☐
200	**73**	2d green and red	28·00	12·00	☐ ☐
201	**74**	2½d purple on blue	22·00	3·00	☐ ☐
203	**75**	3d purple on yellow	22·00	3·25	☐ ☐
205	**76**	4d green and brown	30·00	13·00	☐ ☐
206	**77**	4½d green and red	10·00	40·00	☐ ☐
207a	**78**	5d purple and blue	35·00	11·00	☐ ☐
208	**79**	6d purple on red	30·00	10·00	☐ ☐
209	**80**	9d purple and blue	60·00	40·00	☐ ☐
210	**81**	10d purple and red	45·00	38·00	☐ ☐
211	**82**	1s green	£200	60·00	☐ ☐
214		1s green and red	50·00	£125	☐ ☐
Set of 14			£525	£325	☐ ☐

*The ½d No. 213 in blue is a colour changeling.

KING EDWARD VII

1901 (22 Jan.)–1910 (6 May)

| 83 | 84 | 85 |

| 86 | 87 | 88 |

| 89 | 90 | 91 |

| 92 | 93 | 94 |

| 95 | 96 |

97

297	**83**	6d	purple	30·00	20·00		
249	**90**	7d	grey	12·00	20·00		
307	**91**	9d	purple and blue	60·00	60·00		
311	**92**	10d	purple and red	80·00	60·00		
314	**93**	1s	green and red	55·00	35·00		
260	**94**	2s6d	purple	£225	£140		
263	**95**	5s	red	£350	£200		
265	**96**	10s	blue	£850	£450		
266	**97**	£1	green	£2000	£750		
Set of 15 (to 1s)				£400	£275		
(b) Perf 15 × 14							
279	**83**	½d	green	40·00	45·00		
281		1d	red	15·00	15·00		
283	**86**	2½d	blue	22·00	15·00		
285	**87**	3d	purple on yellow	45·00	15·00		
286	**88**	4d	orange	30·00	15·00		
Set of 5				£130	90·00		

1902–13 Wmks Imperial Crown Type 49 (½d to 1s), Anchor Type 40 (2s 6d to 10s), Three Crowns Type 49 (£1) (a) Perf 14

215	**83**	½d	blue-green	2·00	1·50		
217		½d	yellow-green	2·00	1·50		
219		1d	red	2·00	1·50		
224	**84**	1½d	purple and green	40·00	18·00		
291	**85**	2d	green and red	28·00	20·00		
231	**86**	2½d	blue	20·00	10·00		
232	**87**	3d	purple on yellow	40·00	15·00		
238	**88**	4d	green and brown	40·00	18·00		
240		4d	orange	20·00	15·00		
294	**89**	5d	purple and blue	30·00	20·00		

KING GEORGE V

1910 (6 May)–1936 (20 January)

PERFORATION. All the following issues are Perf 15 × 14 except vertical commemorative stamps which are 14 × 15, unless otherwise stated.

98 (Hair dark) **99** (Lion unshaded) **100**

1911–12 Wmk Imperial Crown Type 49

322	**98**	½d green	4·00	4·00	☐	☐
327	**99**	1d red	4·50	2·50	☐	☐

1912 Wmk Royal Cypher ('Simple') Type 100

335	**98**	½d green	40·00	40·00	☐	☐
336	**99**	1d red	30·00	30·00	☐	☐

101 (Hair light) **102** (Lion shaded) **103**

1912 Wmk Imperial Crown Type 49

339	**101**	½d green	8·00	4·00	☐	☐
341	**102**	1d red	5·00	2·00	☐	☐

1912 Wmk Royal Cypher ('Simple') Type 100

344	**101**	½d green	7·00	3·00	☐	☐
345	**102**	1d red	8·00	4·50	☐	☐

1912 Wmk Royal Cypher ('Multiple') Type 103

346	**101**	½d green	12·00	8·00	☐	☐
350	**102**	1d red	18·00	10·00	☐	☐

104   **105**   **106**

107   **108**

1912–24 Wmk Royal Cypher Type 100

351	**105**	½d green	1·00	1·00	☐	☐
357	**104**	1d red	1·00	1·00	☐	☐
362	**105**	1½d brown	4·00	1·50	☐	☐
368	**106**	2d orange	4·00	3·00	☐	☐
371	**104**	2½d blue	12·00	4·00	☐	☐
375	**106**	3d violet	8·00	3·00	☐	☐
379		4d grey-green	15·00	2·00	☐	☐

381	**107**	5d brown	15·00	5·00	☐	☐
385		6d purple	15·00	7·00	☐	☐
		a. Perf 14	90·00	£110	☐	☐
387		7d olive-green	20·00	10·00	☐	☐
390		8d black on yellow	32·00	11·00	☐	☐
392	**108**	9d black	15·00	6·00	☐	☐
393a		9d olive-green	£110	30·00	☐	☐
394		10d blue	22·00	20·00	☐	☐
395		1s brown	20·00	4·00	☐	☐
Set of 15			£250	95·00	☐	

1913 Wmk Royal Cypher ('Multiple') Type 103

397	**105**	½d green	£150	£180	☐	☐
398	**104**	1d red	£225	£225	☐	☐

See also Nos. 418/29.

109   **110**

T **109**. Background around portrait consists of horizontal lines

1913–18 Wmk Single Cypher Type 110 Perf 11 × 12

413a	**109**	2s 6d brown	£150	90·00	☐	☐
416		5s red	£280	£120	☐	☐
417		10s blue	£375	£160	☐	☐
403		£1 green	£2800	£1250	☐	☐
Set of 4			£3250	£1400	☐	☐

See also Nos. 450/2.

111

1924–26 Wmk Block Cypher Type 111

418	**105**	½d green	1·00	1·00	☐	☐
419	**104**	1d red	1·00	1·00	☐	☐
420	**105**	1½d brown	1·00	1·00	☐	☐
421	**106**	2d orange	2·50	2·50	☐	☐
422	**104**	2½d blue	5·00	3·00	☐	☐
423	**106**	3d violet	10·00	2·50	☐	☐
424		4d grey-green	12·00	2·50	☐	☐
425	**107**	5d brown	20·00	3·00	☐	☐
426a		6d purple	3·00	1·50	☐	☐
427	**108**	9d olive-green	12·00	3·50	☐	☐
428		10d blue	40·00	40·00	☐	☐
429		1s brown	22·00	3·00	☐	☐
Set of 12			£110	60·00	☐	☐

112   **112a**

British Empire Exhibition

1924–25 Wmk 111 Perf 14 (a) 23.4.24. Dated '1924'

430	**112**	1d red	10·00	11·00	☐	☐
431	**112a**	1½d brown	15·00	15·00	☐	☐
First Day Cover				£450		☐

(b) 9.5.25. Dated '1925'

432	**112**	1d red	15·00	30·00	☐	☐
433	**112a**	1½d brown	40·00	70·00	☐	☐
First Day Cover				£1700	☐	

113   **114**   **115**

116 St George and the Dragon

117

Ninth Universal Postal Union Congress

1929 (10 May) (a) Wmk 111

434	**113**	½d green	2·25	2·25	☐	☐
435	**114**	1d red	2·25	2·25	☐	☐
436		1½d brown	2·25	1·75	☐	☐
437	**115**	2½d blue	10·00	10·00	☐	☐
(b) Wmk 117 Perf 12						
438	**116**	£1 black	£750	£550	☐	☐
434/7	*Set of* 4		15·00	14·50	☐	☐
434/7	First Day Cover (4 vals.)			£600	☐	
434/8	First Day Cover (5 vals.)			£10000	☐	

118   **119**   **120**

121   **122**

1934–36 Wmk 111

439	**118**	½d green	50	50	☐	☐
440	**119**	1d red	50	50	☐	☐
441	**118**	1½d brown	50	50	☐	☐
442	**120**	2d orange	75	75	☐	☐
443	**119**	2½d blue	1·50	1·25	☐	☐
444	**120**	3d violet	1·50	1·25	☐	☐

445		4d grey-green	2·00	1·25	☐	☐
446	**121**	5d brown	6·50	2·75	☐	☐
447	**122**	9d olive-green	12·00	2·25	☐	☐
448		10d blue	15·00	10·00	☐	☐
449		1s brown	15·00	1·25	☐	☐
Set of 11			50·00	20·00	☐	☐

T **109** (re-engraved). Background around portrait consists of horizontal and diagonal lines

1934 Wmk 110 Perf 11 × 12

450	**109**	2s 6d brown	80·00	40·00	☐	☐
451		5s red	£175	85·00	☐	☐
452		10s blue	£350	80·00	☐	☐
Set of 3			£575	£190	☐	☐

123   **123a**

123b   **123c**

Silver Jubilee

1935 (7 May) Wmk 111

453	**123**	½d green	1·00	1·00	☐	☐
454	**123a**	1d red	1·50	2·00	☐	☐
455	**123b**	1½d brown	1·00	1·00	☐	☐
456	**123c**	2½d blue	5·00	6·50	☐	☐
Set of 4			7·50	9·50	☐	☐
First Day Cover				£600	☐	

KING EDWARD VIII

1936 (20 Jan.–10 Dec.)

KING GEORGE VI

1936 (11 Dec.)–1952 (6 Feb.)

124 **125**

1936 Wmk 125

457	**124**	½d	green	30	30	☐	☐
458		1d	red	60	50	☐	☐
459		1½d	brown	30	30	☐	☐
460		2½d	blue	30	85	☐	☐
Set of 4				1·25	1·75	☐	☐

First Day Covers			
1 Sept. 1936	Nos. 457, 459/60	£150	☐
14 Sept. 1936	No. 458	£180	☐

Collectors are reminded that for issues from 1936 to date, prices in the unused column are for unmounted mint.

126 King George VI and Queen Elizabeth **127**

Coronation

1937 (13 May) Wmk 127

461	**126**	1½d	brown	30	30	☐	☐
First Day Cover				35·00			☐

128 **129** **130**

King George VI and National Emblems

1937–47 Wmk 127

462	**128**	½d	green	30	25	☐	☐
463		1d	scarlet	30	25	☐	☐
464		1½d	brown	30	25	☐	☐
465		2d	orange	1·20	50	☐	☐
466		2½d	blue	40	25	☐	☐
467		3d	violet	5·00	1·00	☐	☐
468	**129**	4d	green	60	75	☐	☐
469		5d	brown	3·50	85	☐	☐
470		6d	purple	1·50	60	☐	☐
471	**130**	7d	green	5·00	60	☐	☐
472		8d	red	7·50	80	☐	☐
473		9d	deep green	6·50	80	☐	☐
474		10d	blue	7·00	80	☐	☐
474a		11d	plum	3·00	2·75	☐	☐
475		1s	brown	9·00	75	☐	☐
Set of 15				45·00	10·00	☐	☐

First Day Covers			
10 May 1937	Nos. 462/3, 466	45·00	☐
30 July 1937	No. 464	45·00	☐
31 Jan. 1938	Nos. 465, 467	95·00	☐
21 Nov. 1938	Nos. 468/9	60·00	☐
30 Jan. 1939	No. 470	55·00	☐
27 Feb. 1939	Nos. 471/2	80·00	☐
1 May 1939	Nos. 473/4, 475	£450	☐
29 Dec. 1947	No. 474a	50·00	☐

For later printings of the lower values in apparently lighter shades and different colours, see Nos. 485/90 and 503/8.

130a King George VI   131

132   132a

133

1939–48 Wmk 133 Perf 14

476	**130a**	2s 6d	brown	85·00	6·00	☐	☐
476a		2s 6d	green	15·00	1·50	☐	☐
477	**131**	5s	red	20·00	2·00	☐	☐
478	**132**	10s	dark blue	£250	20·00	☐	☐
478a		10s	bright blue	40·00	5·00	☐	☐
478b	**132a**	£1	brown	25·00	26·00	☐	☐
Set of 6				£400	55·00	☐	☐

First Day Covers

21 Aug. 1939	No. 477	£800	☐
4 Sept. 1939	No. 476	£1750	☐
30 Oct. 1939	No. 478	£3000	☐
9 Mar. 1942	No. 476a	£1700	☐
30 Nov. 1942	No. 478a	£3500	☐
1 Oct. 1948	No. 478b	£300	☐

134 Queen Victoria and King George VI

Centenary of First Adhesive Postage Stamps

1940 (6 May) Wmk 127 Perf 14½ × 14

479	**134**	½d	green	30	75	☐	☐
480		1d	red	1·00	75	☐	☐
481		1½d	brown	50	1·50	☐	☐
482		2d	orange	1·00	75	☐	☐
483		2½d	blue	2·25	50	☐	☐
484		3d	violet	3·00	3·50	☐	☐
Set of 6				8·75	5·25	☐	☐
First Day Cover					55·00	☐	

Head as Nos. 462–7, but with lighter background

1941–42 Wmk 127

485	**128**	½d	pale green	30	30	☐	☐
486		1d	pale red	30	30	☐	☐
487		1½d	pale brown	60	80	☐	☐
488		2d	pale orange	50	50	☐	☐
489		2½d	light blue	30	30	☐	☐
490		3d	pale violet	2·50	1·00	☐	☐
Set of 6				3·50	2·75	☐	☐

First Day Covers

21 July 1941	No. 489	45·00	☐
11 Aug. 1941	No. 486	22·00	☐
1 Sept. 1941	No. 485	22·00	☐
6 Oct. 1941	No. 488	60·00	☐
3 Nov. 1941	No. 490	£110	☐
28 Sept. 1942	No. 487	55·00	☐

135 Symbols of Peace and Reconstruction   136 Symbols of Peace and Reconstruction

Victory

1946 (11 June) Wmk 127

491	**135**	2½d	blue	20	20	☐	☐
492	**136**	3d	violet	20	50	☐	☐
First Day Cover					65·00		☐

137 King George VI and Queen Elizabeth   138 King George VI and Queen Elizabeth

Royal Silver Wedding

1948 (26 Apr.) Wmk 127

493	**137**	2½d	blue	35	20	☐	☐
494	**138**	£1	blue	40·00	40·00	☐	☐
First Day Cover					£425		☐

1948 (10 May)

Stamps of 1d and 2½d showing seaweed-gathering were on sale at eight Head Post Offices elsewhere in Great Britain, but were primarily for use in the Channel Islands and are listed there (see after Regional Issues).

139 Globe and Laurel Wreath   140 Speed

141 Olympic Symbol

142 Winged Victory

149 St George and the Dragon **150** Royal Coat of Arms

Olympic Games

1948 (29 July) Wmk 127

495	**139**	2½d	blue	35	10	☐	☐
496	**140**	3d	violet	35	50	☐	☐
497	**141**	6d	purple	2·50	75	☐	☐
498	**142**	1s	brown	3·75	2·00	☐	☐
Set of 4				6·00	3·00	☐	☐
First Day Cover					45·00		☐

1951 (3 May) Wmk 133 Perf 11 × 12

509	**147**	2s 6d	green	7·50	1·00	☐	☐
510	**148**	5s	red	35·00	1·00	☐	☐
511	**149**	10s	blue	15·00	7·50	☐	☐
512	**150**	£1	brown	45·00	18·00	☐	☐
Set of 4				£100	25·00	☐	☐
First Day Cover					£925		☐

143 Two Hemispheres

144 U.P.U. Monument, Berne

151 Commerce and Prosperity **152** Festival Symbol

145 Goddess Concordia, Globe and Points of Compass

146 Posthorn and Globe

Festival of Britain

1951 (3 May) Wmk 127

513	**151**	2½d	red	20	15	☐	☐
514	**152**	4d	blue	30	35	☐	☐
Set of 2				40	40	☐	☐
First Day Cover					38·00		☐

75th Anniversary of Universal Postal Union

1949 (10 Oct.) Wmk 127

499	**143**	2½d	blue	25	10	☐	☐
500	**144**	3d	violet	25	50	☐	☐
501	**145**	6d	purple	50	75	☐	☐
502	**146**	1s	brown	1·00	1·25	☐	☐
Set of 4				1·50	2·50	☐	☐
First Day Cover					80·00		☐

4d as No. 468 and others as Nos. 485/9, but colours changed

1950–51 Wmk 127

503	**128**	½d	pale orange	30	30	☐	☐
504		1d	light blue	30	30	☐	☐
505		1½d	pale green	65	60	☐	☐
506		2d	pale brown	75	40	☐	☐
507		2½d	pale red	60	40	☐	☐
508	**129**	4d	light blue	2·00	1·75	☐	☐
Set of 6				4·00	3·25	☐	☐
First Day Covers							
2 Oct. 1950	No. 508				£120		☐
3 May 1951	Nos. 503/7				55·00		☐

147 HMS Victory

148 White Cliffs of Dover

QUEEN ELIZABETH II

6 February, 1952

153 Tudor Crown

154

155

156

157

158

159

160

1952–54 Wmk 153

515	**154**	½d orange	10	15	
516		1d blue	20	20	
517		1½d green	10	20	
518		2d brown	20	20	
519	**155**	2½d red	15	15	
520		3d lilac	1·50	90	
521	**156**	4d blue	3·25	1·25	
		4½d (See Nos. 577, 594, 609 and 616b)			
522	**157**	5d brown	75	3·50	
523		6d purple	4·00	1·00	
524		7d green	9·50	5·50	
525	**158**	8d magenta	75	85	
526		9d bronze-green	23·00	4·75	
527		10d blue	18·00	4·75	
528		11d plum	35·00	15·00	
529	**159**	1s bistre	80	50	
530	**160**	1s 3d green	4·50	3·25	
531	**159**	1s 6d indigo	14·00	3·75	
Set of 17			£100	40·00	

First Day Covers

5 Dec. 1952	Nos. 517, 519	25·00	
6 July 1953	Nos. 522, 525, 529	50·00	
31 Aug. 1953	Nos. 515/16, 518	50·00	
2 Nov. 1953	Nos. 521, 530/1	£170	
18 Jan. 1954	Nos. 520, 523/4	£110	
8 Feb. 1954	Nos. 526/8	£225	

See also Nos. 540/56, 561/6, 570/94 and 599/618a and for stamps as Types **154/60** with face values in decimal currency see Nos. 2031/3, 2258/9, **MS**2326, **MS**2367 and 2378/9.

161

162

163

164

Coronation

1953 (3 June) Wmk 153

532	**161**	2½d red	20	25	
533	**162**	4d blue	1·10	1·90	
534	**163**	1s 3d green	5·00	3·00	
535	**164**	1s 6d blue	10·00	4·75	
Set of 4			16·00	9·00	
First Day Cover				75·00	

For £1 values as Type **163** see Nos. **MS**2147 and 2380.

165 St Edward's Crown

166 Carrickfergus Castle

167 Caernarvon Castle

168 Edinburgh Castle

169 Windsor Castle

1955 (1–23 Sept.) Wmk 165 Perf 11 × 12

536	**166**	2s 6d brown	13·00	2·00	
537	**167**	5s red	35·00	4·00	
538	**168**	10s blue	85·00	14·00	
539	**169**	£1 black	£130	35·00	
Set of 4			£225	50·00	
First Day Cover (Nos. 538/9) (1 Sept.)				£850	
First Day Cover (Nos. 536/7) (23 Sept.)				£650	

See also Nos. 595a/8a and 759/62.

1955–58 Wmk 165

540	**154**	½d orange	15	15	
541		1d blue	30	15	
542		1½d green	25	30	
543		2d red-brown	20	35	
543b		2d light red-brown	20	20	
544	**155**	2½d red	20	25	
545		3d lilac	25	25	
546	**156**	4d blue	1·25	45	
547	**157**	5d brown	6·00	6·00	
548		6d purple	4·50	1·25	

549		7d green	50·00	10·00	☐	☐
550	**158**	8d magenta	7·00	1·25	☐	☐
551		9d bronze-green	20·00	2·75	☐	☐
552		10d blue	20·00	2·75	☐	☐
553		11d plum	50	1·10	☐	☐
554	**159**	1s bistre	22·00	65	☐	☐
555	**160**	1s 3d green	30·00	1·60	☐	☐
556	**159**	1s 6d indigo	23·00	1·60	☐	☐
Set of 18			£160	27·00	☐	☐

170 Scout Badge and 'Rolling Hitch' **171** 'Scouts coming to Britain'

172 Globe within a Compass **173**

World Scout Jubilee Jamboree

1957 (1 Aug.) Wmk 165

557	**170**	2½d red	50	50	☐	☐
558	**171**	4d blue	75	1·50	☐	☐
559	**172**	1s 3d green	4·50	4·50	☐	☐
Set of 3			5·00	5·75	☐	☐
First Day Cover				25·00		☐

46th Inter Parliamentary Union Conference

1957 (12 Sept.) Wmk 165

560	**173**	4d blue	1·00	1·00	☐	☐
First Day Cover				£140		☐

Graphite-lined and Phosphor Issues

These are used in connection with automatic sorting machinery, originally experimentally at Southampton but now also operating elsewhere. In such areas these stamps were the normal issue, but from mid 1967 all low-value stamps bear phosphor markings.

The graphite lines were printed in black on the back, beneath the gum; two lines per stamp except for the 2d (see below).

174   **175 (2d only)**

(Stamps viewed from back)

In November 1959, phosphor bands, printed on the front, replaced the graphite. They are wider than the graphite, not easy to see, but show as broad vertical bands at certain angles to the light.

Values representing the rate for printed papers (and second class mail from 1968) have one band and others have two, three or four bands according to size and format. From 1972 onwards some commemorative stamps were printed with 'all-over' phosphor.

In the small stamps the bands are on each side with the single band at left (except where otherwise stated). In the large-size commemorative stamps the single band may be at left, centre or right varying in different issues. The bands are vertical on both horizontal and vertical designs except where otherwise stated.

See also notes on page 33.

Graphite-lined issue

1957 (19 Nov.) Two graphite lines on the back, except 2d value, which has one line. Wmk 165

561	**154**	½d orange	25	25	☐	☐
562		1d blue	40	40	☐	☐
563		1½d green	1·20	1·40	☐	☐
564		2d light red-brown	1·60	2·25	☐	☐
565	**155**	2½d red	8·50	7·00	☐	☐
566		3d lilac	80	50	☐	☐
Set of 6			12·00	10·50	☐	☐
First Day Cover				85·00		☐

See also Nos. 587/94.

176 Welsh Dragon **177** Flag and Games Emblem

178 Welsh Dragon

Sixth British Empire and Commonwealth Games, Cardiff

1958 (18 July) Wmk 165

567	**176**	3d lilac	20	20	☐	☐
568	**177**	6d mauve	40	45	☐	☐
569	**178**	1s 3d green	2·25	2·40	☐	☐
Set of 3			2·50	2·75	☐	☐
First Day Cover				85·00		☐

179 Multiple Crowns

WATERMARK. All the following issues to No. 755 are Watermark 179 (sideways on the vertical commemorative stamps) unless otherwise stated.

1958–65 Wmk 179

570	**154**	½d orange	10	10	☐	☐
571		1d blue	10	10	☐	☐
572		1½d green	10	15	☐	☐
573		2d light red-brown	10	10	☐	☐
574	**155**	2½d red	10	20	☐	☐
575		3d lilac	10	20	☐	☐
576a	**156**	4d blue	15	15	☐	☐
577		4½d brown	10	25	☐	☐
578	**157**	5d brown	30	40	☐	☐
579		6d purple	30	25	☐	☐
580		7d green	50	45	☐	☐
581	**158**	8d magenta	60	40	☐	☐

582		9d	bronze-green	60	40	☐ ☐
583		10d	blue	1·00	50	☐ ☐
584	**159**	1s	bistre	45	30	☐ ☐
585	**160**	1s 3d	green	45	30	☐ ☐
586	**159**	1s 6d	indigo	4·00	40	☐ ☐
Set of 17				8·00	4·25	☐ ☐
First Day Cover (No. 577) (9 Feb. 1959)					£250	☐

Graphite-lined issue

1958–59 Two graphite lines on the back, except 2d value, which has one line. Wmk 179

587	**154**	½d	orange	3·25	4·00	☐ ☐
588		1d	blue	2·00	1·50	☐ ☐
589		1½d	green	75·00	60·00	☐ ☐
590		2d	light red-brown	9·00	3·50	☐ ☐
591	**155**	2½d	red	10·00	10·00	☐ ☐
592		3d	lilac	50	65	☐ ☐
593	**156**	4d	blue	5·50	5·00	☐ ☐
594		4½d	brown	6·50	5·00	☐ ☐
Set of 8				£100	70·00	☐ ☐

The prices quoted for Nos. 587 and 589 are for examples with inverted watermark. Stamps with upright watermark are priced at: ½d £9 *mint*, £9 *used* and 1½d £90 *mint*, £80 *used*.

1959–63 Wmk 179 Perf 11 × 12

595a	**166**	2s 6d	brown	35	40	☐ ☐
596a	**167**	5s	red	1·20	50	☐ ☐
597a	**168**	10s	blue	4·50	4·50	☐ ☐
598a	**169**	£1	black	13·00	8·00	☐ ☐
Set of 4				15·00	11·00	☐ ☐

Phosphor-Graphite issue

1959 (18 Nov.) Two phosphor bands on front and two graphite lines on back, except 2d value, which has one band on front and one line on back

			(a) Wmk 165			
599	**154**	½d	orange	4·00	3·75	☐ ☐
600		1d	blue	11·00	11·00	☐ ☐
601		1½d	green	4·00	4·00	☐ ☐

			(b) Wmk 179			
605	**154**	2d	light red-brown			
			(1 band)	5·00	4·25	☐ ☐
606	**155**	2½d	red	22·00	18·00	☐ ☐
607		3d	lilac	10·00	8·00	☐ ☐
608	**156**	4d	blue	20·00	16·00	☐ ☐
609		4½d	brown	30·00	20·00	☐ ☐
Set of 8				85·00	70·00	☐ ☐

Phosphor issue

1960–67 Two phosphor bands on front, except where otherwise stated. Wmk 179

610	**154**	½d	orange	10	15	☐ ☐
611		1d	blue	10	10	☐ ☐
612		1½d	green	15	15	☐ ☐
613		2d	light red-brown			
			(1 band)	16·00	18·00	☐ ☐
613a		2d	light red-brown			
			(2 bands)	10	15	☐ ☐
614	**155**	2½d	red (2 bands)	20	30	☐ ☐
614a		2½d	red (1 band)	60	75	☐ ☐
615		3d	lilac (2 bands)	60	55	☐ ☐
615c		3d	lilac (1 side band)	60	55	☐ ☐
615e		3d	lilac (1 centre band)	40	45	☐ ☐
616a	**156**	4d	blue	25	25	☐ ☐

616b		4½d	brown	25	30	☐ ☐
616c	**157**	5d	brown	25	35	☐ ☐
617		6d	purple	30	30	☐ ☐
617a		7d	green	55	50	☐ ☐
617b	**158**	8d	magenta	40	45	☐ ☐
617c		9d	bronze-green	60	55	☐ ☐
617d		10d	blue	70	60	☐ ☐
617e	**159**	1s	bistre	40	35	☐ ☐
618	**160**	1s 3d	green	1·90	2·50	☐ ☐
618a	**159**	1s 6d	indigo	2·00	2·00	☐ ☐
Set of 17 (one of each value)				7·50	8·00	☐ ☐

No. 615c exists with the phosphor band at the left or right of the stamp.

| **180** Postboy of 1660 | **181** Posthorn of 1660 |

Tercentenary of Establishment of 'General Letter Office'

1960 (7 July)

619	**180**	3d	lilac	50	50	☐ ☐
620	**181**	1s 3d	green	3·75	4·25	☐ ☐
Set of 2				3·75	4·25	☐ ☐
First Day Cover					65·00	☐

182 Conference Emblem

First Anniversary of European Postal and Telecommunications Conference

1960 (19 Sept.)

621	**182**	6d	green and purple	2·00	50	☐ ☐
622		1s 6d	brown and blue	9·50	5·00	☐ ☐
Set of 2				11·00	5·50	☐ ☐
First Day Cover					65·00	☐

183 Thrift Plant

184 'Growth of Savings'

185 Thrift Plant

Centenary of Post Office Savings Bank

1961 (28 Aug.)

623A	**183**	2½d black and red	25	25	☐	☐
624A	**184**	3d orange-brown and violet	20	20	☐	☐
625A	**185**	1s 6d red and blue	2·50	2·25	☐	☐
Set of 3			2·75	2·50	☐	☐
First Day Cover				75·00	☐	

186 C.E.P.T. Emblem   **187** Doves and Emblem

188 Doves and Emblem

European Postal and Telecommunications (C.E.P.T.) Conference, Torquay

1961 (18 Sept.)

626	**186**	2d orange, pink and brown	15	10	☐	☐
627	**187**	4d buff, mauve and ultramarine	15	15	☐	☐
628	**188**	10d turquoise, green and blue	15	50	☐	☐
Set of 3			40	60	☐	☐
First Day Cover				6·00	☐	

189 Hammer Beam Roof, Westminster Hall   **190** Palace of Westminster

Seventh Commonwealth Parliamentary Conference

1961 (25 Sept.)

629	**189**	6d purple and gold	25	25	☐	☐
630	**190**	1s 3d green and blue	2·50	2·75	☐	☐
Set of 2			2·75	3·00	☐	☐
First Day Cover				30·00	☐	

191 'Units of Productivity'.   **192** 'National Productivity'

193 'Unified Productivity'

National Productivity Year

1962 (14 Nov.) Wmk 179 (inverted on 2½d and 3d)

631	**191**	2½d green and red	20	20	☐	☐
		p. Phosphor	60	50	☐	☐
632	**192**	3d blue and violet	50	25	☐	☐
		p. Phosphor	1·50	80	☐	☐
633	**193**	1s 3d red, blue and green	1·50	1·75	☐	☐
		p. Phosphor	35·00	22·00	☐	☐
Set of 3 (Ordinary)			2·00	1·90	☐	☐
Set of 3 (Phosphor)			30·00	22·00	☐	☐
First Day Cover (Ordinary)				55·00	☐	
First Day Cover (Phosphor)				£150	☐	

194 Campaign Emblem and Family   **195** Children of Three Races

Freedom from Hunger

1963 (21 Mar.) Wmk 179 (inverted)

634	**194**	2½d crimson and pink	25	10	☐	☐
		p. Phosphor	3·00	1·25	☐	☐
635	**195**	1s 3d brown and yellow	1·90	1·90	☐	☐
		p. Phosphor	30·00	23·00	☐	☐
Set of 2 (Ordinary)			2·00	2·00	☐	☐
Set of 2 (Phosphor)			30·00	24·00	☐	☐
First Day Cover (Ordinary)				35·00	☐	
First Day Cover (Phosphor)				52·00	☐	

196 'Paris Conference'

Paris Postal Conference Centenary

1963 (7 May) Wmk 179 (inverted)

636	**196**	6d green and mauve	50	50	☐	☐
		p. Phosphor	6·00	7·00	☐	☐
First Day Cover (Ordinary)				16·00	☐	
First Day Cover (Phosphor)				37·00	☐	

197 Posy of Flowers   **198** Woodland Life

National Nature Week

1963 (16 May)

637	**197**	3d multicoloured	15	15	☐	☐
		p. Phosphor	60	60	☐	☐
638	**198**	4½d multicoloured	35	35	☐	☐
		p. Phosphor	3·00	3·00	☐	☐
Set of 2 (Ordinary)			50	50	☐	☐
Set of 2 (Phosphor)			3·50	3·50	☐	☐
First Day Cover (Ordinary)				22·00	☐	
First Day Cover (Phosphor)				40·00	☐	

199 Rescue at Sea

200 19th-century Lifeboat

201 Lifeboatmen

Ninth International Lifeboat Conference, Edinburgh

1963 (31 May)

639	**199**	2½d blue, black and red	25	25	☐	☐
		p. Phosphor	50	60	☐	☐
640	**200**	4d multicoloured	50	50	☐	☐
		p. Phosphor	50	60	☐	☐
641	**201**	1s 6d sepia, yellow and blue	3·00	3·25	☐	☐
		p. Phosphor	48·00	28·00	☐	☐
Set of 3 (Ordinary)			3·25	3·50	☐	☐
Set of 3 (Phosphor)			48·00	28·00	☐	☐
First Day Cover (Ordinary)				35·00		☐
First Day Cover (Phosphor)				55·00		☐

202 Red Cross   **203**

204

Red Cross Centenary Congress

1963 (15 Aug.)

642	**202**	3d red and lilac	25	25	☐	☐
		p. Phosphor	1·10	1·00	☐	☐
643	**203**	1s 3d red, blue and grey	3·00	3·00	☐	☐
		p. Phosphor	35·00	27·00	☐	☐
644	**204**	1s 6d red, blue and bistre	3·00	3·00	☐	☐
		p. Phosphor	35·00	27·00	☐	☐
Set of 3 (Ordinary)			5·00	5·75	☐	☐
Set of 3 (Phosphor)			65·00	55·00	☐	☐
First Day Cover (Ordinary)				40·00		☐
First Day Cover (Phosphor)				90·00		☐

205 'Commonwealth Cable'

Opening of COMPAC (Trans-Pacific Telephone Cable)

1963 (3 Dec.)

645	**205**	1s 6d blue and black	2·75	2·50	☐	☐
		p. Phosphor	16·00	15·50	☐	☐
First Day Cover (Ordinary)				28·00		☐
First Day Cover (Phosphor)				40·00		☐

206 Puck and Bottom
(A Midsummer Nights Dream)

207 Feste
(Twelfth Night)

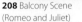

208 Balcony Scene
(Romeo and Juliet)

209 'Eve of Agincourt'
(Henry V)

210 Hamlet contemplating
Yorick's skull (Hamlet)
and Queen Elizabeth II

Shakespeare Festival

1964 (23 Apr.) Perf 11 × 12 (2s 6d) or 15 × 14 (others)

646	**206**	3d bistre, black and violet-blue	15	15	☐	☐
		p. Phosphor	25	30	☐	☐
647	**207**	6d multicoloured	30	30	☐	☐
		p. Phosphor	75	1·00	☐	☐
648	**208**	1s 3d multicoloured	75	1·00	☐	☐
		p. Phosphor	4·00	6·50	☐	☐
649	**209**	1s 6d multicoloured	1·00	85	☐	☐
		p. Phosphor	8·00	8·00	☐	☐
650	**210**	2s 6d deep slate-purple	2·75	2·75	☐	☐
Set of 5 (Ordinary)			4·50	4·50	☐	☐
Set of 4 (Phosphor)			12·00	14·00	☐	☐
First Day Cover (Ordinary)				12·00		☐
First Day Cover (Phosphor)				17·00		☐
Presentation Pack (Ordinary)				22·00		☐

PRESENTATION PACKS were first introduced by the G.P.O. for the Shakespeare Festival issue. The packs include one set of stamps and details of the designs, the designer and the stamp printer. They were issued for almost all later definitive and special issues.

211 Flats near Richmond Park
('Urban Development')

212 Shipbuilding Yards, Belfast
('Industrial Activity')

213 Beddgelert Forest Park, Snowdonia ('Forestry')

214 Nuclear Reactor, Dounreay ('Technological Development')

20th International Geographical Congress, London

1964 (1 July)

651	**211**	2½d multicoloured	10	10	☐	☐
		p. Phosphor	40	50	☐	☐
652	**212**	4d multicoloured	30	30	☐	☐
		p. Phosphor	1·25	1·25	☐	☐
653	**213**	8d multicoloured	75	85	☐	☐
		p. Phosphor	2·50	2·75	☐	☐
654	**214**	1s 6d multicoloured	3·50	3·50	☐	☐
		p. Phosphor	28·00	22·00	☐	☐
Set of 4 (Ordinary)			4·50	4·50	☐	☐
Set of 4 (Phosphor)			30·00	24·00	☐	☐
First Day Cover (Ordinary)				22·00		☐
First Day Cover (Phosphor)				40·00		☐
Presentation Pack (Ordinary)			£160			☐

215 Spring Gentian

216 Dog Rose

217 Honeysuckle

218 Fringed Water Lily

Tenth International Botanical Congress, Edinburgh

1964 (5 Aug.)

655	**215**	3d violet, blue and green	25	25	☐	☐
		p. Phosphor	40	40	☐	☐
656	**216**	6d multicoloured	50	50	☐	☐
		p. Phosphor	2·50	2·75	☐	☐
657	**217**	9d multicoloured	1·75	2·25	☐	☐
		p. Phosphor	4·50	4·00	☐	☐
658	**218**	1s 3d multicoloured	2·50	2·50	☐	☐
		p. Phosphor	25·00	20·00	☐	☐
Set of 4 (Ordinary)			4·50	4·50	☐	☐
Set of 4 (Phosphor)			30·00	24·00	☐	☐
First Day Cover (Ordinary)				30·00		☐
First Day Cover (Phosphor)				40·00		☐
Presentation Pack (Ordinary)			£160			☐

219 Forth Road Bridge

220 Forth Road and Railway Bridges

Opening of Forth Road Bridge

1964 (4 Sept.)

659	**219**	3d black, blue and violet	10	10	☐	☐
		p. Phosphor	1·00	1·50	☐	☐
660	**220**	6d blackish lilac, blue and red	40	40	☐	☐
		p. Phosphor	4·50	4·75	☐	☐
Set of 2 (Ordinary)			50	50	☐	☐
Set of 2 (Phosphor)			5·00	5·75	☐	☐
First Day Cover (Ordinary)				7·00		☐
First Day Cover (Phosphor)				18·00		☐
Presentation Pack (Ordinary)			£400			☐

221 Sir Winston Churchill

221a Sir Winston Churchill

Churchill Commemoration

1965 (8 July)

661	**221**	4d black and drab	10	10	☐	☐
		p. Phosphor	25	25	☐	☐
662	**221a**	1s 3d black and grey	30	40	☐	☐
		p. Phosphor	2·50	3·00	☐	☐
Set of 2 (Ordinary)			40	50	☐	☐
Set of 2 (Phosphor)			2·75	3·25	☐	☐
First Day Cover (Ordinary)				7·00		☐
First Day Cover (Phosphor)				9·00		☐
Presentation Pack (Ordinary)			70·00			☐

222 Simon de Montfort's Seal

223 Parliament Buildings (after engraving by Hollar, 1647)

700th Anniversary of Simon de Montfort's Parliament

1965 (19 July)

663	**222**	6d green	20	20	☐	☐
		p. Phosphor	60	1·00	☐	☐
664	**223**	2s 6d black, grey and drab	80	1·50	☐	☐
Set of 2 (Ordinary)			1·00	1·25	☐	☐
First Day Cover (Ordinary)				15·00		☐
First Day Cover (Phosphor)				26·00		☐
Presentation Pack (Ordinary)			75·00			☐

224 Bandsmen and Banner

225 Three Salvationists

Salvation Army Centenary

1965 (9 Aug.)

665	**224**	3d multicoloured	25	25	☐	☐
		p. Phosphor	25	40	☐	☐
666	**225**	1s 6d multicoloured	1·00	1·50	☐	☐
		p. Phosphor	2·50	2·75	☐	☐
Set of 2 (Ordinary)			1·00	1·50	☐	☐
Set of 2 (Phosphor)			2·50	3·00	☐	☐
First Day Cover (Ordinary)				23·00		☐
First Day Cover (Phosphor)				33·00		☐

226 Lister's Carbolic Spray

227 Lister and Chemical Symbols

Centenary of Joseph Lister's Discovery of Antiseptic Surgery

1965 (1 Sept.)

667	**226**	4d indigo, chestnut and grey	25	15	☐	☐
		p. Phosphor	25	25	☐	☐
668	**227**	1s black, purple and blue	1·00	1·10	☐	☐
		p. Phosphor	2·00	2·50	☐	☐
Set of 2 (Ordinary)			1·00	1·25	☐	☐
Set of 2 (Phosphor)			2·25	2·50	☐	☐
First Day Cover (Ordinary)				12·00		☐
First Day Cover (Phosphor)				15·00		☐

228 Trinidad Carnival Dancers

229 Canadian Folk Dancers

Commonwealth Arts Festival

1965 (1 Sept.)

669	**228**	6d black and orange	20	20	☐	☐
		p. Phosphor	30	50	☐	☐
670	**229**	1s 6d black and violet	80	1·10	☐	☐
		p. Phosphor	2·50	3·50	☐	☐
Set of 2 (Ordinary)			1·00	1·25	☐	☐
Set of 2 (Phosphor)			2·75	3·50	☐	☐
First Day Cover (Ordinary)				16·50		☐
First Day Cover (Phosphor)				22·00		☐

230 Flight of Supermarine Spitfires

231 Pilot in Hawker Hurricane Mk I

232 Wing-tips of Supermarine Spitfire and Messerschmitt Bf 109

233 Supermarine Spitfires attacking Heinkel HE 111H Bomber

234 Supermarine Spitfire attacking Junkers Ju 87B 'Stuka' Dive Bomber

235 Hawker Hurricanes Mk I over Wreck of Dornier Do-17Z Bomber

The above were issued together *se-tenant* in blocks of six (3 × 2) within the sheet.

236 Anti-aircraft Artillery in Action

237 Air Battle over St Paul's Cathedral

25th Anniversary of Battle of Britain

1965 (13 Sept.)

671	**230**	4d olive and black	25	25	☐	☐
	a.	Block of 6. Nos. 671/6	8·00	8·00	☐	☐
		p. Phosphor	50	50	☐	☐
	pa.	Block of 6. Nos. 671p/6p	10·00	12·00	☐	☐
672	**231**	4d olive, blackish olive and black	25	25	☐	☐
		p. Phosphor	50	50	☐	☐
673	**232**	4d multicoloured	25	25	☐	☐
		p. Phosphor	50	50	☐	☐
674	**233**	4d olive and black	25	25	☐	☐
		p. Phosphor	50	50	☐	☐
675	**234**	4d olive and black	25	25	☐	☐
		p. Phosphor	50	50	☐	☐
676	**235**	4d multicoloured	25	25	☐	☐
		p. Phosphor	50	50	☐	☐
677	**236**	9d violet, orange and purple	1·75	1·75	☐	☐
		p. Phosphor	1·75	2·50	☐	☐
678	**237**	1s 3d multicoloured	1·75	1·75	☐	☐
		p. Phosphor	1·75	2·50	☐	☐
Set of 8 (Ordinary)			8·00	8·00	☐	☐
Set of 8 (Phosphor)			10·00	12·00	☐	☐
First Day Cover (Ordinary)				25·00		☐
First Day Cover (Phosphor)				28·00		☐
Presentation Pack (Ordinary)			70·00			☐

238 Tower and Georgian Buildings

239 Tower and Nash Terrace, Regent's Park

Opening of Post Office Tower

1965 (8 Oct.)

679	**238**	3d yellow, blue and green	10	15	☐	☐
		p. Phosphor	15	15	☐	☐
680	**239**	1s 3d green and blue	30	45	☐	☐
		p. Phosphor	30	50	☐	☐
Set of 2 (Ordinary)			40	60	☐	☐
Set of 2 (Phosphor)			45	65	☐	☐
First Day Cover (Ordinary)				6·50		☐
First Day Cover (Phosphor)				7·00		☐
Presentation Pack (Ordinary)			6·50		☐	
Presentation Pack (Phosphor)			6·50		☐	

240 U.N. Emblem

241 I.C.Y. Emblem

20th Anniversary of UNO and International Co-operation Year

1965 (25 Oct.)

681	**240**	3d black, orange and blue	25	20	☐	☐
		p. Phosphor	25	30	☐	☐
682	**241**	1s 6d black, purple and blue	1·00	80	☐	☐
		p. Phosphor	2·75	3·00	☐	☐
Set of 2 (Ordinary)			1·00	1·00	☐	☐
Set of 2 (Phosphor)			2·50	3·25	☐	☐
First Day Cover (Ordinary)				12·00		☐
First Day Cover (Phosphor)				14·00		☐

242 Telecommunications Network

243 Radio Waves and Switchboard

I.T.U. Centenary

1965 (15 Nov.)

683	**242**	9d multicoloured	50	40	☐	☐
		p. Phosphor	1·00	75	☐	☐
684	**243**	1s 6d multicoloured	1·50	1·25	☐	☐
		p. Phosphor	4·25	5·25	☐	☐
Set of 2 (Ordinary)			1·50	1·60	☐	☐
Set of 2 (Phosphor)			4·25	6·00	☐	☐
First Day Cover (Ordinary)				17·00		☐
First Day Cover (Phosphor)				20·00		☐

244 Robert Burns (after Skirving chalk drawing)

245 Robert Burns (after Nasmyth portrait)

Burns Commemoration

1966 (25 Jan.)

685	**244**	4d black, indigo and blue	15	15	☐	☐
		p. Phosphor	25	50	☐	☐
686	**245**	1s 3d black, blue and orange	40	70	☐	☐
		p. Phosphor	2·25	2·25	☐	☐

Set of 2 (Ordinary)		55	85	☐ ☐
Set of 2 (Phosphor)		2·50	2·25	☐ ☐
First Day Cover (Ordinary)			4·00	☐
First Day Cover (Phosphor)			6·00	☐
Presentation Pack (Ordinary)		60·00		☐

246 Westminster Abbey

247 Fan Vaulting, Henry VII Chapel

900th Anniversary of Westminster Abbey

1966 (28 Feb.) Perf 15 × 14 (3d) or 11 × 12 (2s 6d)

687	**246**	3d black, brown and blue	15	20	☐	☐
		p. Phosphor	20	25	☐	☐
688	**247**	2s 6d black	55	80	☐	☐
Set of 2			70	1·00	☐	☐
First Day Cover (Ordinary)				6·00		☐
First Day Cover (Phosphor)				14·00		☐
Presentation Pack (Ordinary)			55·00		☐	

248 View near Hassocks, Sussex

249 Antrim, Northern Ireland

250 Harlech Castle, Wales

251 Cairngorm Mountains, Scotland

Landscapes

1966 (2 May)

689	**248**	4d black, yellow-green and blue	10	15	☐	☐
		p. Phosphor	10	15	☐	☐
690	**249**	6d black, green and blue	15	20	☐	☐
		p. Phosphor	15	20	☐	☐
691	**250**	1s 3d black, yellow and blue	25	35	☐	☐
		p. Phosphor	25	35	☐	☐
692	**251**	1s 6d black, orange and blue	40	35	☐	☐
		p. Phosphor	40	40	☐	☐
Set of 4 (Ordinary)			80	95	☐	☐
Set of 4 (Phosphor)			80	1·00	☐	☐
First Day Cover (Ordinary)				7·00		☐
First Day Cover (Phosphor)				8·50		☐

252 Players with Ball

253 Goalmouth Mêlée

254 Goalkeeper saving Goal

World Cup Football Championship

1966 (1 June)

693	**252**	4d	multicoloured	10	25	☐	☐
		p.	Phosphor	10	25	☐	☐
694	**253**	6d	multicoloured	15	25	☐	☐
		p.	Phosphor	15	25	☐	☐
695	**254**	1s 3d	multicoloured	50	1·00	☐	☐
		p.	Phosphor	50	1·00	☐	☐
Set of 3 (Ordinary)				70	1·00	☐	
Set of 3 (Phosphor)				50	1·00	☐	
First Day Cover (Ordinary)					20·00	☐	
First Day Cover (Phosphor)					22·00	☐	
Presentation Pack (Ordinary)				15·00		☐	

255 Black-headed Gull

256 Blue Tit

257 European Robin

258 Blackbird

The above were issued *se-tenant* in blocks of four within the sheet.

British Birds

1966 (8 Aug.)

696	**255**	4d	multicoloured	20	20	☐	☐
		a.	Block of 4. Nos. 696/9	1·00	2·00	☐	☐
		p.	Phosphor	20	20	☐	☐
		pa.	Block of 4. Nos. 696p/9p	75	2·00	☐	☐
697	**256**	4d	multicoloured	20	20	☐	☐
		p.	Phosphor	20	20	☐	☐
698	**257**	4d	multicoloured	20	20	☐	☐
		p.	Phosphor	20	20	☐	☐
699	**258**	4d	multicoloured	20	20	☐	☐
		p.	Phosphor	20	20	☐	☐
Set of 4 (Ordinary)				1·00	2·00	☐	
Set of 4 (Phosphor)				75	2·00	☐	
First Day Cover (Ordinary)					8·00	☐	
First Day Cover (Phosphor)					8·00	☐	
Presentation Pack (Ordinary)				11·00		☐	

259 Cup Winners

England's World Cup Football Victory

1966 (18 Aug.)

700	**259**	4d	multicoloured	30	30	☐	☐
First Day Cover					13·00		☐

260 Jodrell Bank Radio Telescope

261 British Motor-cars

262 SR N6 Hovercraft

263 Windscale Reactor

British Technology

1966 (19 Sept.)

701	**260**	4d	black and lemon	15	10	☐	☐
		p.	Phosphor	10	10	☐	☐
702	**261**	6d	red, blue and orange	25	20	☐	☐
		p.	Phosphor	15	25	☐	☐
703	**262**	1s 3d	multicoloured	50	40	☐	☐
		p.	Phosphor	35	40	☐	☐
704	**263**	1s 6d	multicoloured	50	60	☐	☐
		p.	Phosphor	50	60	☐	☐
Set of 4 (Ordinary)				1·00	1·10	☐	
Set of 4 (Phosphor)				1·00	1·10	☐	
First Day Cover (Ordinary)					5·00	☐	
First Day Cover (Phosphor)					5·00	☐	
Presentation Pack (Ordinary)				12·00		☐	

264

265

266

267

268

269

The above show battle scenes, they were issued together *se-tenant* in horizontal strips of six within the sheet.

270 Norman Ship

271 Norman Horsemen attacking Harold's Troops

900th Anniversary of Battle of Hastings

1966 (14 Oct.) Designs show scenes from Bayeux Tapestry
Wmk 179 (sideways on 1s 3d)

705	**264**	4d	multicoloured	10	10	☐	☐
		a.	Strip of 6. Nos. 705/10	1·90	2·25	☐	☐
		p.	Phosphor	10	10	☐	☐
		pa.	Strip of 6. Nos.				
			705p/10p	1·90	2·25	☐	☐
706	**265**	4d	multicoloured	10	10	☐	☐
		p.	Phosphor	10	10	☐	☐
707	**266**	4d	multicoloured	10	10	☐	☐
		p.	Phosphor	10	10	☐	☐
708	**267**	4d	multicoloured	10	10	☐	☐
		p.	Phosphor	10	10	☐	☐
709	**268**	4d	multicoloured	10	10	☐	☐
		p.	Phosphor	10	10	☐	☐
710	**269**	4d	multicoloured	10	10	☐	☐
		p.	Phosphor	10	25	☐	☐
711	**270**	6d	multicoloured	10	10	☐	☐
		p.	Phosphor	10	10	☐	☐
712	**271**	1s 3d	multicoloured	20	75	☐	☐
		p.	Phosphor	20	75	☐	☐
Set of 8 (Ordinary)				2·00	2·25	☐	☐
Set of 8 (Phosphor)				2·00	2·25	☐	
First Day Cover (Ordinary)					8·00	☐	
First Day Cover (Phosphor)					9·00	☐	
Presentation Pack (Ordinary)				9·00		☐	

272 King of the Orient

273 Snowman

Christmas

1966 (1 Dec.) Wmk 179 (upright on 1s 6d)

713	**272**	3d	multicoloured	10	25	☐	☐
		p.	Phosphor	10	25	☐	☐
714	**273**	1s 6d	multicoloured	30	50	☐	☐
		p.	Phosphor	30	50	☐	☐
Set of 2 (Ordinary)				40	40	☐	☐
Set of 2 (Phosphor)				40	40	☐	
First Day Cover (Ordinary)					2·50	☐	
First Day Cover (Phosphor)					2·00	☐	
Presentation Pack (Ordinary)				12·00		☐	

274 Sea Freight

275 Air Freight

European Free Trade Association (EFTA)

1967 (20 Feb.)

715	**274**	9d	multicoloured	25	20	☐	☐
		p.	Phosphor	25	20	☐	☐
716	**275**	1s 6d	multicoloured	50	45	☐	☐
		p.	Phosphor	25	40	☐	☐
Set of 2 (Ordinary)				50	65	☐	☐
Set of 2 (Phosphor)				50	60	☐	☐
First Day Cover (Ordinary)					3·00	☐	
First Day Cover (Phosphor)					3·00	☐	
Presentation Pack (Ordinary)				3·50		☐	

276 Hawthorn and Bramble

277 Larger Bindweed and Viper's Bugloss

278 Ox-eye Daisy, Coltsfoot and Buttercup

279 Bluebell, Red Campion and Wood Anemone

T **276/9** were issued together *se-tenant* in blocks of four within the sheet.

280 Dog Violet

281 Primroses

British Wild Flowers

1967 (24 Apr.)

717	**276**	4d	multicoloured	20	20	☐	☐
		a.	Block of 4. Nos. 717/20	80	2·25	☐	☐
		p.	Phosphor	10	15	☐	☐
		pa	Block of 4. Nos.				
			717p/20p	50	2·00	☐	☐
718	**277**	4d	multicoloured	20	20	☐	☐
		p.	Phosphor	10	15	☐	☐
719	**278**	4d	multicoloured	20	20	☐	☐
		p.	Phosphor	10	15	☐	☐
720	**279**	4d	multicoloured	20	20	☐	☐
		p.	Phosphor	10	15	☐	☐
721	**280**	9d	multicoloured	20	25	☐	☐
		p.	Phosphor	15	25	☐	☐
722	**281**	1s 9d	multicoloured	25	35	☐	☐
		p.	Phosphor	20	30	☐	☐
Set of 6 (Ordinary)				1·00	2·25	☐	☐
Set of 6 (Phosphor)				75	2·00	☐	☐
First Day Cover (Ordinary)					5·00	☐	
First Day Cover (Phosphor)					5·00	☐	
Presentation Pack (Ordinary)				6·00		☐	
Presentation Pack (Phosphor)				6·00		☐	

282 (value at left)

282a (value at right)

285 'Children Coming Out of School' (L. S. Lowry)

Two types of the 2d.

I.   Value spaced away from left side of stamp.
II. Value close to left side from new multi-positive. This results in the portrait appearing in the centre, thus conforming with the other values.

1967–69 Two phosphor bands, except where otherwise stated. No wmk.

723	**282**	½d orange-brown	10	20	☐	☐
724		1d olive (2 bands)	10	10	☐	☐
725		1d olive (1 centre band)	30	35	☐	☐
726		2d lake-brown (Type I) (2 bands)	10	15	☐	☐
727		2d lake-brown (Type II) (2 bands)	15	20	☐	☐
728		2d lake-brown (Type II) (1 centre band)	70	90	☐	☐
729		3d violet (1 centre band)	15	10	☐	☐
730		3d violet (2 bands)	30	35	☐	☐
731		4d sepia (2 bands)	10	10	☐	☐
732		4d olive-brown (1 centre band)	10	10	☐	☐
733		4d vermilion (1 centre band)	10	10	☐	☐
734		4d vermilion (1 side band)	1·50	1·90	☐	☐
735		5d blue	10	10	☐	☐
736		6d purple	20	25	☐	☐
737	**282a**	7d emerald	40	35	☐	☐
738		8d vermilion	20	45	☐	☐
739		8d turquoise-blue	50	60	☐	☐
740		9d green	40	25	☐	☐
741	**282**	10d drab	50	50	☐	☐
742		1s violet	15	75	☐	☐
743		1s 6d blue and deep blue	50	50	☐	☐
		c. Phosphorised paper	80	80	☐	☐
744		1s 9d orange and black	50	45	☐	☐
Set of 16 (one of each value and colour)			4·00	4·00		☐
Presentation Pack (one of each value)			12·00		☐	
Presentation Pack (German)			£140		☐	
First Day Covers						
5 June 1967		Nos. 731, 742, 744	3·00		☐	
8 Aug. 1967		Nos. 729, 740, 743	3·00		☐	
5 Feb. 1968		Nos. 723/4, 726, 736	3·00		☐	
1 July 1968		Nos. 735, 737/8, 741	3·00		☐	

No. 734 exists with phosphor band at the left or right.

283 'Master Lambton' (Sir Thomas Lawrence)

284 'Mares and Foals in a Landscape' (George Stubbs)

British Paintings

1967 (10 July) Two phosphor bands. No wmk

748	**283**	4d multicoloured	10	10	☐	☐
749	**284**	9d multicoloured	15	15	☐	☐
750	**285**	1s 6d multicoloured	25	35	☐	☐
Set of 3			30	50	☐	☐
First Day Cover				2·50		☐
Presentation Pack			5·50		☐	

286 Gipsy Moth IV

Sir Francis Chichester's World Voyage

1967 (24 July) Three phosphor bands. No wmk

751	**286**	1s 9d multicoloured	20	20	☐	☐
First Day Cover				1·00		☐

287 Radar Screen

288 *Penicillium notatum*

289 Vickers VC-10 Jet Engines   **290** Television Equipment

British Discovery and Invention

1967 (19 Sept.) Two phosphor bands (except 4d. three bands). Wmk 179 (sideways on 1s 9d)

752	**287**	4d yellow, black and vermilion	10	10	☐	☐
753	**288**	1s multicoloured	10	20	☐	☐
754	**289**	1s 6d multicoloured	20	25	☐	☐
755	**290**	1s 9d multicoloured	20	30	☐	☐
Set of 4			50	75	☐	☐
First Day Cover				2·00		☐
Presentation Pack			4·00		☐	

NO WATERMARK. All the following issues are on unwatermarked paper unless otherwise stated.

291 'The Adoration of the Shepherds' (School of Seville)

292 'Madonna and Child' (Murillo)

293 'The Adoration of the Shepherds' (Louis le Nain)

Christmas

1967 Two phosphor bands (except 3d, one phosphor band)

756	**291**	3d multicoloured (27 Nov.)	10	15	☐	☐
757	**292**	4d multicoloured (18 Oct.)	10	15	☐	☐
758	**293**	1s 6d multicoloured (27 Nov.)	15	15	☐	☐
Set of 3			30	30	☐	☐
First Day Covers (2)				1·50	☐	

Gift Pack 1967

1967 (27 Nov.) Comprises Nos. 715p/22p and 748/58

GP758c Gift Pack		3·00	☐

1967–68 No wmk. Perf 11 × 12

759	**166**	2s 6d brown	30	45	☐	☐
760	**167**	5s red	70	75	☐	☐
761	**168**	10s blue	7·75	4·00	☐	☐
762	**169**	£1 black	7·50	4·50	☐	☐
Set of 4			15·00	8·00	☐	☐

294 Tarr Steps, Exmoor

295 Aberfeldy Bridge

296 Menai Bridge

297 M4 Viaduct

British Bridges

1968 (29 Apr.) Two phosphor bands

763	**294**	4d multicoloured	10	10	☐	☐
764	**295**	9d multicoloured	10	15	☐	☐
765	**296**	1s 6d multicoloured	15	25	☐	☐
766	**297**	1s 9d multicoloured	20	30	☐	☐
Set of 4			50	70	☐	☐
First Day Cover				1·50	☐	
Presentation Pack		3·00			☐	

298 'TUC' and Trades Unionists

299 Mrs Emmeline Pankhurst (statue)

300 Sopwith Camel and English Electric Lightning Fighters

301 Captain Cook's *Endeavour* and Signature

British Anniversaries. Events described on stamps

1968 (29 May) Two phosphor bands

767	**298**	4d multicoloured	10	10	☐	☐
768	**299**	9d violet, grey and black	10	15	☐	☐
769	**300**	1s multicoloured	15	15	☐	☐
770	**301**	1s 9d ochre and brown	35	35	☐	☐
Set of 4			50	50	☐	☐
First Day Cover				4·00	☐	
Presentation Pack			3·00		☐	

302 'Queen Elizabeth I' (Unknown Artist)

303 'Pinkie' (Lawrence)

304 'Ruins of St Mary Le Port' (John Piper)

305 'The Hay Wain' (John Constable)

British Paintings

1968 (12 Aug.) Two phosphor bands

771	**302**	4d multicoloured	10	10	☐	☐
772	**303**	1s multicoloured	10	20	☐	☐
773	**304**	1s 6d multicoloured	20	25	☐	☐
774	**305**	1s 9d multicoloured	25	40	☐	☐
Set of 4			50	85	☐	☐
First Day Cover				2·00	☐	
Presentation Pack			3·50		☐	
Presentation Pack (German)			12·00		☐	

Gift Pack 1968

1968 (16 Sept.) Comprises Nos. 763/74

GP774c Gift Pack	6·00	☐
GP774d Gift Pack (German)	38·00	☐

Collectors Pack 1968

1968 (16 Sept.) Comprises Nos. 752/8 and 763/74

CP774e Collectors Pack	7·00	☐

306 Girl and Boy with Rocking Horse

307 Girl with Doll's House   **308** Boy with Train Set

Christmas

1968 (25 Nov.) Two phosphor bands (except 4d, one centre phosphor band)

775	**306**	4d multicoloured	10	15	☐	☐
776	**307**	9d multicoloured	15	25	☐	☐
777	**308**	1s 6d multicoloured	15	50	☐	☐
Set of 3			30	50	☐	☐
First Day Cover				1·00		☐
Presentation Pack			5·00		☐	
Presentation Pack (German)			14·00		☐	

309 *Queen Elizabeth 2*

310 Elizabethan Galleon   **311** East Indiaman

312 *Cutty Sark*

313 *Great Britain*

314 *Mauretania I*

The 9d and 1s values were arranged in horizontal strips of three and pairs respectively throughout the sheet.

British Ships

1969 (15 Jan.) One horiz phosphor band (5d), two phosphor bands (9d) or two vertical phosphor bands at right (1s)

778	**309**	5d multicoloured	10	15	☐	☐
779	**310**	9d multicoloured	10	25	☐	☐
		a. Strip of 3. Nos. 779/81	1·25	1·50	☐	☐
780	**311**	9d multicoloured	10	25	☐	☐
781	**312**	9d multicoloured	10	25	☐	☐
782	**313**	1s multicoloured	40	35	☐	☐
		a. Pair. Nos. 782/3	1·25	1·50	☐	☐
783	**314**	1s multicoloured	40	35	☐	☐
Set of 6			2·50	3·00	☐	☐
First Day Cover				5·00		☐
Presentation Pack			4·50		☐	
Presentation Pack (German)			40·00		☐	

315 Concorde in Flight   **316** Plan and Elevation Views

317 Concorde's Nose and Tail

First Flight of Concorde

1969 (3 Mar.) Two phosphor bands

784	**315**	4d multicoloured	25	25	☐	☐
785	**316**	9d multicoloured	55	75	☐	☐
786	**317**	1s 6d deep blue, grey and light blue	75	1·00	☐	☐
Set of 3			1·00	1·50	☐	☐
First Day Cover				3·00		☐
Presentation Pack			12·00		☐	
Presentation Pack (German)			40·00		☐	

318 (See also Type **357**)

1969 (5 Mar.) Perf 12

787	**318**	2s 6d brown	35	30	☐	☐
788		5s lake	1·75	60	☐	☐
789		10s ultramarine	6·00	7·00	☐	☐
790		£1 black	3·25	1·50	☐	☐
Set of 4			10·00	8·50	☐	☐

First Day Cover		9·50		☐	
Presentation Pack		16·00		☐	
Presentation Pack (German)		80·00		☐	

319 Page from the *Daily Mail*, and Vickers FB-27 Vimy Aircraft

320 Europa and C.E.P.T. Emblems

321 I.L.O. Emblem

322 Flags of N.A.T.O. Countries

323 Vickers FB-27 Vimy Aircraft and Globe showing Flight

Anniversaries. Events described on stamps

1969 (2 Apr.) Two phosphor bands

791	**319**	5d	multicoloured	10	15	☐ ☐
792	**320**	9d	multicoloured	15	25	☐ ☐
793	**321**	1s	claret, red and blue	15	25	☐ ☐
794	**322**	1s 6d	multicoloured	15	30	☐ ☐
795	**323**	1s 9d	olive, yellow and turquoise-green	20	40	☐ ☐
Set of 5				50	1·00	☐ ☐
First Day Cover					3·00	☐
Presentation Pack				3·50		☐
Presentation Pack (German)				65·00		☐

324 Durham Cathedral

325 York Minster

326 St Giles' Cathedral, Edinburgh

327 Canterbury Cathedral

The above were issued together *se-tenant* in blocks of four within the sheet.

328 St Paul's Cathedral

329 Liverpool Metropolitan Cathedral

British Architecture (Cathedrals)

1969 (28 May) Two phosphor bands

796	**324**	5d multicoloured	10	10	☐ ☐
		a. Block of 4. Nos. 796/9	1·10	1·25	☐ ☐
797	**325**	5d multicoloured	10	10	☐ ☐
798	**326**	5d multicoloured	10	10	☐ ☐
799	**327**	5d multicoloured	10	10	☐ ☐
800	**328**	9d multicoloured	25	30	☐ ☐
801	**329**	1s 6d multicoloured	25	35	☐ ☐
Set of 6			1·10	1·50	☐ ☐
First Day Cover				3·00	☐
Presentation Pack			3·25		☐
Presentation Pack (German)			30·00		☐

330 The King's Gate, Caernarvon Castle

331 The Eagle Tower, Caernarvon Castle

332 Queen Eleanor's Gate, Caernarvon Castle

333 Celtic Cross, Margam Abbey

The 5d values were printed *se-tenant* in strips of three throughout the sheet

334 Prince Charles

Investiture of H.R.H. The Prince of Wales

1969 (1 July) Two phosphor bands

802	**330**	5d multicoloured	10	15	☐ ☐
		a. Strip of 3. Nos. 802/4	50	1·00	☐ ☐
803	**331**	5d multicoloured	10	15	☐ ☐
804	**332**	5d multicoloured	10	15	☐ ☐
805	**333**	9d multicoloured	15	30	☐ ☐
806	**334**	1s black and gold	15	30	☐ ☐
Set of 5			60	1·20	☐ ☐
First Day Cover				1·50	☐
Presentation Pack			3·00		☐
Presentation Pack (German)			30·00		☐

335 Mahatma Gandhi

Gandhi Centenary Year

1969 (13 Aug.) Two phosphor bands

807	**335**	1s 6d	multicoloured	30	30	☐ ☐
First Day Cover					1·00	☐

Collectors Pack 1969

1969 (15 Sept.) Comprises Nos. 775/86 and 791/807

CP807b	Collectors Pack	25·00	☐

336 National Giro

337 Telecommunications –
International Subscriber Dialling

338 Telecommunications –
Pulse Code Modulation

339 Postal Mechanisation –
Automatic Sorting

British Post Office Technology

1969 (1 Oct.) Two phosphor bands. Perf 13½ × 14

808	**336**	5d	multicoloured	10	10	☐ ☐
809	**337**	9d	green, blue and black	20	25	☐ ☐
810	**338**	1s	green, lavender and black	20	25	☐ ☐
811	**339**	1s 6d	multicoloured	25	50	☐ ☐
Set of 4				70	1·00	☐ ☐
First Day Cover					1·50	☐
Presentation Pack				3·00		☐

340 Herald Angel

341 The Three Shepherds

342 The Three Kings

Christmas

1969 (26 Nov.) Two phosphor bands (5d, 1s 6d) or one centre band (4d)

812	**340**	4d	multicoloured	10	10	☐ ☐
813	**341**	5d	multicoloured	15	15	☐ ☐
814	**342**	1s 6d	multicoloured	20	20	☐ ☐
Set of 3				30	30	☐ ☐
First Day Cover					1·00	☐
Presentation Pack				3·00		☐

343 Fife Harling

344 Cotswold Limestone

345 Welsh Stucco

346 Ulster Thatch

British Rural Architecture

1970 (11 Feb.) Two phosphor bands

815	**343**	5d	multicoloured	10	10	☐ ☐
816	**344**	9d	multicoloured	10	25	☐ ☐
817	**345**	1s	multicoloured	15	25	☐ ☐
818	**346**	1s 6d	multicoloured	20	40	☐ ☐
Set of 4				50	75	☐ ☐
First Day Cover					1·50	☐
Presentation Pack				4·00		☐

347 Signing the Declaration of Arbroath

348 Florence Nightingale attending Patients

349 Signing of International Co-operative Alliance

350 Pilgrims and *Mayflower*

351 Sir William Herschel, Francis Baily, Sir John Herschel and Telescope

Anniversaries. Events described on stamps

1970 (1 Apr.) Two phosphor bands

819	**347**	5d	multicoloured	10	10	☐ ☐
820	**348**	9d	multicoloured	15	15	☐ ☐
821	**349**	1s	multicoloured	20	25	☐ ☐
822	**350**	1s 6d	multicoloured	20	30	☐ ☐
823	**351**	1s 9d	multicoloured	25	30	☐ ☐
Set of 5				75	1·00	☐ ☐
First Day Cover					2·00	☐
Presentation Pack				3·00		☐

352 'Mr Pickwick and Sam' *(Pickwick Papers)*

353 'Mr and Mrs Micawber' *(David Copperfield)*

354 'David Copperfield and Betsy Trotwood' *(David Copperfield)*

355 'Oliver asking for more' *(Oliver Twist)*

356 'Grasmere' (from engraving by J. Farrington, R.A.)

The 5d values were issued together *se-tenant* in blocks of four within the sheet.

Literary Anniversaries. Events described on stamps

1970 (3 June) Two phosphor bands.

824	**352**	5d multicoloured	10	25	☐	☐
		a. Block of 4. Nos. 824/7	75	1·50	☐	☐
825	**353**	5d multicoloured	10	25	☐	☐
826	**354**	5d multicoloured	10	25	☐	☐
827	**355**	5d multicoloured	10	25	☐	☐
828	**356**	1s 6d multicoloured	25	50	☐	☐
Set of 5			1·00	1·50	☐	☐
First Day Cover				2·00		☐
Presentation Pack			3·00		☐	

356a

357 (Value redrawn)

Decimal Currency

1970 (17 June)–**72** 10p and some printings of the 50p were issued on phosphor paper. Perf 12

829	**356a**	10p cerise	50	75	☐	☐
830		20p olive-green	60	25	☐	☐
831		50p ultramarine	1·50	40	☐	☐
831b	**357**	£1 black (6 Dec. 1972)	3·50	80	☐	☐
Set of 4			6·00	2·00	☐	☐
First Day Cover (Nos. 829/31)				2·75		☐
First Day Cover (No. 831b)				3·00		☐
Presentation Pack (P.O Pack No. 18)						
		(Nos. 829/31)	10·00		☐	
Presentation Pack (P.O Pack No. 38)						
		(Nos. 830/1, 790				
		or 831b)	17·00		☐	

358 Runners

359 Swimmers

360 Cyclists

Ninth British Commonwealth Games, Edinburgh

1970 (15 July) Two phosphor bands. Perf 13½ × 14

832	**358**	5d pink, emerald, greenish yellow and yellow-green	25	25	☐	☐
833	**359**	1s 6d greenish blue, lilac, brown and Prussian blue	50	50	☐	☐
834	**360**	1s 9d yellow-orange, lilac, salmon and red-brown	50	50	☐	☐
Set of 3			75	75	☐	☐
First Day Cover				1·20		☐
Presentation Pack			3·00		☐	

Collectors Pack 1970

1970 (14 Sept.) Comprises Nos. 808/28 and 832/4

CP834a	Collectors Pack	35·00	☐

361 1d Black (1840)

362 1s Green (1847)

363 4d Carmine (1855)

'Philympia 70' Stamp Exhibition

1970 (18 Sept.) Two phosphor bands. Perf 14 × 14½

835	**361**	5d multicoloured	25	10	☐	☐
836	**362**	9d multicoloured	25	30	☐	☐
837	**363**	1s 6d multicoloured	25	45	☐	☐
Set of 3			50	75	☐	☐
First Day Cover				1·50		☐
Presentation Pack			3·00		☐	

364 Shepherds and Apparition of the Angel

365 Mary, Joseph and
Christ in Manger

366 The Wise Men
bearing Gifts

Christmas

1970 (25 Nov.) Two phosphor bands (5d, 1s 6d) or one centre
phosphor band (4d)

838	**364**	4d	multicoloured	15	10	☐ ☐
839	**365**	5d	multicoloured	15	15	☐ ☐
840	**366**	1s 6d	multicoloured	25	30	☐ ☐
Set of 3				50	50	☐ ☐
First Day Cover					1·00	☐
Presentation Pack				2·75		☐

PRINTING PROCESSES

There is a basic distinction between stamps printed
byphotogravure and those printed by lithography. Sorting the
two is not as difficult as it sounds and with a little experience
it should become easy to tell which method of production
was employed for a particular stamp.

The tiny dots of the printing screen give uneven edges to the
values on photogravure stamps (right). Litho values have clean,
clear outlines (left).

All you need is a reasonably good glass giving a magnification
of 34 or more (310 is even better!).

The image on a photogravure stamp is created from a pattern
or 'screen', of minute dots which are not evident when looking
at the stamp without a glass but show up quite clearly under
magnification, especially in the Queen's face and around
the margin of the stamp design where it meets the white
background of the paper. Now look at the value; here also,
what looks to the naked eye like a straight line is in fact made
up of rows of tiny little dots.

'Screens' of dots are also used in the production of litho
printed stamps but they are only required where the printer
is attempting to produce shades and tints as is necessary in
the Queen's head portion of the stamp. Where solid colour is
used, as in the background of the majority of values, there is
no need to resort to a screen of dots and the background is
printed as a solid mass of colour. If you look at the margins or
the values of stamps produced in this way you will not see any
evidence of dots—just a clear clean break between the inked
portion of the stamp and the uninked white of the paper.

367   **367a**

Two types of the 3p., 10p. and 26p. (Nos. X930/c, X886/b and
X971/b).

I   II

I   II

I   II

Decimal Currency

1971–96. Type 367

(a) Printed in photogravure by Harrison and Sons (except for
some ptgs of Nos. X879 and X913 which were produced by
Enschedé) with phosphor bands. Perf 15×14

X841	½p	turquoise-blue (2 bands)	10	10	☐ ☐
X842	½p	turquoise-blue (1 side band)	55·00	30·00	☐ ☐
X843	½p	turquoise-blue (1 centre band)	40	25	☐ ☐
X844	1p	crimson (2 bands)	10	15	☐ ☐
X845	1p	crimson (1 centre band)	25	20	☐ ☐
X846	1p	crimson ('all-over' phosphor)	15	25	☐ ☐
X847	1p	crimson (1 side band)	1·00	1·25	☐ ☐
X848	1½p	black (2 bands)	15	25	☐ ☐
X849	2p	myrtle-green (face value as in T **367**) (2 bands)	15	20	☐ ☐
X850	2p	myrtle-green (face value as in T **367**) ('all-over' phosphor)	25	30	☐ ☐
X851	2½p	magenta (1 centre band)	20	15	☐ ☐
X852	2½p	magenta (1 side band)	1·50	1·75	☐ ☐
X853	2½p	magenta (2 bands)	25	50	☐ ☐
X854	2½p	rose-red (2 bands)	40	60	☐ ☐
X855	3p	ultramarine (2 bands)	20	25	☐ ☐
X856	3p	ultramarine (1 centre band)	15	20	☐ ☐
X857	3p	bright magenta (Type I) (2 bands)	35	35	☐ ☐
X858	3½p	olive-grey (2 bands)	25	30	☐ ☐
X859	3½p	olive-grey (1 centre band)	30	35	☐ ☐

X860	3½p	purple-brown (1 centre band)	1·25	1·25	☐	☐
X861	4p	ochre-brown (2 bands)	20	25	☐	☐
X862	4p	greenish blue (2 bands)	1·75	2·00	☐	☐
X863	4p	greenish blue (1 centre band)	1·50	1·90	☐	☐
X864	4p	greenish blue (1 side band)	2·00	2·00	☐	☐
X865	4½p	grey-blue (2 bands)	25	30	☐	☐
X866	5p	pale violet (2 bands)	20	20	☐	☐
X867	5p	claret (1 centre band)	2·00	2·25	☐	☐
X868	5½p	violet (2 bands)	25	30	☐	☐
X869	5½p	violet (1 centre band)	25	30	☐	☐
X870	6p	light emerald (2 bands)	25	20	☐	☐
X871	6½p	greenish blue (2 bands)	30	35	☐	☐
X872	6½p	greenish blue (1 centre band)	25	20	☐	☐
X873Ea	6½p	greenish blue (1 side band)	60	60	☐	☐
X874	7p	purple-brown (2 bands)	30	35	☐	☐
X875	7p	purple-brown (1 centre band)	25	30	☐	☐
X876Ea	7p	purple-brown (1 side band)	45	50	☐	☐
X877	7½p	chestnut (2 bands)	25	35	☐	☐
X878	8p	rosine (2 bands)	30	30	☐	☐
X879	8p	rosine (1 centre band)	30	30	☐	☐
X880	8p	rosine (1 side band)	60	75	☐	☐
X881	8½p	yellowish green (2 bands)	30	30	☐	☐
X882	9p	yellow-orange and black (2 bands)	45	55	☐	☐
X883	9p	deep violet (2 bands)	35	30	☐	☐
X884	9½p	purple (2 bands)	35	45	☐	☐
X885	10p	orange-brown and chestnut (2 bands)	35	35	☐	☐
X886	10p	orange-brown (Type I) (2 bands)	35	30	☐	☐
		b. Type II	22·00	22·00	☐	☐
X887	10p	orange-brown (Type I) ('all-over' phosphor)	35	45	☐	☐
X888	10p	orange-brown (Type I) (1 centre band)	35	25	☐	☐
X889	10p	orange-brown (Type I) (1 side band)	70	80	☐	☐
X890	10½p	yellow (2 bands)	40	45	☐	☐
X891	10½p	blue (2 bands)	45	50	☐	☐
X892	11p	brown-red (2 bands)	40	30	☐	☐
X893	11½p	drab (1 centre band)	40	35	☐	☐
X894	11½p	drab (1 side band)	55	70	☐	☐
X895	12p	yellowish green (2 bands)	45	45	☐	☐
X896	12p	bright emerald (1 centre band)	45	45	☐	☐
X897	12p	bright emerald (1 sideband)	80	85	☐	☐
X898	12½p	light emerald (1 centre band)	45	40	☐	☐
X899	12½p	light emerald (1 side band)	70	75	☐	☐
X900	13p	pale chestnut (1 centre band)	40	40	☐	☐
X901	13p	pale chestnut (1 side band)	50	60	☐	☐

X902	14p	grey-blue (2 bands)	75	80	☐	☐
X903	14p	deep blue (1 centre band)	45	50	☐	☐
X904	14p	deep blue (1 side band)	4·00	4·00	☐	☐
X905	15p	bright blue (1 centre band)	65	65	☐	☐
X906Ea	15p	bright blue (1 side band)	3.00	3·00	☐	☐
X907	15½p	pale violet (2 bands)	60	65	☐	☐
X908	16p	olive-drab (2 bands)	1·25	1·40	☐	☐
X909	17p	grey-blue (2 bands)	60	60	☐	☐
X910	17p	deep blue (1 centre band)	80	85	☐	☐
X911Ea	17p	deep blue (1 side band)	1·25	1.25	☐	☐
X912	18p	deep olive-grey (2 bands)	70	80	☐	☐
X913	18p	bright green (1 centre band)	60	60	☐	☐
X914	19p	bright orange-red (2 bands)	1·50	1·50	☐	☐
X915	20p	dull purple (2 bands)	1·20	90	☐	☐
X916	20p	brownish black (2 bands)	1·50	1·60	☐	☐
X917	22p	bright orange-red (2 bands)	1·50	1·25	☐	☐
X917a	25p	rose-red (2 bands)	7·00	7·00	☐	☐
X918	26p	rosine (Type I) (2 bands)	15·00	16·00	☐	☐
X919	31p	purple (2 bands)	15·00	15·00	☐	☐
X920	34p	ochre-brown (2 bands)	7·00	7·50	☐	☐
X921	50p	ochre-brown (2 bands)	2·00	75	☐	☐
X922	50p	ochre (2 bands)	4·50	4·50	☐	☐

(b) Printed in photogravure by Harrison and Sons on phosphorised paper. Perf 15×14

X924	½p	turquoise-blue	10	15	☐	☐
X925	1p	crimson	10	15	☐	☐
X926	2p	myrtle-green (face value as in T **367**)	15	20	☐	☐
X927	2p	deep green (smaller value as in T **367a**)	20	20	☐	☐
X928	2p	myrtle-green (smaller value as in T 367a)	3·25	3·25	☐	☐
X929	2½p	rose-red	15	20	☐	☐
X930	3p	bright magenta (Type I)	20	25	☐	☐
		c. Type II	90	70	☐	☐
X931	3½p	purple-brown	50	60	☐	☐
X932	4p	greenish blue	25	40	☐	☐
X933	4p	new blue	20	25	☐	☐
X934	5p	pale violet	30	35	☐	☐
X935	5p	dull red-brown	25	30	☐	☐
X936	6p	yellow-olive	30	30	☐	☐
X937	7p	brownish red	1·10	1·25	☐	☐
X938	8½p	yellowish green	40	50	☐	☐
X939	10p	orange-brown (Type I)	35	35	☐	☐
X940	10p	dull orange (Type II)	40	35	☐	☐
X941	11p	brown-red	70	80	☐	☐
X942	11½p	ochre-brown	55	55	☐	☐
X943	12p	yellowish green	45	45	☐	☐
X944	13p	olive-grey	45	50	☐	☐
X945	13½p	purple-brown	60	60	☐	☐
X946	14p	grey-blue	50	50	☐	☐
X947	15p	ultramarine	60	60	☐	☐
X948	15½p	pale violet	60	50	☐	☐

X949	16p	olive-drab	55	55	☐	☐
X950	16½p	pale chestnut	80	80	☐	☐
X951	17p	light emerald	60	60	☐	☐
X952	17p	grey-blue	60	60	☐	☐
X953	17½p	pale chestnut	70	75	☐	☐
X954	18p	deep violet	70	70	☐	☐
X955	18p	deep olive-grey	75	60	☐	☐
X956	19p	bright orange-red	80	60	☐	☐
X957	19½p	olive-grey	2·00	2·00	☐	☐
X958	20p	dull purple	1·00	75	☐	☐
X959	20p	turquoise-green	75	70	☐	☐
X960	20p	brownish black	1·00	1·00	☐	☐
X961	20½p	ultramarine	1·25	1·25	☐	☐
X962	22p	blue	90	75	☐	☐
X963	22p	yellow-green	90	80	☐	☐
X964	22p	bright orange-red	90	80	☐	☐
X965	23p	brown-red	1·25	1·10	☐	☐
X966	23p	bright green	1·10	1·10	☐	☐
X967	24p	violet	1·40	1·50	☐	☐
X968	24p	Indian red	2·00	1·60	☐	☐
X969	24p	chestnut	80	80	☐	☐
X970	25p	purple	1·00	1·00	☐	☐
X971	26p	rosine (Type I)	1·10	80	☐	☐
	b.	Type II	3·50	4·00	☐	☐
X972	26p	drab	1·50	1·25	☐	☐
X973	27p	chestnut	1·25	1·25	☐	☐
X974	27p	violet	1·50	1·25	☐	☐
X975	28p	deep violet	1·25	1·25	☐	☐
X976	28p	ochre	1·40	1·25	☐	☐
X977	28p	deep bluish grey	1·40	1·25	☐	☐
X978	29p	ochre-brown	1·75	1·75	☐	☐
X979	29p	deep mauve	1·75	1·75	☐	☐
X980	30p	deep olive-grey	1·25	1·25	☐	☐
X981	31p	purple	1·25	1·25	☐	☐
X982	31p	ultramarine	1·60	1·50	☐	☐
X983	32p	greenish blue	1·90	1·75	☐	☐
X984	33p	light emerald	1·75	1·60	☐	☐
X985	34p	ochre-brown	1·75	1·75	☐	☐
X986	34p	deep bluish grey	2·00	1·90	☐	☐
X987	34p	deep mauve	1·75	1·75	☐	☐
X988	35p	sepia	1·60	1·60	☐	☐
X989	35p	yellow	1·75	1·60	☐	☐
X990	37p	rosine	2·00	1·75	☐	☐
X991	39p	bright mauve	1·75	1·75	☐	☐

(c) Printed in photogravure by Harrison and Sons on ordinary paper. Perf 15×14

X992	50p	ochre-brown	1·75	70	☐	☐
X993	75p	grey-black (smaller values as T **367a**)	3·25	1·50	☐	☐

(d) Printed in photogravure by Harrison and Sons on ordinary paper or phosphorised paper. Perf 15 × 14

X994	50p	ochre	2·00	70	☐	☐

(e) Printed in lithography by John Waddington. Perf 14

X996	4p	greenish blue (2 bands)	25	35	☐	☐
X997	4p	greenish blue (phosphorised paper)	45	40	☐	☐
X998	20p	dull purple (2 bands)	1·25	1·20	☐	☐
X999	20p	dull purple (phosphorised paper)	1·75	1·20	☐	☐

(f) Printed in lithography by Questa. Perf 14 (Nos. X1000, X1003/4 and X1023) or 15×14 (others)

X1000	2p	emerald-green (face value as in T **367**) (phosphorised paper)	20	25	☐	☐
	a.	Perf 15 × 14	35	35	☐	☐

X1001	2p	bright green and deep green (smaller value as in T **367a**) (phosphorised paper)	75	70	☐	☐
X1002	4p	greenish blue (phosphorised paper)	70	75	☐	☐
X1003	5p	light violet (phosphorised paper)	40	40	☐	☐
X1004	5p	claret (phosphorised paper)	50	50	☐	☐
	a.	Perf 15 × 14	65	60	☐	☐
X1005	13p	pale chestnut (1 centre band)	70	75	☐	☐
X1006	13p	pale chestnut (1 side band)	75	75	☐	☐
X1007	14p	deep blue (1 centre band)	2·00	2·00	☐	☐
X1008	17p	deep blue (1 centre band)	80	80	☐	☐
X1009	18p	deep olive-grey (phosphorised paper)	90	95	☐	☐
X1010	18p	deep olive-grey (2 bands)	7·50	7·50	☐	☐
X1011	18p	bright green (1 centre band)	75	75	☐	☐
X1012	18p	bright green (1 side band)	1·25	1·40	☐	☐
X1013	19p	bright orange-red (phosphorised paper)	2·20	2·00	☐	☐
X1014	20p	dull purple (phosphorised paper)	1·40	1·40	☐	☐
X1015	22p	yellow-green (2 bands)	9·00	9·00	☐	☐
X1016	22p	bright orange-red (phosphorised paper)	1·00	90	☐	☐
X1017	24p	chestnut (phosphorised paper)	90	1·10	☐	☐
X1018	24p	chestnut (2 bands)	1·40	1·40	☐	☐
X1019	33p	light emerald (phosphorised paper)	2·50	2·50	☐	☐
X1020	33p	light emerald (2 bands)	1·50	1·50	☐	☐
X1021	34p	bistre-brown (2 bands)	7·50	7·50	☐	☐
X1022	39p	bright mauve (2 bands)	1·50	1·60	☐	☐
X1023	75p	black (face value as T **367**) (ordinary paper)	3·00	1·50	☐	☐
	a.	Perf 15×14	4·00	2·25	☐	☐
X1024	75p	brownish grey and black (smaller value as T **367a**) (ordinary paper)	9·00	8·50	☐	☐

(g) Printed in lithography by Walsall. Perf 14

X1050	2p	deep green (phosphorised paper)	1·10	1·10	☐	☐
X1051	14p	deep blue (1 side band)	4·50	4·50	☐	☐
X1052	19p	bright orange-red (2 bands)	3·00	3·00	☐	☐
X1053	24p	chestnut (phosphorised paper)	1·10	1·25	☐	☐
X1054	29p	deep mauve (2 bands)	3·00	3·00	☐	☐
X1055	29p	deep mauve (phosphorised paper)	4·50	4·50	☐	☐
X1056	31p	ultramarine (phosphorised paper)	1·40	1·40	☐	☐
X1057	33p	light emerald (phosphorised paper)	1·25	1·25	☐	☐
X1058	39p	bright mauve (phosphorised paper)	1·60	1·60	☐	☐

Presentation Pack (P.O. Pack No. 26) (contains ½p
(X841), 1p (X844), 1½p (X848), 2p (X849), 2½p
(X851), 3p (X855), 3½p (X858), 4p (X861), 5p
(X866), 6p (X870), 7½p(X877), 9p (X882))   5·00   ☐

Presentation Pack ('Scandinavia 71')
(contents as above)   30·00   ☐

Presentation Pack (P.O. Pack No. 37) (contains ½p
(X841), 1p (X844), 1½p (X848), 2p (X849), 2½p
(X851), 3p (X855 or X856), 3½p (X858 or X859),
4p (X861), 4½p (X865), 5p (X866), 5½p (X868 or
X869), 6p (X870), 7½p (X877),8p (X878), 9p
(X882), 10p (X885))   30·00   ☐

Later issues of this pack included the 6½p (X871) or the 6½p
(X872) and 7p (X874).

Presentation Pack (P.O. Pack No. 90) (contains ½p
(X841), 1p (X844), 1½p (X848), 2p (X849), 2½p
(X851), 3p (X856), 5p (X866), 6½p (X872), 7p
(X874 or X875), 7½p (X877), 8p (X878), 8½p
(X881), 9p (X883), 9½p (X884), 10p (X886),
10½p (X890), 11p (X892), 20p (X915), 50p
(X921))   5·00   ☐

Presentation Pack (P.O. Pack No. 129a) (contains
2½p (X929), 3p (X930), 4p (X996), 10½p (X891),
11½p (X893), 11½p (X942), 12p (X943), 13p
(X944), 13½p (X945), 14p (X946), 15p (X947),
15½p (X948), 17p (X951), 17½p (X953),18p
(X954), 22p (X962), 25p (X970), 75p
(X1023))   20·00   ☐

Presentation Pack (P.O. Pack No. 1) (contains ½p
(X924), 1p (X925), 2p (X1000), 3p (X930), 3½p
(X931), 4p (X997), 5p (X1004), 10p (X888), 12½p
(X898), 16p (X949), 16½p (X950), 17p (X952),
20p (X999), 20½p (X961), 23p (X965), 26p
(X971), 28p (X975), 31p (X981), 50p (X992),
75p (X1023))   40·00   ☐

Presentation Pack (P.O. Pack No. 5) (contains ½p
(X924), 1p (X925), 2p (X1000a), 3p (X930), 4p
(X997), 5p (X1004a), 10p (X939), 13p (X900),
16p (X949), 17p (X952), 18p (X955), 20p (X999),
22p (X963), 24p (X967), 26p (X971), 28p (X975),
31p (X981), 34p (X985), 50p (X992), 75p
(X1023a))   36·00   ☐

Presentation Pack (P.O. Pack No. 9) (contains 1p
(X925), 2p (X1000a), 3p (X930), 4p (X997), 5p
(X1004a), 7p (X937), 10p (X939), 12p (X896),
13p (X900), 17p (X952), 18p (X955), 20p (X999),
22p (X963), 24p (X967), 26p (X971), 28p (X975),
31p (X981), 34p (X985), 50p (X992), 75p
(X1023a))   40·00   ☐

Presentation Pack (P.O. Pack No. 15) (contains
14p (X903), 19p (X956), 20p (X959), 23p (X966),
27p (X973), 28p (X976), 32p (X983), 35p
(X988))   12·00   ☐

Presentation Pack (P.O. Pack No. 19) (contains
15p (X905), 20p (X960), 24p (X968), 29p (X979),
30p (X980), 34p (X986), 37p (X990))   10·00   ☐

Presentation Pack (P.O. Pack No. 22) (contains
10p (X940), 17p (X910), 22p (X964), 26p (X972),
27p (X974),31p (X982), 33p (X984))   9·00   ☐

Presentation Pack (P.O. Pack No. 24) (contains
1p (X925), 2p (X927), 3p (X930), 4p (X933), 5p
(X935), 10p (X940), 17p (X910), 20p (X959), 22p
(X964), 26p (X972), 27p (X974), 30p (X980), 31p
(X982), 32p (X983), 33p (X984), 37p (X990), 50p
(X994), 75p (X993))   30·00   ☐

Presentation Pack (P.O. Pack No. 25) (contains 6p
(X936), 18p (X913), 24p (X969), 28p (X977), 34p
(X987), 35p (X989), 39p (X991))   9·00   ☐

First Day Covers

Date	Stamps	Price	
15 Feb. 1971	½p, 1p, 1½p, 2p, 2½p, 3p, 3½p, 4p, 5p, 6p, 7½p, 9p (Nos. X841, X844, X848/9, X851, X855, X858, X861, X866, X870, X877, X882) (Covers carry 'POSTING DELAYED BY THE POST OFFICE STRIKE 1971' cachet)	2·50	☐
11 Aug. 1971	10p (No. X885)	1·50	☐
24 Oct. 1973	4½p, 5½p, 8p (Nos. X865, X868, X878)	1·50	☐
4 Sept. 1974	6½p (No. X871)	1·50	☐
15 Jan. 1975	7p (No. X874)	1·00	☐
24 Sept. 1975	8½p (No. X881)	1·50	☐
25 Feb. 1976	9p, 9½p, 10p, 10½p, 11p, 20p (Nos. X883/4, X886, X890, X892, X915)	3·50	☐
2 Feb. 1977	50p (No. X921)	1·75	☐
26 April 1978	10½p (No. X891)	1·20	☐
15 Aug. 1979	11½p, 13p, 15p (Nos. X942, X944, X947)	1·75	☐
30 Jan. 1980	4p, 12p, 13½p, 17p, 17½p, 75p (Nos. X996, X943, X945, X951, X953, X1023)	3·25	☐
22 Oct. 1980	3p, 22p (Nos. X930, X962)	1·50	☐
14 Jan. 1981	2½p, 11½p, 14p, 15½p, 18p, 25p (Nos. X929, X893, X946, X948, X954, X970)	2·00	☐
27 Jan. 1982	5p, 12½p, 16½p, 19½p, 26p, 29p (Nos. X1004, X898, X950, X957, X971, X978)	3·50	☐
30 Mar. 1983	3½p, 16p, 17p, 20½p, 23p, 28p, 31p (Nos. X931, X949, X952, X961, X965, X975, X981)	5·00	☐
28 Aug. 1984	13p, 18p, 22p, 24p, 34p (Nos. X900, X955, X963, X967, X985)	3·00	☐
29 Oct. 1985	7p, 12p (Nos. X937, X896)	3·00	☐
23 Aug. 1988	14p, 19p, 20p, 23p, 27p, 28p, 32p, 35p (Nos. X903, X956, X959, X966, X973, X976, X983, X988)	6·00	☐
26 Sept. 1989	15p, 20p, 24p, 29p, 30p, 34p, 37p (Nos. X905, X960, X968, X979/80, X986, X990)	5·00	☐
4 Sept. 1990	10p, 17p, 22p, 26p, 27p, 31p, 33p (Nos. X940, X910, X964, X972, X974, X982, X984)	5·50	☐
10 Sept. 1991	6p, 18p, 24p, 28p, 34p, 35p, 39p (Nos. X936, X913, X969, X977, X987, X989, X991)	6·00	☐

For similar stamps, but with elliptical perforations see Nos.
Y1667/1803 in 1993.

PHOSPHOR BANDS. See notes on page 15.
Phosphor bands are applied to the stamps, after the design
has been printed, by a separate cylinder. On issues with 'all-
over' phosphor the 'band' covers the entire stamp. Parts of the
stamp covered by phosphor bands, or the entire surface for
'all-over' phosphor versions, appear matt.
Nos. X847, X852, X864, X873, X876, X880, X889, X894, X897,
X899, X901, X906, X911, X1006 and X1012 exist with the
phosphor band at the left or right of the stamp.

PHOSPHORISED PAPER. First introduced as an experiment for a limited printing of the 1s 6d value (No. 743c) in 1969, this paper has the phosphor, to activate the automatic sorting machinery, added to the paper coating before the stamps were printed. Issues on this paper have a completely shiny surface. Although not adopted after this first trial further experiments on the 8½p in 1976 led to this paper being used for new printings of current values.

368 'A Mountain Road' (T.P. Flanagan)

369 'Deer's Meadow' (Tom Carr)

370 'Slieve na brock' (Colin Middleton)

'Ulster '71' Paintings

1971 (16 June) Two phosphor bands

881	**368**	3p multicoloured	25	25	☐	☐
882	**369**	7½p multicoloured	50	50	☐	☐
883	**370**	9p multicoloured	50	50	☐	☐
Set of 3			1·00	1·00	☐	☐
First Day Cover				1·75		☐
Presentation Pack			6·00		☐	

371 John Keats (150th Death Anniv)

372 Thomas Gray (Death Bicentenary)

373 Sir Walter Scott (Birth Bicentenary)

Literary Anniversaries. Events described above

1971 (28 July) Two phosphor bands

884	**371**	3p black, gold and blue	25	10	☐	☐
885	**372**	5p black, gold and olive	45	50	☐	☐
886	**373**	7½p black, gold and brown	45	45	☐	☐
Set of 3			1·00	1·10	☐	☐
First Day Cover				2·00		☐
Presentation Pack			6·00		☐	

374 Servicemen and Nurse of 1921

375 Roman Centurion

376 Rugby Football, 1871

British Anniversaries. Events described on stamps

1971 (25 Aug.) Two phosphor bands

887	**374**	3p multicoloured	25	25	☐	☐
888	**375**	7½p multicoloured	50	50	☐	☐
889	**376**	9p multicoloured	50	50	☐	☐
Set of 3			1·00	1·00	☐	☐
First Day Cover				2·50		☐
Presentation Pack			6·00		☐	

377 Physical Sciences Building, University College of Wales, Aberystwyth

378 Faraday Building, Southampton University

379 Engineering Department, Leicester University

380 Hexagon Restaurant, Essex University

British Architecture (Modern University Buildings)

1971 (22 Sept.) Two phosphor bands

890	**377**	3p multicoloured	10	10	☐	☐
891	**378**	5p multicoloured	25	20	☐	☐
892	**379**	7½p ochre, black and purple-brown	45	55	☐	☐
893	**380**	9p multicoloured	75	80	☐	☐
Set of 4			1·25	1·50	☐	☐
First Day Cover				2·00		☐
Presentation Pack			8·00		☐	

Collectors Pack 1971

1971 (29 Sept.) Comprises Nos. 835/40 and 881/93

CP893a	Collectors Pack	60·00	☐

381 Dream of the Wise Men

382 Adoration of the Magi

390 Ralph Vaughan Williams and Score

383 Ride of the Magi

Christmas

1971 (13 Oct.) Two phosphor bands (3p, 7½p) or one centre phosphor band (2½p)

894	**381**	2½p multicoloured	10	10	☐	☐
895	**382**	3p multicoloured	10	10	☐	☐
896	**383**	7½p multicoloured	55	75	☐	☐
Set of 3			55	75	☐	☐
First Day Cover				2·00	☐	
Presentation Pack			4·50		☐	

Anniversaries. Events described on stamps

1972 (26 Apr.) Two phosphor bands

901	**388**	3p multicoloured	25	25	☐	☐
902	**389**	7½p multicoloured	50	50	☐	☐
903	**390**	9p multicoloured	50	50	☐	☐
Set of 3			1·00	1·00	☐	☐
First Day Cover				2·25		☐
Presentation Pack			4·25		☐	

391 St Andrew's, Greensted - juxta-Ongar, Essex

392 All Saints, Earls Barton, Northants

384 Sir James Clark Ross

385 Sir Martin Frobisher

386 Henry Hudson

387 Capt. Robert F. Scott

393 St Andrew's, Letheringsett, Norfolk

394 St Andrew's, Helpringham, Lincs

395 St Mary the Virgin, Huish Episcopi, Somerset

British Polar Explorers

1972 (16 Feb.) Two phosphor bands

897	**384**	3p multicoloured	10	10	☐	☐
898	**385**	5p multicoloured	15	15	☐	☐
899	**386**	7½p multicoloured	45	50	☐	☐
900	**387**	9p multicoloured	70	85	☐	☐
Set of 4			1·25	1·50	☐	☐
First Day Cover				2·50		☐
Presentation Pack			5·25		☐	

British Architecture (Village Churches)

1972 (21 June) Two phosphor bands

904	**391**	3p multicoloured	10	10	☐	☐
905	**392**	4p multicoloured	10	20	☐	☐
906	**393**	5p multicoloured	15	20	☐	☐
907	**394**	7½p multicoloured	50	75	☐	☐
908	**395**	9p multicoloured	50	80	☐	☐
Set of 5			1·25	1·90	☐	☐
First Day Cover				2·75		☐
Presentation Pack			10·00		☐	

388 Statuette of Tutankhamun

389 19th-century Coastguard

'Belgica '72' Souvenir Pack

1972 (24 June) Comprises Nos. 894/6 and 904/8
CP908b Souvenir Pack   10·00   ☐

396 Microphones, 1924–69   397 Horn Loudspeaker

398 TV Camera, 1972   399 Oscillator and Spark
Transmitter, 1897

Broadcasting Anniversaries. Events described on stamps

1972 (13 Sept.) Two phosphor bands

909	**396**	3p multicoloured	10	10	☐	☐
910	**397**	5p multicoloured	10	20	☐	☐
911	**398**	7½p multicoloured	45	50	☐	☐
912	**399**	9p multicoloured	50	50	☐	☐
Set of 4			1·00	1·25	☐	☐
First Day Cover				2·75	☐	
Presentation Pack			4·25		☐	

400 Angel holding
Trumpet   401 Angel playing
Lute

402 Angel playing Harp

Christmas

1972 (18 Oct.) Two phosphor bands (3p, 7½p) or one centre
phosphor band (2½p)

913	**400**	2½p multicoloured	10	10	☐	☐
914	**401**	3p multicoloured	10	10	☐	☐
915	**402**	7½p multicoloured	50	45	☐	☐
Set of 3			60	45	☐	☐
First Day Cover				1·50	☐	
Presentation Pack			4·00		☐	

403 Queen Elizabeth II
and Prince Philip   404 Europe

Royal Silver Wedding

1972 (20 Nov.) 3p 'all-over' phosphor, 20p without phosphor

916	**403**	3p brownish black, deep blue and silver	25	25	☐	☐
917		20p brownish black, reddish purple and silver	1·00	1·00	☐	☐
Set of 2			1·00	1·00	☐	☐
First Day Cover				1·50		☐
Presentation Pack			4·00		☐	
Presentation Pack (Japanese)			9·50		☐	
Souvenir Book			4·00		☐	
Gutter Pair (3p)			80		☐	
Traffic Light Gutter Pair (3p)			20·00		☐	

Collectors Pack 1972

1972 (20 Nov.) Comprises Nos. 897/917
CP918a Collectors Pack   35·00   ☐
Nos. 920/1 were issued horizontally *se-tenant* throughout the
sheet.

Britain's Entry into European Communities

1973 (3 Jan.) Two phosphor bands

919	**404**	3p multicoloured	25	25	☐	☐
920		5p multicoloured (blue jigsaw)	25	50	☐	☐
		a. Pair. Nos. 920/1	1·00	1·00	☐	☐
921		5p multicoloured (green jigsaw)	25	50	☐	☐
Set of 3			1·00	1·00	☐	☐
First Day Cover				2·00		☐
Presentation Pack			3·00		☐	

405 Oak Tree

British Trees (1st Issue)

1973 (28 Feb.) Two phosphor bands

922	**405**	9p multicoloured	35	40	☐	☐
First Day Cover				1·75		☐
Presentation Pack			2·75		☐	

See also No. 949

406 David Livingstone

407 H. M. Stanley

The above were issued horizontally *se-tenant* throughout the sheet.

408 Sir Francis Drake

409 Sir Walter Raleigh

410 Charles Sturt

British Explorers

1973 (18 Apr.) 'All-over' phosphor

923	**406**	3p multicoloured	40	25	☐	☐
		a. Pair. Nos. 923/4	80	1·00	☐	☐
924	**407**	3p multicoloured	40	25	☐	☐
925	**408**	5p multicoloured	40	50	☐	☐
926	**409**	7½p multicoloured	40	50	☐	☐
927	**410**	9p multicoloured	40	75	☐	☐
Set of 5			1·50	2·50	☐	☐
First Day Cover				2·50		☐
Presentation Pack			4·50		☐	

411

412

413

County Cricket 1873–1973

1973 (16 May) Designs show sketches of W. G. Grace by Harry Furniss. Queen's head in gold. 'All-over' phosphor

928	**411**	3p black and brown	25	25	☐	☐
929	**412**	7½p black and green	75	75	☐	☐
930	**413**	9p black and blue	1·25	1·00	☐	☐
Set of 3			1·75	1·50	☐	☐
First Day Cover				3·00		☐
Presentation Pack			4·50		☐	
Souvenir Book			7·00		☐	
PHQ Card (No. 928)			70·00	£275	☐	☐

The PHQ Card did not become available until mid-July. The used price quoted is for an example used in July or August 1973.

414 'Self-portrait' (Sir Joshua Reynolds)

415 'Self-portrait' (Sir Henry Raeburn)

416 'Nelly O'Brien' (Sir Joshua Reynolds)

417 'Rev R. Walker (The Skater)' (Sir Henry Raeburn)

British Paintings. 250th Birth Anniv of Sir Joshua Reynolds and 150th Death Anniv of Sir Henry Raeburn

1973 (4 July) 'All-over' phosphor

931	**414**	3p multicoloured	10	10	☐	☐
932	**415**	5p multicoloured	30	30	☐	☐
933	**416**	7½p multicoloured	30	30	☐	☐
934	**417**	9p multicoloured	60	60	☐	☐
Set of 4			1·20	1·20	☐	☐
First Day Cover				2·00		☐
Presentation Pack			3·25		☐	

418 Court Masque Costumes	**419** St Paul's Church, Covent Garden		
420 Prince's Lodging, Newmarket	**421** Court Masque Stage Scene		

The 3p and 5p values were printed horizontally *se-tenant* within the sheet.

400th Anniversary of the Birth of Inigo Jones (architect and designer)

1973 (15 Aug.) 'All-over' phosphor
935	**418**	3p deep mauve, black and gold	10	25	
		a. Pair. Nos. 935/6	30	50	
936	**419**	3p deep brown, black and gold	10	25	
937	**420**	5p blue, black and gold	35	50	
		a. Pair. Nos. 937/8	1·00	1·00	
938	**421**	5p grey-olive, black and gold	35	50	
Set of 4			1·25	1·25	
First Day Cover				2·00	
Presentation Pack			3·50		
PHQ Card (No. 936)			£200	£200	

422 Palace of Westminster seen from Whitehall   **423** Palace of Westminster seen from Millbank

19th Commonwealth Parliamentary Conference

1973 (12 Sept.) 'All-over' phosphor
939	**422**	8p black, grey and pale buff	45	50	
940	**423**	10p gold and black	45	40	
Set of 2			75	75	
First Day Cover				1·50	
Presentation Pack			3·00		
Souvenir Book			7·00		
PHQ Card (No. 939)			40·00	£150	

424 Princess Anne and Captain Mark Phillips

Royal Wedding

1973 (14 Nov.) 'All-over' phosphor
941	**424**	3½p violet and silver	25	25	
942		20p brown and silver	1·00	75	
Set of 2			1·00	75	
First Day Cover				1·50	
Presentation Pack			2·75		
PHQ Card (No. 941)			9·00	50·00	
Set of 2 Gutter Pairs			2·75		
Set of 2 Traffic Light Gutter Pairs			£110		

425   **426**

427   **428**

429   **430** 'Good King Wenceslas, the Page and Peasant'

The 3p values depict the carol 'Good King Wenceslas' and were printed horizontally *se-tenant* within the sheet.

Christmas

1973 (28 Nov.) One phosphor band (3p) or 'all-over' phosphor (3½p)
943	**425**	3p multicoloured	20	25	
		a. Strip of 5. Nos. 943/7	2·25	2·50	
944	**426**	3p multicoloured	20	25	
945	**427**	3p multicoloured	20	25	
946	**428**	3p multicoloured	20	25	
947	**429**	3p multicoloured	20	25	
948	**430**	3½p multicoloured	20	25	
Set of 6			2·25	2·50	
First Day Cover				2·50	
Presentation Pack			4·00		

Collectors Pack 1973

1973 (28 Nov.) Comprises Nos. 919/48
| CP948k Collectors Pack | 27·00 | |

431 Horse Chestnut

British Trees (2nd issue)

1974 (27 Feb.) 'All-over' phosphor

949	**431**	10p multicoloured	40	35	☐ ☐
First Day Cover				1·25	☐
Presentation Pack			2·50		☐
PHQ Card			£150	£150	☐ ☐
Gutter Pair			2·00		☐
Traffic Light Gutter Pair			65·00		☐

432 First Motor Fire-engine, 1904

433 Prize-winning Fire-engine, 1863

434 First Steam Fire-engine, 1830

435 Fire-engine, 1766

Bicentenary of the Fire Prevention (Metropolis) Act

1974 (24 Apr.) 'All-over' phosphor

950	**432**	3½p multicoloured	25	10	☐ ☐
951	**433**	5½p multicoloured	25	30	☐ ☐
952	**434**	8p multicoloured	50	50	☐ ☐
953	**435**	10p multicoloured	50	50	☐ ☐
Set of 4			1·25	1·25	☐ ☐
First Day Cover				3·00	☐
Presentation Pack			3·00		☐
PHQ Card (No. 950)			£140	£150	☐ ☐
Set of 4 Gutter Pairs			4·00		☐
Set of 4 Traffic Light Gutter Pairs			60·00		☐

436 P & O Packet *Peninsular*, 1888

437 Farman H.F. III Biplane, 1911

438 Airmail-blue Van and Postbox, 1930

439 Imperial Airways Short S.21 Flying Boat *Maia*, 1937

Centenary of Universal Postal Union

1974 (12 June) 'All-over' phosphor

954	**436**	3½p multicoloured	25	10	☐ ☐
955	**437**	5½p multicoloured	25	30	☐ ☐
956	**438**	8p multicoloured	25	35	☐ ☐
957	**439**	10p multicoloured	50	40	☐ ☐
Set of 4			1·00	1·00	☐ ☐

First Day Cover		2·00	☐
Presentation Pack		3·00	☐
Set of 4 Gutter Pairs		3·00	☐
Set of 4 Traffic Light Gutter Pairs		45·00	☐

440 Robert the Bruce

441 Owain Glyndŵr

442 Henry V

443 The Black Prince

Medieval Warriors

1974 (10 July) 'All-over' phosphor

958	**440**	4½p multicoloured	25	10	☐ ☐
959	**441**	5½p multicoloured	25	35	☐ ☐
960	**442**	8p multicoloured	50	50	☐ ☐
961	**443**	10p multicoloured	50	50	☐ ☐
Set of 4			1·25	1·25	☐ ☐
First Day Cover				3·00	☐
Presentation Pack			4·00		☐
PHQ Cards (*set of* 4)			28·00	65·00	☐ ☐
Set of 4 Gutter Pairs			4·00		☐
Set of 4 Traffic Light Gutter Pairs			60·00		☐

444 Churchill in Royal yacht Squadron Uniform

445 Prime Minister, 1940

446 Secretary for War and Air, 1919

447 War Correspondent, South Africa, 1899

Birth Centenary of Sir Winston Churchill

1974 (9 Oct.) Queen's head and inscription in silver. 'All-over' phosphor

962	**444**	4½p green and blue	20	15	☐ ☐
963	**445**	5½p grey and black	35	35	☐ ☐
964	**446**	8p rose and lake	60	50	☐ ☐
965	**447**	10p stone and brown	60	50	☐ ☐
Set of 4			1·60	1·50	☐ ☐
First Day Cover				2·00	☐

Presentation Pack	3·50		☐
Souvenir Book	3·00		☐
PHQ Card (No. 963)	6·00	32·00	☐ ☐
Set of 4 Gutter Pairs	4·00		☐
Set of 4 Traffic Light Gutter Pairs	34·00		☐

448 Adoration of the Magi (York Minister, *c* 1355)

449 The Nativity (St Helen's Church, Norwich, *c* 1480)

450 Virgin and Child (Ottery St Mary Church, *c* 1350)

451 Virgin and Child (Worcester Cathedral, *c* 1224)

Christmas

1974 (27 Nov.) Designs show church roof bosses. One phosphor band (3½p) or 'all-over' phosphor (others)

966	**448**	3½p multicoloured	10	10	☐ ☐
967	**449**	4½p multicoloured	10	10	☐ ☐
968	**450**	8p multicoloured	25	50	☐ ☐
969	**451**	10p multicoloured	50	50	☐ ☐
Set of 4			1·00	1·00	☐ ☐
First Day Cover				2·00	☐
Presentation Pack			3·00		☐
Set of 4 Gutter Pairs			3·50		☐
Set of 4 Traffic Light Gutter Pairs			36·00		☐

Collectors Pack 1974

1974 (27 Nov.) Comprises Nos. 949/69

CP969a Collectors Pack	15·00		☐

452 Invalid in Wheelchair

Health and Handicap Funds

1975 (22 Jan.) 'All-over' phosphor

970	**452**	4½p + 1½p azure and blue	25	25	☐ ☐
First Day Cover				1·00	☐
Gutter Pair			50		☐
Traffic Light Gutter Pair			2·25		☐

453 'Peace – Burial at Sea'

454 'Snowstorm – Steamer off a Harbour's Mouth'

455 'The Arsenal, Venice'

456 'St Laurent'

Birth Bicentenary of J. M. W. Turner (painter)

1975 (19 Feb.) 'All-over' phosphor

971	**453**	4½p multicoloured	25	25	☐ ☐
972	**454**	5½p multicoloured	25	25	☐ ☐
973	**455**	8p multicoloured	25	50	☐ ☐
974	**456**	10p multicoloured	50	50	☐ ☐
Set of 4			1·00	1·00	☐ ☐
First Day Cover				1·50	☐
Presentation Pack			3·00		☐
PHQ Card (No. 972)			42·00	34·00	☐ ☐
Set of 4 Gutter Pairs			2·25		☐
Set of 4 Traffic Light Gutter Pairs			8·00		☐

457 Charlotte Square, Edinburgh

458 The Rows, Chester

The above were printed horizontally *se-tenant* throughout the sheet.

459 Royal Observatory, Greenwich

460 St George's Chapel, Windsor

461 National Theatre, London

European Architectural Heritage Year

1975 (23 Apr.) 'All-over' phosphor

975	**457**	7p multicoloured	15	15	☐ ☐
		a. Pair. Nos. 975/6	90	1·00	☐ ☐
976	**458**	7p multicoloured	15	15	☐ ☐
977	**459**	8p multicoloured	40	30	☐ ☐
978	**460**	10p multicoloured	40	30	☐ ☐
979	**461**	12p multicoloured	40	35	☐ ☐
Set of 5			1·50	1·40	☐ ☐
First Day Cover				2·50	☐
Presentation Pack			3·00		☐
PHQ Cards (Nos. 975/7)			11·00	40·00	☐ ☐
Set of 5 Gutter Pairs			5·50		☐
Set of 5 Traffic Light Gutter Pairs			22·00		☐

462 Sailing Dinghies

463 Racing Keel Boats

464 Cruising Yachts

465 Multihulls

Sailing

1975 (11 June) 'All-over' phosphor

980	**462**	7p multicoloured	25	20	☐	☐
981	**463**	8p multicoloured	35	40	☐	☐
982	**464**	10p multicoloured	35	45	☐	☐
983	**465**	12p multicoloured	50	50	☐	☐
Set of 4			1·25	1·25	☐	☐
First Day Cover				2·00		☐
Presentation Pack			2·50		☐	
PHQ Card (No. 981)			5·75	30·00	☐	☐
Set of 4 Gutter Pairs			2·50		☐	
Set of 4 Traffic Light Gutter Pairs			25·00		☐	

466 Stephenson's *Locomotion*, 1825 **467** *Abbotsford*, 1876

468 *Caerphilly Castle*, 1923 **469** High Speed Train, 1975

150th Anniversary of Public Railways

1975 (13 Aug.) 'All-over' phosphor

984	**466**	7p multicoloured	25	25	☐	☐
985	**467**	8p multicoloured	50	50	☐	☐
986	**468**	10p multicoloured	50	50	☐	☐
987	**469**	12p multicoloured	40	50	☐	☐
Set of 4			1·50	1·50	☐	☐
First Day Cover				2·50		☐
Presentation Pack			3·00		☐	
Souvenir Book			4·00		☐	
PHQ Cards (*set of 4*)			70·00	72·00	☐	☐
Set of 4 Gutter Pairs			3·00		☐	
Set of 4 Traffic Light Gutter Pairs			12·00		☐	

470 Palace of Westminster

62nd Inter-Parliamentary Union Conference

1975 (3 Sept.) 'All-over' phosphor

988	**470**	12p multicoloured	50	40	☐	☐
First Day Cover				80		☐
Presentation Pack			1·75		☐	
Gutter Pair			1·00		☐	
Traffic Light Gutter Pair			3·00		☐	

471 Emma and Mr Woodhouse (*Emma*)

472 Catherine Morland (*Northanger Abbey*)

473 Mr Darcy (*Pride and Prejudice*)

474 Mary and Henry Crawford (*Mansfield Park*)

Birth Bicentenary of Jane Austen (novelist)

1975 (22 Oct.) 'All-over' phosphor

989	**471**	8½p multicoloured	25	20	☐	☐
990	**472**	10p multicoloured	45	45	☐	☐
991	**473**	11p multicoloured	45	45	☐	☐
992	**474**	13p multicoloured	50	50	☐	☐
Set of 4			1·50	1·25	☐	☐
First Day Cover				2·50		☐
Presentation Pack			3·00		☐	
PHQ Cards (*set of 4*)			24·00	42·00	☐	☐
Set of 4 Gutter Pairs			2·50		☐	
Set of 4 Traffic Light Gutter Pairs			7·00		☐	

475 Angels with Harp and Lute **476** Angel with Mandolin

477 Angel with Horn   **478** Angel with Trumpet

485 Chimney Cleaning (Lord Shaftesbury)   **486** Hands clutching Prison Bars (Elizabeth Fry)

Christmas

1975 (26 Nov.) One phosphor band (6½p). phosphor-inked (8½p) (background) or 'all-over' phosphor (others)

993	**475**	6½p multicoloured	25	25	☐	☐
994	**476**	8½p multicoloured	25	40	☐	☐
995	**477**	11p multicoloured	50	45	☐	☐
996	**478**	13p multicoloured	50	45	☐	☐
Set of 4			1·25	1·25	☐	☐
First Day Cover				1·50		☐
Presentation Pack			3·00		☐	
Set of 4 Gutter Pairs			2·75		☐	
Set of 4 Traffic Light Gutter Pairs			9·00		☐	

Collectors Pack 1975

1975 (26 Nov.) Comprises Nos. 970/96

CP996a Collectors Pack		9·00	☐

479 Housewife   **480** Policeman

481 District Nurse   **482** Industrialist

Telephone Centenary

1976 (10 Mar.) 'All-over' phosphor

997	**479**	8½p multicoloured	25	20	☐	☐
998	**480**	10p multicoloured	40	40	☐	☐
999	**481**	11p multicoloured	50	50	☐	☐
1000	**482**	13p multicoloured	60	60	☐	☐
Set of 4			1·50	1·50	☐	☐
First Day Cover				1·50		☐
Presentation Pack			3·00		☐	
Set of 4 Gutter Pairs			2·75		☐	
Set of 4 Traffic Light Gutter Pairs			9·00		☐	

483 Hewing Coal (Thomas Hepburn)   **484** Machinery (Robert Owen)

Social Reformers

1976 (28 Apr.) 'All-over' phosphor

1001	**483**	8½p multicoloured	25	20	☐	☐
1002	**484**	10p multicoloured	40	40	☐	☐
1003	**485**	11p black, slate-grey and drab	50	50	☐	☐
1004	**486**	13p slate-grey, black and green	60	60	☐	☐
Set of 4			1·50	1·50	☐	☐
First Day Cover				1·50		☐
Presentation Pack			2·75		☐	
PHQ Card (No. 1001)			6·00	20·00	☐	☐
Set of 4 Gutter Pairs			2·75		☐	
Set of 4 Traffic Light Gutter Pairs			9·00		☐	

487 Benjamin Franklin (bust by Jean-Jacques Caffieri)

Bicentenary of American Revolution

1976 (2 June) 'All-over' phosphor

1005	**487**	11p multicoloured	50	50	☐	☐
First Day Cover				1·50		☐
Presentation Pack			1·50		☐	
PHQ Card			5·00	20·00	☐	☐
Gutter Pair			75		☐	
Traffic Light Gutter Pair			2·50		☐	

488 'Elizabeth of Glamis'   **489** 'Grandpa Dickson'

490 'Rosa Mundi'   **491** 'Sweet Briar'

Centenary of Royal National Rose Society

1976 (30 June) 'All-over' phosphor

1006	**488**	8½p multicoloured	15	10	☐	☐
1007	**489**	10p multicoloured	40	40	☐	☐
1008	**490**	11p multicoloured	50	50	☐	☐
1009	**491**	13p multicoloured	65	65	☐	☐
Set of 4			1·50	1·50	☐	
First Day Cover				1·50		☐
Presentation Pack			3·00		☐	
PHQ Cards (*set of* 4)			30·00	38·00	☐	☐
Set of 4 Gutter Pairs			3·00		☐	
Set of 4 Traffic Light Gutter Pairs			10·00		☐	

492 Archdruid

493 Morris Dancing

494 Scots Piper

495 Welsh Harpist

British Cultural Traditions

1976 (4 Aug.) 'All-over' phosphor

1010	**492**	8½p multicoloured	25	20	☐	☐
1011	**493**	10p multicoloured	40	40	☐	☐
1012	**494**	11p multicoloured	45	45	☐	☐
1013	**495**	13p multicoloured	60	60	☐	☐
Set of 4			1·50	1·50	☐	☐
First Day Cover				2·00		☐
Presentation Pack			2·50		☐	
PHQ Cards (*set of* 4)			18·00	30·00	☐	☐
Set of 4 Gutter Pairs			3·00		☐	
Set of 4 Traffic Light Gutter Pairs			12·00		☐	

496 The Canterbury Tales

497 The Tretyse of Love

William Caxton 1476 **11**ᴾ

498 *Game and Playe of Chesse*

William Caxton 1476 **13**ᴾ

499 Early Printing Press

500th Anniversary of British Printing

1976 (29 Sept.) 'All-over' phosphor

1014	**496**	8½p black, blue and gold	25	20	☐	☐
1015	**497**	10p black, olive-green and gold	40	40	☐	☐
1016	**498**	11p black, grey and gold	45	45	☐	☐
1017	**499**	13p brown, ochre and gold	60	60	☐	☐
Set of 4			1·50	1·50	☐	☐
First Day Cover				1·75		☐
Presentation Pack			2·75		☐	
PHQ Cards (*set of* 4)			10·00	28·00	☐	☐
Set of 4 Gutter Pairs			3·00		☐	
Set of 4 Traffic Light Gutter Pairs			7·00		☐	

500 Virgin and Child

501 Angel with Crown

502 Angel appearing to Shepherds

503 The Three Kings

Christmas

1976 (24 Nov.) Designs show English medieval embroidery. One phosphor band (6½p) or 'all-over' phosphor (others)

1018	**500**	6½p multicoloured	25	25	☐	☐
1019	**501**	8½p multicoloured	35	25	☐	☐
1020	**502**	11p multicoloured	40	45	☐	☐
1021	**503**	13p multicoloured	45	50	☐	☐
Set of 4			1·25	1·25	☐	☐
First Day Cover				1·50		☐
Presentation Pack			2·75		☐	
PHQ Cards (*set of* 4)			4·50	26·00	☐	☐
Set of 4 Gutter Pairs			2·75		☐	
Set of 4 Traffic Light Gutter Pairs			7·00		☐	

Collectors Pack 1976

1976 (24 Nov.) Comprises Nos. 997/1021

CP1021a	Collectors Pack	13·50	☐

504 Lawn Tennis

505 Table Tennis

506 Squash

507 Badminton

Racket Sports

1977 (12 Jan.) Phosphorised paper

1022	**504**	8½p multicoloured	25	20	☐	☐
1023	**505**	10p multicoloured	40	40	☐	☐
1024	**506**	11p multicoloured	45	40	☐	☐
1025	**507**	13p multicoloured	45	50	☐	☐
Set of 4			1·25	1·25	☐	☐
First Day Cover				2·00	☐	
Presentation Pack			3·00		☐	
PHQ Cards (set of 4)			8·00	24·00	☐	☐
Set of 4 Gutter Pairs			3·00		☐	
Set of 4 Traffic Light Gutter Pairs			7·50		☐	

508

1977 (2 Feb.)–**87** Type 508 Ordinary paper

1026		£1 green and olive	3·00	25	☐	☐
1026b		£1·30 drab and deep greenish blue	5·50	6·00	☐	☐
1026c		f1·33 pale mauve and grey-black	7·50	8·00	☐	☐
1026d		£1·41 drab and deep greenish blue	8·50	8·50	☐	☐
1026e		£1·50 pale mauve and grey-black	6·00	5·00	☐	☐
1026f		£1·60 drab and deep greenish blue	6·50	7·00	☐	☐
1027		£2 green and brown	9·00	50	☐	☐
1028		£5 pink and blue	22·00	3·00	☐	☐
Set of 8			60·00	32·00	☐	☐
Presentation pack (P.O. Pack No. 91 (small size)) (Nos. 1026, 1027/8)			48·00		☐	
Presentation Pack (P.O. Pack No 13 (large size)) (Nos. 1026, 1027/8)			£180		☐	
Presentation Pack (P.O. Pack No. 14) (No. 1026f)			22·00		☐	
Set of 8 Gutter Pairs			£140		☐	
Set of 8 Gutter Pairs			£170		☐	

First Day Covers

2 Feb. 1977	Nos. 1026, 1027/8	14·00	☐
3 Aug. 1983	No. 1026b	6·50	☐
28th Aug. 1984	No. 1026c.	8·00	☐
17 Sept. 1985	No. 1026d	9·00	☐
2 Sept. 1986	No. 1026e	6·50	☐
15 Sept. 1987	No. 1026f	8·50	☐

509 Steroids — Conformational Analysis

510 Vitamin C — Synthesis

511 Starch — Chromatography

512 Salt — Crystallography

Centenary of Royal Institute of Chemistry

1977 (2 Mar.) 'All-over' phosphor

1029	**509**	8½p multicoloured	25	20	☐	☐
1030	**510**	10p multicoloured	45	45	☐	☐
1031	**511**	11p multicoloured	45	45	☐	☐
1032	**512**	13p multicoloured	45	45	☐	☐
Set of 4			1·25	1·25	☐	☐
First Day Cover				1·50	☐	
Presentation Pack			3·00		☐	
PHQ Cards (set of 4)			8·00	18·00	☐	☐
Set of 4 Gutter Pairs			3·00		☐	
Set of 4 Traffic Light Gutter Pairs			7·00		☐	

513

Silver Jubilee

1977 (11 May–15 June) 'All-over' phosphor

1033	**513**	8½p multicoloured	25	25	☐	☐
1034		9p multicoloured	25	25	☐	☐
1035		10p multicoloured	25	25	☐	☐
1036		11p multicoloured	50	50	☐	☐
10347		13p multicoloured	50	50	☐	☐
Set of 5			1·75	1·75	☐	☐
First Day Cover (2)				2·50	☐	
Presentation Pack (ex 9p)			2·00		☐	
Souvenir Book (ex 9p)			3·00		☐	
PHQ Cards (set of 5)			14·00	20·00	☐	☐
Set of 5 Gutter Pairs			3·50		☐	
Set of 5 Traffic Light Gutter Pairs			6·00		☐	

517 'Gathering of Nations'

Commonwealth Heads of Government Meeting, London

1977 (8 June) 'All-over' phosphor

1038 **517**	13p black, deep green, rose and silver	50	50	☐	☐
First Day Cover			1·50		☐
Presentation Pack		1·50		☐	
PHQ Card		5·00	6·00	☐	☐
Gutter Pair		1·00		☐	
Traffic Light Gutter Pair		1·50		☐	

518 Hedgehog

519 Brown Hare

520 Red Squirrel

521 Otter

522 Badger

T **518/22** were printed together, *se-tenant*, throughout the sheet.

British Wildlife

1977 (5 Oct.) 'All-over' phosphor

1039 **518**	9p multicoloured	25	20	☐	☐
	a. Strip of 5. Nos.1039/43	1·50	1·75	☐	☐
1040 **519**	9p multicoloured	25	20	☐	☐
1041 **520**	9p multicoloured	25	20	☐	☐
1042 **521**	9p multicoloured	25	20	☐	☐
1043 **522**	9p multicoloured	25	20	☐	☐
Set of 5		1·50	1·75	☐	☐

First Day Cover		3·00	☐
Presentation Pack		2·50	☐
PHQ Cards (*set of 5*)	3·00	7·00	☐ ☐
Gutter Strip of 10		3·00	☐
Traffic Light Gutter Strip of 10		5·00	☐

523 'Three French Hens, Two Turtle Doves and a Partridge in a Pear Tree'

524 'Six Geese a laying, Five Gold Rings, Four Colly Birds'

525 'Eight Maids a-milking, Seven Swans a-swimming'

526 'Ten Pipers piping, Nine Drummers drumming'

527 'Twelve Lords a-leaping, Eleven Ladies Dancing'

528 'A Partridge in a Pear Tree'

T **523/8** depict the carol 'The Twelve Days of Christmas'.
T **523/7** were printed horizontally *se-tenant* throughout the sheet.

Christmas

1977 (23 Nov.) One centre phosphor band (7p) or 'all-over' phosphor (9p)

1044 **523**	7p	multicoloured	20	15	☐	☐
	a.	Strip of 5. Nos. 1044/8	1·50	1·50	☐	☐
1045 **524**	7p	multicoloured	20	15	☐	☐
1046 **525**	7p	multicoloured	20	15	☐	☐
1047 **526**	7p	multicoloured	20	15	☐	☐
1048 **527**	7p	multicoloured	20	15	☐	☐
1049 **528**	9p	multicoloured	35	30	☐	☐
Set of 6			1·25	1·50	☐	☐
First Day Cover				2·25		☐
Presentation Pack			2·25		☐	
PHQ Cards (*set of 6*)			3·00	6·00	☐	☐
Set of 6 Gutter Pairs			3·00		☐	
Set of 6 Traffic Light Gutter Pairs		5·50		☐	

Collectors Pack 1977

1977 (23 Nov.) Comprises Nos. 1022/5, 1029/49

CP1049b	Collectors Pack	9·00	☐

529 Oil — North Sea Production Platform

530 Coal — Modern Pithead

531 Natural Gas — Flame Rising from Sea

532 Electricity — Nuclear Power Station and Uranium Atom

Energy Resources

1978 (25 Jan.) 'All-over' phosphor

1050	**529**	9p multicoloured	25	25		
1051	**530**	10½p multicoloured	25	25		
1052	**531**	11p multicoloured	50	50		
1053	**532**	13p multicoloured	50	50		
Set of 4			1·25	1·25		
First Day Cover				1·50		
Presentation Pack			2·00			
PHQ Cards (*set of* 4)			3·00	6·00		
Set of 4 Gutter Pairs			2·75			
Set of 4 Traffic Light Gutter Pairs			4·50			

533 Tower of London

534 Holyroodhouse

535 Caernarvon Castle

536 Hampton Court Palace

British Architecture (Historic Buildings)

1978 (1 Mar.) 'All-over' phosphor

1054	**533**	9p multicoloured	25	20		
1055	**534**	10½p multicoloured	25	40		
1056	**535**	11p multicoloured	60	40		
1057	**536**	13p multicoloured	60	40		
Set of 4			1·50	1·25		
First Day Cover				1·50		

Presentation Pack	2·00		
PHQ Cards (*set of* 4)	3·00	6·00	
Set of 4 Gutter Pairs	3·00		
Set of 4 Traffic Light Gutter Pairs	4·50		
MS1058 121 × 90 mm. Nos. 1054/7	1·50	1·75	
First Day Cover		2·00	

No. **MS**1058 was sold at 53½p, the premium being used for the London 1980 Stamp Exhibition.

537 State Coach

538 St Edward's Crown

539 The Sovereign's Orb

540 Imperial State Crown

25th Anniversary of Coronation

1978 (31 May) 'All-over' phosphor

1059	**537**	9p gold and blue	35	25		
1060	**538**	10½p gold and red	45	45		
1061	**539**	11p gold and green	45	45		
1062	**540**	13p gold and violet	50	50		
Set of 4			1·50	1·50		
First Day Cover				1·50		
Presentation Pack			2·00			
Souvenir Book			3·00			
PHQ Cards (*set of* 4)			3·00	6·00		
Set of 4 Gutter Pairs			3·00			
Set of 4 Traffic Light Gutter Pairs			4·25			

541 Shire Horse

542 Shetland Pony

543 Welsh Pony

544 Thoroughbred

Horses

1978 (5 July) 'All-over' phosphor

1063	**541**	9p multicoloured	20	10	☐	☐
1064	**542**	10½p multicoloured	35	40	☐	☐
1065	**543**	11p multicoloured	35	45	☐	☐
1066	**544**	13p multicoloured	45	50	☐	☐
Set of 4			1·25	1·25	☐	☐
First Day Cover				1·50	☐	
Presentation Pack			1·75		☐	
PHQ Cards (set of 4)			2·25	5·75	☐	☐
Set of 4 Gutter Pairs			3·00		☐	
Set of 4 Traffic Light Gutter Pairs			4·50		☐	

545 Penny-farthing and 1884 Safety Bicycle

546 1920 Touring Bicycles

547 Modern Small-wheel Bicycles

548 1978 Road-racers

Centenaries of Cyclists Touring Club and British Cycling Federation

1978 (2 Aug.) 'All-over' phosphor

1067	**545**	9p multicoloured	25	20	☐	☐
1068	**546**	10½p multicoloured	35	40	☐	☐
1069	**547**	11p multicoloured	40	40	☐	☐
1070	**548**	13p multicoloured	50	50	☐	☐
Set of 4			1·25	1·25	☐	☐
First Day Cover				1·50	☐	
Presentation Pack			1·75		☐	
PHQ Cards (set of 4)			2·25	5·00	☐	☐
Set of 4 Gutter Pairs			2·75		☐	
Set of 4 Traffic Light Gutter Pairs			4·50		☐	

549 Singing Carols round the Christmas Tree

550 The Waits

551 18th-Century Carol Singers **552** 'The Boar's Head Carol'

Christmas

1978 (22 Nov.) One centre phosphor band (7p) or 'all-over' phosphor (others)

1071	**549**	7p multicoloured	25	25	☐	☐
1072	**550**	9p multicoloured	25	25	☐	☐
1073	**551**	11p multicoloured	50	50	☐	☐
1074	**552**	13p multicoloured	50	50	☐	☐
Set of 4			1·25	1·25	☐	☐
First Day Cover				1·50	☐	
Presentation Pack			1·75		☐	
PHQ Cards (set of 4)			2·25	5·00	☐	☐
Set of 4 Gutter Pairs			2·50		☐	
Set of 4 Traffic Light Gutter Pairs			4·25		☐	

Collectors Pack 1978

1978 (22 Nov.) Comprises Nos. 1050/7, 1059/74

CP1074a Collectors Pack		10·00	☐

553 Old English Sheepdog

554 Welsh Springer Spaniel

555 West Highland Terrier

556 Irish Setter

Dogs

1979 (7 Feb.) 'All-over' phosphor

1075	**553**	9p multicoloured	25	20	☐	☐
1076	**554**	10½p multicoloured	40	40	☐	☐
1077	**555**	11p multicoloured	40	40	☐	☐
1078	**556**	13p multicoloured	40	50	☐	☐
Set of 4			1·25	1·25	☐	☐
First Day Cover				1·50	☐	
Presentation Pack			1·75		☐	
PHQ Cards (set of 4)			2·50	5·00	☐	☐
Set of 4 Gutter Pairs			2·50		☐	
Set of 4 Traffic Light Gutter Pairs			4·25		☐	

557 Primrose

558 Daffodil

559 Bluebell   **560** Snowdrop

Spring Wild Flowers

1979 (21 Mar.) 'All-over' phosphor

1079	**557**	9p multicoloured	25	20	☐	☐
1080	**558**	10½p multicoloured	25	45	☐	☐
1081	**559**	11p multicoloured	50	45	☐	☐
1082	**560**	13p multicoloured	50	40	☐	☐
Set of 4			1·25	1·25	☐	☐
First Day Cover				1·50	☐	
Presentation Pack			1·75		☐	
PHQ Cards (*set of* 4)			2·50	4·50	☐	☐
Set of 4 Gutter Pairs			2·50		☐	
Set of 4 Traffic Light Gutter Pairs			4·25		☐	

561   **562**

563   **564**

T **561/4** show hands placing the flags of the member nations into ballot boxes.

First Direct Elections to European Assembly

1979 (9 May) Phosphorised paper

1083	**561**	9p multicoloured	25	20	☐	☐
1084	**562**	10½p multicoloured	35	35	☐	☐
1085	**563**	11p multicoloured	40	40	☐	☐
1086	**564**	13p multicoloured	45	40	☐	☐
Set of 4			1·25	1·25	☐	☐
First Day Cover				1·50	☐	
Presentation Pack			1·75		☐	
PHQ Cards (*set of* 4)			2·25	4·50	☐	☐
Set of 4 Gutter Pairs			2·50		☐	
Set of 4 Traffic Light Gutter Pairs			4·25		☐	

565 'Saddling "Mahmoud" for the Derby, 1936' (Sir Alfred Munnings)

566 'The Liverpool Great National Steeple Chase, 1839' (aquatint by F. C.Turner)

567 'The First Spring Meeting, Newmarket, 1793' (J.N. Sartorius)

568 'Racing at Dorsett Ferry, Windsor, 1684' (Francis Barlow)

Horseracing Paintings and Bicentenary of The Derby (9p)

1979 (6 June) 'All-over' phosphor

1087	**565**	9p multicoloured	25	25	☐	☐
1088	**566**	10½p multicoloured	25	25	☐	☐
1089	**567**	11p multicoloured	50	50	☐	☐
1090	**568**	13p multicoloured	50	50	☐	☐
Set of 4			1·25	1·25	☐	☐
First Day Cover				1·50	☐	
Presentation Pack			1·75		☐	
PHQ Cards (*set of* 4)			2·25	4·50	☐	☐
Set of 4 Gutter Pairs			2·50		☐	
Set of 4 Traffic Light Gutter Pairs			4·25		☐	

569 *The Tale of Peter Rabbit* (Beatrix Potter)

570 *The Wind in the Willows* (Kenneth Grahame)

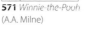

571 *Winnie-the-Pooh* (A.A. Milne)

572 *Alice's Adventures in Wonderland* (Lewis Carroll)

T **569/72** depict original illustrations from the four books.

International Year of the Child

1979 (11 July) 'All-over' phosphor

1091	**569**	9p multicoloured	30	25	☐	☐
1092	**570**	10½p multicoloured	35	35	☐	☐
1093	**571**	11p multicoloured	40	40	☐	☐
1094	**572**	13p multicoloured	60	60	☐	☐
Set of 4			1·50	1·50	☐	☐
First Day Cover				1·50	☐	
Presentation Pack			1·75		☐	
PHQ Cards (*set of* 4)			2·50	4·50	☐	☐
Set of 4 Gutter Pairs			3·50		☐	
Set of 4 Traffic Light Gutter Pairs			4·25		☐	

573 Sir Rowland Hill, 1795-1879

574 General Post, c 1839

575 London Post, c 1839

576 Uniform Postage, 1840

Death Centenary of Sir Rowland Hill (postal reformer)

1979 (22 Aug.–24 Oct.) 'All-over' phosphor

1095	**573**	10p multicoloured	25	20	☐	☐
1096	**574**	11½p multicoloured	25	35	☐	☐
1097	**575**	13p multicoloured	50	45	☐	☐
1098	**576**	15p multicoloured	75	50	☐	☐
Set of 4			1·50	1·50	☐	☐
First Day Cover				1·50	☐	
Presentation Pack			1·50		☐	
PHQ Cards (*set of* 4)			2·25	4·25	☐	☐
Set of 4 Gutter Pairs			3·00		☐	
Set of 4 Traffic Light Gutter Pairs			4·25		☐	
MS1099 89 × 121 mm. Nos. 1095/8			1·25	1·50	☐	☐
First Day Cover (24 Oct.)				1·50	☐	

No. **MS**1099 was sold at 59½p, the premium being used for the London 1980 Stamp Exhibition.

577 Policeman on the Beat

578 Policeman directing Traffic

579 Mounted Policewoman

580 River Patrol Boat

150th Anniversary of Metropolitan Police

1979 (26 Sept.) Phosphorised paper

1100	**577**	10p multicoloured	30	20	☐	☐
1101	**578**	11½p multicoloured	35	35	☐	☐
1102	**579**	13p multicoloured	40	55	☐	☐
1103	**580**	15p multicoloured	60	55	☐	☐

Set of 4		1·50	1·50	☐ ☐
First Day Cover			1·50	☐
Presentation Pack		1·75		☐
PHQ Cards (*set of* 4)		2·25	4·25	☐ ☐
Set of 4 Gutter Pairs		3·00		☐
Set of 4 Traffic Light Gutter Pairs		4·25		☐

581 The Three Kings

582 Angel appearing to the Shepherds

583 The Nativity

584 Mary and Joseph travelling to Bethlehem

585 The Annunciation

Christmas

1979 (21 Nov.) One centre phosphor band (8p) or phosphorised paper (others)

1104	**581**	8p multicoloured	25	20	☐	☐
1105	**582**	10p multicoloured	25	25	☐	☐
1106	**583**	11½p multicoloured	25	35	☐	☐
1107	**584**	13p multicoloured	50	50	☐	☐
1108	**585**	15p multicoloured	50	50	☐	☐
Set of 5			1·50	1·50	☐	☐
First Day Cover				1·50	☐	
Presentation Pack			2·00		☐	
PHQ Cards (*set of* 5)			2·50	4·25	☐	☐
Set of 5 Gutter Pairs			3·50		☐	
Set of 5 Traffic Light Gutter Pairs			4·50		☐	

Collectors Pack 1979

1979 (21 Nov.) Comprises Nos. 1075/98, 1100/8

CP1108a	Collectors Pack	12·00	☐

586 Common Kingfisher

587 Dipper

588 Moorhen

589 Yellow Wagtails

Centenary of Wild Bird Protection Act

1980 (16 Jan.) Phosphorised paper

1109	**586**	10p multicoloured	20	10	☐	☐
1110	**587**	11½p multicoloured	40	35	☐	☐
1111	**588**	13p multicoloured	50	55	☐	☐
1112	**589**	15p multicoloured	50	55	☐	☐
Set of 4			1·50	1·50	☐	☐
First Day Cover				1·50	☐	
Presentation Pack			1·50		☐	
PHQ Cards (set of 4)			2·25	4·50	☐	☐
Set of 4 Gutter Pairs			3·50		☐	

590 Rocket approaching Moorish Arch, Liverpool

591 First and Second Class Carriages passing through Olive Mount Cutting

592 Third Class Carriage and Sheep Truck crossing Chat Moss

593 Horsebox and Carriage Truck near Bridgewater Canal

594 Goods Truck and Mail - coach at Manchester

T **590/4** were printed together, se-tenant, in horizontal strips of 5 throughout the sheet.

150th Anniversary of Liverpool and Manchester Railway

1980 (12 Mar.) Phosphorised paper

1113	**590**	12p multicoloured	20	15	☐	☐
		a. Strip of 5.				
		Nos. 1113/17	1·75	1·75	☐	☐
1114	**591**	12p multicoloured	20	15	☐	☐
1115	**592**	12p multicoloured	20	15	☐	☐
1116	**593**	12p multicoloured	20	15	☐	☐
1117	**594**	12p multicoloured	20	15	☐	☐

Set of 5		1·75	1·75	☐ ☐
First Day Cover			1·75	☐
Presentation Pack		2·00		☐
PHQ Cards (set of 5)		3·25	4·50	☐ ☐
Gutter block of 10		3·75		☐

595 Montage of London Buildings

'London 1980' International Stamp Exhibition

1980 (9 Apr.–7 May) Phosphorised paper. Perf 14½ × 14

1118	**595**	50p agate	1·50	1·50	☐	☐
First Day Cover				1·50	☐	
Presentation Pack			1·75		☐	
PHQ Card			2·25	3·00	☐	☐
Gutter Pair			3·25		☐	
MS1119 90 × 123 mm. No. 1118			1·50	1·75	☐	☐
First Day Cover (7 May)				2·00	☐	

No. **MS**1119 was sold at 75p, the premium being used for the exhibition.

596 Buckingham Palace

597 The Albert Memorial

598 Royal Opera House

599 Hampton Court

600 Kensington Palace

London Landmarks

1980 (7 May) Phosphorised paper

1120	**596**	10½p multicoloured	25	10	☐	☐
1121	**597**	12p multicoloured	25	15	☐	☐
1122	**598**	13½p multicoloured	40	50	☐	☐
1123	**599**	15p multicoloured	50	75	☐	☐
1124	**600**	17½p multicoloured	75	75	☐	☐
Set of 5			2·00	2·00	☐	☐
First Day Cover				2·00		☐
Presentation Pack			2·00		☐	
PHQ Cards (*set of 5*)			2·25	3·00	☐	☐
Set of 5 Gutter Pairs			4·25		☐	

601 Charlotte Brontë (*Jane Eyre*)

602 George Eliot (*The Mill on the Floss*)

603 Emily Brontë (*Wuthering Heights*)

604 Mrs Gaskell (*North and South*)

T **601/4** show authoresses and scenes from their novels.
T **601/2** also include the 'Europa' C.E.P.T. emblem.

Famous Authoresses

1980 (9 July) Phosphorised paper

1125	**601**	12p multicoloured	35	20	☐	☐
1126	**602**	13½p multicoloured	40	45	☐	☐
1127	**603**	15p multicoloured	40	45	☐	☐
1128	**604**	17½p multicoloured	50	50	☐	☐
Set of 4			1·50	1·50	☐	☐
First Day Cover				1·50		☐
Presentation Pack			1·75		☐	
PHQ Cards (*set of 4*)			2·50	3·00	☐	☐
Set of 4 Gutter Pairs			3·75		☐	

605 Queen Elizabeth the Queen Mother

80th Birthday of Queen Elizabeth the Queen Mother

1980 (4 Aug.) Phosphorised paper

1129	**605**	12p multicoloured	75	75	☐	☐
First Day Cover				1·50		☐
PHQ Card			2·25	2·00	☐	☐
Gutter Pair			1·50		☐	

606 Sir Henry Wood

607 Sir Thomas Beecham

608 Sir Malcolm Sargent

609 Sir John Barbirolli

British Conductors

1980 (10 Sept.) Phosphorised paper

1130	**606**	12p multicoloured	30	10	☐	☐
1131	**607**	13½p multicoloured	45	40	☐	☐
1132	**608**	15p multicoloured	50	55	☐	☐
1133	**609**	17½p multicoloured	50	55	☐	☐
Set of 4			1·50	1·50	☐	☐
First Day Cover				1·75		☐
Presentation Pack			1·75		☐	
PHQ Cards (*set of 4*)			2·25	3·75	☐	☐
Set of 4 Gutter Pairs			3·75		☐	

610 Running

611 Rugby

612 Boxing

613 Cricket

Sports Centenaries

1980 (10 Oct.) Phosphorised paper. Perf 14 × 14½

1134	**610**	12p multicoloured	25	20	☐	☐
1135	**611**	13½p multicoloured	50	50	☐	☐
1136	**612**	15p multicoloured	50	45	☐	☐
1137	**613**	17½p multicoloured	50	50	☐	☐

Set of 4	1·50	1·50	☐	☐
First Day Cover		1·75		☐
Presentation Pack	1·75		☐	
PHQ Cards (*set of 4*)	2·25	3·75	☐	☐
Set of 4 Gutter Pairs	3·75		☐	

Centenaries:—12p Amateur Athletics Association; 13½p Welsh Rugby Union; 15p Amateur Boxing Association; 17½p First England v Australia Test Match.

614 Christmas Tree

615 Candles

616 Apples and Mistletoe

617 Crown, Chains and Bell

618 Holly

Christmas

1980 (19 Nov.) One centre phosphor band (10p) or phosphorised paper (others)

1138	**614**	10p multicoloured	20	10	☐	☐
1139	**615**	12p multicoloured	20	20	☐	☐
1140	**616**	13½p multicoloured	40	40	☐	☐
1141	**617**	15p multicoloured	55	50	☐	☐
1142	**618**	17½p multicoloured	55	50	☐	☐
Set of 5			1·75	1·50	☐	☐
First Day Cover				1·75		☐
Presentation Pack			2·00		☐	
PHQ Cards (*set of 5*)			2·25	4·00	☐	☐
Set of 5 Gutter Pairs			4·50		☐	

Collectors Pack 1980

1980 (19 Nov.) Comprises Nos. 1109/18, 1120/42

CP1142a	Collectors Pack	15·00	☐

619 St Valentine's Day

620 Morris Dancers

621 Lammastide

622 Medieval Mummers

T **619/20** also include the 'Europa' C.E.P.T. emblem.

Folklore

1981 (6 Feb.) Phosphorised paper

1143	**619**	14p multicoloured	25	25	☐	☐
1144	**620**	18p multicoloured	50	50	☐	☐
1145	**621**	22p multicoloured	75	80	☐	☐
1146	**622**	25p multicoloured	1·00	1·10	☐	☐
Set of 4			2·25	2·50	☐	☐
First Day Cover				2·00		☐
Presentation Pack			2·25		☐	
PHQ Cards (*set of 4*)			2·25	3·25	☐	☐
Set of 4 Gutter Pairs			5·25		☐	

623 Blind Man with Guide Dog

624 Hands spelling 'Deaf' in Sign Language

625 Disabled Man in Wheelchair

626 Disabled Artist painting with Foot

International Year of the Disabled

1981 (25 Mar.) Phosphorised paper

1147	**623**	14p multicoloured	50	25	☐	☐
1148	**624**	18p multicoloured	50	50	☐	☐
1149	**625**	22p multicoloured	75	85	☐	☐
1150	**626**	25p multicoloured	1·00	1·00	☐	☐
Set of 4			2·25	2·50	☐	☐
First Day Cover				2·50		☐
Presentation Pack			2·25		☐	
PHQ Cards (*set of 4*)			2·25	3·25	☐	☐
Set of 4 Gutter Pairs			4·25		☐	

627 *Aglais urticae*

628 *Maculinea arion*

629 *Inachis io*

630 *Carterocephalus palaemon*

636 Prince Charles and Lady Diana Spencer

Butterflies

1981 (13 May) Phosphorised paper

1151	**627**	14p multicoloured	25	20	☐	☐
1152	**628**	18p multicoloured	75	70	☐	☐
1153	**629**	22p multicoloured	70	85	☐	☐
1154	**630**	25p multicoloured	75	85	☐	☐
Set of 4			2·25	2·50	☐	☐
First Day Cover				2·50	☐	
Presentation Pack			2·25		☐	
PHQ Cards (*set of* 4)			2·25	6·00	☐	☐
Set of 4 Gutter Pairs			4·75		☐	

631 Glenfinnan, Scotland

632 Derwentwater, England

633 Stackpole Head, Wales

634 Giant's Causeway, N. Ireland

635 St Kilda, Scotland

50th Anniversary of National Trust for Scotland (British landscapes)

1981 (24 June) Phosphorised paper

1155	**631**	14p multicoloured	15	25	☐	☐
1156	**632**	18p multicoloured	45	50	☐	☐
1157	**633**	20p multicoloured	70	75	☐	☐
1158	**634**	22p multicoloured	75	1·00	☐	☐
1159	**635**	25p multicoloured	90	1·00	☐	☐
Set of 5			2·50	3·00	☐	☐
First Day Cover				3·25	☐	
Presentation Pack			3·00		☐	
PHQ Cards (*set of* 5)			2·50	5·00	☐	☐
Set of 5 Gutter Pairs			6·00		☐	

Royal Wedding

1981 (22 July) Phosphorised paper

1160	**636**	14p multicoloured	75	25	☐	☐
1161		25p multicoloured	1·50	1·50	☐	☐
Set of 2			2·25	1·50	☐	☐
First Day Cover				2·75		☐
Presentation Pack			3·00		☐	
Souvenir Book			3·00		☐	
PHQ Cards (*set of* 2)			2·50	5·00	☐	☐
Set of 2 Gutter Pairs			4·00		☐	

637 'Expeditions'

638 'Skills'

639 'Service'

640 'Recreation'

25th Anniversary of Duke of Edinburgh's Award Scheme

1981 (12 Aug.) Phosphorised paper. Perf 14

1162	**637**	14p multicoloured	25	20	☐	☐
1163	**638**	18p multicoloured	45	50	☐	☐
1164	**639**	22p multicoloured	80	80	☐	☐
1165	**640**	25p multicoloured	90	1·00	☐	☐
Set of 4			2·25	2·50	☐	☐
First Day Cover				2·50		☐
Presentation Pack			2·50		☐	
PHQ Cards (*set of* 4)			2·50	4·50	☐	☐
Set of 4 Gutter Pairs			5·00		☐	

641 Cockle-dredging from *Lindsey II*

642 Hauling Trawl Net

643 Lobster Potting **644** Hoisting Seine Net

Fishing Industry

1981 (23 Sept.) Phosphorised paper

1166	**641**	14p multicoloured	25	25	☐	☐
1167	**642**	18p multicoloured	50	50	☐	☐
1168	**643**	22p multicoloured	85	85	☐	☐
1169	**644**	25p multicoloured	85	85	☐	☐
Set of 4			2·25	2·50	☐	☐
First Day Cover				2·00	☐	
Presentation Pack			2·50		☐	
PHQ Cards (set of 4)			2·25	4·50	☐	☐
Set of 4 Gutter Pairs			5·00		☐	

Nos. 1166/9 were issued on the occasion of the centenary of
Royal National Mission to Deep Sea Fishermen.

645 Father Christmas **646** Jesus Christ

647 Flying Angel **648** Joseph and Mary arriving at Bethlehem

649 Three Kings approaching Bethlehem

Christmas. Children's Pictures

1981 (18 Nov.) One phosphor band (11½p) or phosphorised
paper (others)

1170	**645**	11½p multicoloured	25	20	☐	☐
1171	**646**	14p multicoloured	35	20	☐	☐
1172	**647**	18p multicoloured	50	60	☐	☐
1173	**648**	22p multicoloured	75	75	☐	☐
1174	**649**	25p multicoloured	85	85	☐	☐
Set of 5			2·50	2·50	☐	☐
First Day Cover				2·75	☐	
Presentation Pack			3·00		☐	
PHQ Cards (set of 5)			2·25	5·50	☐	☐
Set of 5 Gutter Pairs			5·50		☐	

Collectors Pack 1981

1981 (18 Nov.) Comprises Nos. 1143/74

CP1174a	Collectors Pack	19·00	☐

650 Charles Darwin and Giant Tortoises **651** Darwin and Marine Iguanas

652 Darwin, Cactus Ground Finch and Large Ground Finch **653** Darwin and Prehistoric Skulls

Death Centenary of Charles Darwin

1982 (10 Feb.) Phosphorised paper

1175	**650**	15½p multicoloured	50	20	☐	☐
1176	**651**	19½p multicoloured	50	60	☐	☐
1177	**652**	26p multicoloured	75	85	☐	☐
1178	**653**	29p multicoloured	95	90	☐	☐
Set of 4			2·50	2·50	☐	☐
First Day Cover				2·75	☐	
Presentation Pack			3·00		☐	
PHQ Cards (set of 4)			2·50	6·00	☐	☐
Set of 4 Gutter Pairs			5·25		☐	

654 Boys' Brigade **655** Girls' Brigade

656 Boy Scout Movement **657** Girl Guide Movement

Youth Organizations

1982 (24 Mar.) Phosphorised paper

1179	**654**	15½p multicoloured	25	15	☐	☐
1180	**655**	19½p multicoloured	50	50	☐	☐
1181	**656**	26p multicoloured	85	85	☐	☐
1182	**657**	29p multicoloured	1·00	1·10	☐	☐
Set of 4			2·50	2·50	☐	☐

First Day Cover		2·75	☐	
Presentation Pack	3·00		☐	
PHQ Cards (set of 4)	2·50	6·00	☐	☐
Set of 4 Gutter Pairs	5·50		☐	

Nos. 1179/82 were issued on the occasion of the 75th anniversary of the Boy Scout Movement, the 125th birth anniversary of Lord Baden-Powell and the centenary of the Boys' Brigade (1983).

658 Ballerina

659 Harlequin

660 Hamlet

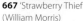
661 Opera Singer

Europa. British Theatre

1982 (28 Apr.) Phosphorised paper

1183	**658**	15½p multicoloured	25	15	☐	☐
1184	**659**	19½p multicoloured	50	50	☐	☐
1185	**660**	26p multicoloured	1·25	1·00	☐	☐
1186	**661**	29p multicoloured	1·50	1·00	☐	☐
Set of 4			3·25	2·50	☐	☐
First Day Cover				2·75	☐	
Presentation Pack			3·00		☐	
PHQ Cards (set of 4)			2·50	6·00	☐	☐
Set of 4 Gutter Pairs			8·00		☐	

662 Henry VIII and *Mary Rose*

663 Admiral Blake and *Triumph*

664 Lord Nelson and HMS *Victory*

665 Lord Fisher and HMS *Dreadnought*

666 Viscount Cunningham and HMS *Warspite*

Maritime Heritage

1982 (16 June) Phosphorised paper

1187	**662**	15½p multicoloured	35	25	☐	☐
1188	**663**	19½p multicoloured	50	50	☐	☐
1189	**664**	24p multicoloured	75	85	☐	☐
1190	**665**	26p multicoloured	75	85	☐	☐
1191	**666**	29p multicoloured	1·00	1·00	☐	☐
Set of 5			3·00	3·50	☐	
First Day Cover				3·75	☐	
Presentation Pack			3·50		☐	
PHQ Cards (set of 5)			2·50	6·00	☐	☐
Set of 5 Gutter Pairs			7·00		☐	

667 'Strawberry Thief' (William Morris)

668 Untitled (Steiner and Co)

669 'Cherry Orchard' (Paul Nash)

670 'Chevron' (Andrew Foster)

British Textiles

1982 (23 July) Phosphorised paper

1192	**667**	15½p multicoloured	25	25	☐	☐
1193	**668**	19½p multicoloured	75	75	☐	☐
1194	**669**	26p multicoloured	75	1·00	☐	☐
1195	**670**	29p multicoloured	1·00	1·25	☐	☐
Set of 4			2·50	2·75	☐	
First Day Cover				3·00	☐	
Presentation Pack			2·75		☐	
PHQ Cards (set of 4)			2·50	6·00	☐	☐
Set of 4 Gutter Pairs			5·50		☐	

Nos 1192/5 were issued on the occasion of the 250th birth anniversary of Sir Richard Arkwright (inventor of spinning machine).

671 Development of Communications

672 Modern Technological Aids

Information Technology

1982 (8 Sept.) Phosphorised paper. Perf 14 × 15

1196	**671**	15½p multicoloured	50	25	☐	☐
1197	**672**	26p multicoloured	75	1·00	☐	☐
Set of 2			1·25	1·25	☐	☐
First Day Cover				1·75	☐	
Presentation Pack			1·50		☐	
PHQ Cards (*set of 2*)			2·00	5·25	☐	☐
Set of 2 Gutter Pairs			2·75			

673 Austin 'Seven' and 'Metro' **674** Ford 'Model T' and 'Escort'

675 Jaguar 'SS1' and 'XJ6' **676** Rolls-Royce 'Silver Ghost' and 'Silver Spirit'

British Motor Industry

1982 (13 Oct.) Phosphorised paper. Perf 14½ × 14

1198	**673**	15½p multicoloured	50	25	☐	☐
1199	**674**	19½p multicoloured	75	75	☐	☐
1200	**675**	26p multicoloured	75	75	☐	☐
1201	**676**	29p multicoloured	1·00	1·00	☐	☐
Set of 4			2·50	2·50	☐	☐
First Day Cover				2·50	☐	
Presentation Pack			3·00		☐	
PHQ Cards (*set of 4*)			2·50	6·00	☐	☐
Set of 4 Gutter Pairs			6·25		☐	

677 'While Shepherds Watched' **678** 'The Holly and the Ivy'

679 'I Saw Three Ships' **680** 'We Three Kings'

681 'Good King Wenceslas'

Christmas. Carols

1982 (17 Nov.) One phosphor band (12½p) or phosphorised paper (others).

1202	**677**	12½p multicoloured	25	20	☐	☐
1203	**678**	15½p multicoloured	50	20	☐	☐
1204	**679**	19½p multicoloured	65	75	☐	☐
1205	**680**	26p multicoloured	75	90	☐	☐
1206	**681**	29p multicoloured	1·00	1·00	☐	☐
Set of 5			3·00	2·75	☐	☐
First Day Cover				2·50	☐	
Presentation Pack			3·25		☐	
PHQ Cards (*set of 5*)			2·50	6·00	☐	☐
Set of 5 Gutter Pairs			5·25		☐	

Collectors Pack 1982

1982 (17 Nov.) Comprises Nos. 1175/1206

CP1206a	Collectors Pack	26·00		☐

682 Atlantic Salmon **683** Northern Pike

684 Brown Trout **685** Eurasian Perch

British River Fish

1983 (26 Jan.) Phosphorised paper

1207	**682**	15½p multicoloured	30	25	☐	☐
1208	**683**	19½p multicoloured	60	60	☐	☐
1209	**684**	26p multicoloured	75	85	☐	☐
1210	**685**	29p multicoloured	1·00	1·10	☐	☐
Set of 4			2·50	2·50	☐	☐
First Day Cover				2·50	☐	
Presentation Pack			2·75		☐	
PHQ Cards (*set of 4*)			3·00	7·00	☐	☐
Set of 4 Gutter Pairs			5·00		☐	

686 Tropical Island **687** Desert

688 Temperate
Farmland

689 Mountain Range

Commonwealth Day. Geographical Regions

1983 (9 Mar.) Phosphorised paper

1211	**686**	15½p multicoloured	40	25	☐	☐
1212	**687**	19½p multicoloured	75	75	☐	☐
1213	**688**	26p multicoloured	75	75	☐	☐
1214	**689**	29p multicoloured	1·00	1·00	☐	☐
Set of 4			2·50	2·50	☐	☐
First Day Cover				2·50	☐	
Presentation Pack			3·00		☐	
PHQ Cards (*set of* 4)			2·50	6·50	☐	☐
Set of 4 Gutter Pairs			6·00		☐	

690 Humber Bridge

691 Thames Flood Barrier

692 Iolair (oilfield emergency
support vessel)

Europa. Engineering Achievements

1983 (25 May) Phosphorised paper

1215	**690**	16p multicoloured	50	25	☐	☐
1216	**691**	20½p multicoloured	1·00	1·00	☐	☐
1217	**692**	28p multicoloured	1·00	1·00	☐	☐
Set of 3			2·25	2·00	☐	☐
First Day Cover				2·25	☐	
Presentation Pack			2·50		☐	
PHQ Cards (*set of* 3)			2·50	5·75	☐	☐
Set of 3 Gutter Pairs			7·00		☐	

693 Musketeer and
Pikeman, The Royal
Scots (1633)

694 Fusilier and Ensign,
The Royal Welch Fusiliers
(mid-18th century)

695 Riflemen, 95th
Rifles (The Royal Green
Jackets) (1805)

696 Sergeant (khaki
service uniform) and
Guardsman full dress),
The Irish Guards (1900).

697 Paratroopers,
The Parachute Regiment (1983)

British Army Uniforms

1983 (6 July) Phosphorised paper

1218	**693**	16p multicoloured	50	10	☐	☐
1219	**694**	20½p multicoloured	50	60	☐	☐
1220	**695**	26p multicoloured	75	90	☐	☐
1221	**696**	28p multicoloured	75	90	☐	☐
1222	**697**	31p multicoloured	75	85	☐	☐
Set of 5			3·00	3·25	☐	☐
First Day Cover				3·25	☐	
Presentation Pack			3·50		☐	
PHQ Cards (*set of* 5)			3·50	6·50	☐	☐
Set of 5 Gutter Pairs			7·50		☐	

Nos. 1218/22 were issued on the occasion of the 350th
anniversary of The Royal Scots, the senior line regiment of the
British Army.

698 20th-Century
Garden, Sissinghurst

699 19th-Century
Garden, Biddulph
Grange

700 18th-Century
Garden, Blenheim

701 17th-Century
Garden, Pitmedden

British Gardens

1983 (24 Aug.) Phosphorised paper. Perf 14

1223	**698**	16p multicoloured	50	10	☐	☐
1224	**699**	20½p multicoloured	50	55	☐	☐
1225	**700**	28p multicoloured	75	1·00	☐	☐
1226	**701**	31p multicoloured	1·00	1·00	☐	☐
Set of 4			2·50	2·50	☐	☐
First Day Cover				2·25		☐
Presentation Pack			3·00		☐	
PHQ Cards (*set of* 4)			3·00	6·25	☐	☐
Set of 4 Gutter Pairs			6·00		☐	

702 Merry-go-round

703 Big Wheel, Helter-skelter and Performing Animals

704 Side-shows

705 Early Produce Fair

British Fairs

1983 (5 Oct.) Phosphorised paper

1227	**702**	16p multicoloured	35	25	☐	☐
1228	**703**	20½p multicoloured	75	75	☐	☐
1229	**704**	28p multicoloured	75	1·00	☐	☐
1230	**705**	31p multicoloured	1·00	1·00	☐	☐
Set of 4			2·50	2·75	☐	☐
First Day Cover				3·00		☐
Presentation Pack			3·00		☐	
PHQ Cards (*set of* 4)			3·00	6·25	☐	☐
Set of 4 Gutter Pairs			6·00		☐	

Nos. 1227/30 were issued to mark the 850th anniversary of St Bartholomew's Fair, Smithfield, London.

706 'Christmas Post' (Pillar box)

707 'The Three Kings' (chimney-pots)

708 'World at Peace' (Dove and Blackbird)

709 'Light of Christmas' (street lamp)

710 'Christmas Dove' (hedge sculpture)

Christmas

1983 (16 Nov.) One phosphor band (12½p) or phosphorised paper (others)

1231	**706**	12½p multicoloured	25	25	☐	☐
1232	**707**	16p multicoloured	50	25	☐	☐
1233	**708**	20½p multicoloured	75	1·00	☐	☐
1234	**709**	28p multicoloured	75	1·00	☐	☐
1235	**710**	31p multicoloured	1·25	1·25	☐	☐
Set of 5			3·25	3·25	☐	☐
First Day Cover				3·50		☐
Presentation Pack			3·50		☐	
PHQ Cards (*set of* 5)			3·00	6·25	☐	☐
Set of 5 Gutter Pairs			6·50		☐	

Collectors Pack 1983

1983 (16 Nov.) Comprises Nos. 1207/35

CP1235a	Collectors Pack		32·00	☐

711 Arms of the College of Arms

712 Arms of King Richard III (founder)

713 Arms of the Earl Marshal of England

714 Arms of the City of London

500th Anniversary of College of Arms

1984 (17 Jan.) Phosphorised paper. Perf 14½

1236	**711**	16p multicoloured	50	15	☐	☐
1237	**712**	20½p multicoloured	50	65	☐	☐
1238	**713**	28p multicoloured	1·00	1·10	☐	☐
1239	**714**	31p multicoloured	1·25	1·25	☐	☐
Set of 4			3·00	3·00	☐	☐
First Day Cover				3·00		☐
Presentation Pack			3·25		☐	
PHQ Cards (*set of* 4)			3·00	6·50	☐	☐
Set of 4 Gutter Pairs			6·25		☐	

715 Highland Cow

716 Chillingham Wild Bull

717 Hereford Bull

718 Welsh Black Bull

719 Irish Moiled Cow

British Cattle

1984 (6 Mar.) Phosphorised paper

1240	**715**	16p multicoloured	35	15	☐	☐
1241	**716**	20½p multicoloured	60	60	☐	☐
1242	**717**	26p multicoloured	80	80	☐	☐
1243	**718**	28p multicoloured	90	90	☐	☐
1244	**719**	31p multicoloured	1·00	1·20	☐	☐
Set of 5			3·50	3·50	☐	
First Day Cover				3·50	☐	
Presentation Pack			4·00		☐	
PHQ Cards (*set of* 5)			3·00	6·50	☐	
Set of 5 Gutter Pairs			7·25		☐	

Nos. 1240/4 marked the centenary of the Highland Cattle Society and the bicentenary of the Royal Highland and Agricultural Society of Scotland.

720 Festival Hall, Liverpool

721 Milburngate Shopping Centre, Durham

722 Bush House, Bristol

723 Commercial Street Housing Scheme, Perth

Urban Renewal

1984 (10 Apr.) Phosphorised paper

1245	**720**	16p multicoloured	30	10	☐	☐
1246	**721**	20½p multicoloured	50	60	☐	☐
1247	**722**	28p multicoloured	1·25	1·25	☐	☐
1248	**723**	31p multicoloured	1·25	1·25	☐	☐

Set of 4		3·00	3·00	☐ ☐
First Day Cover			2·50	☐
Presentation Pack		3·00		☐
PHQ Cards (*set of* 4)		3·00	6·25	☐ ☐
Set of 4 Gutter Pairs		6·50		☐

Nos. 1245/8 marked the opening of the International Gardens Festival, Liverpool, and the 150th anniversaries of the Royal Institute of British Architects and the Chartered Institute of Building.

724 C.E.P.T. 25th Anniversary Logo   **725** Abduction of Europa

Nos. 1249/50 and 1251/2 were each printed together, *se-tenant*, in horizontal pairs throughout the sheets.

Europa. 25th Anniversary of C.E.P.T. and 2nd European Parliamentary Elections

1984 (15 May) Phosphorised paper

1249	**724**	16p greenish slate, deep blue and gold	50	25	☐	☐
		a. Horiz pair. Nos. 1249/50	1·50	1·50	☐	☐
1250	**725**	16p greenish slate, deep blue, black and gold	50	25	☐	☐
1251	**724**	20½p Venetian red, deep magenta and gold	70	40	☐	☐
		a. Horiz pair. Nos. 1251/2	2·50	2·50	☐	☐
1252	**725**	20½p Venetian red, deep magenta, black and gold	70	40	☐	☐
Set of 4			3·00	3·00	☐	☐
First Day Cover				3·50	☐	
Presentation Pack			4·00		☐	
PHQ Cards (*set of* 4)			3·00	6·25	☐	☐
Set of 2 Gutter Blocks of 4			8·00		☐	

726 Lancaster House

London Economic Summit Conference

1984 (5 June) Phosphorised paper

1253	**726**	31p multicoloured	1·25	1·25	☐	☐
First Day Cover				2·25		☐
PHQ Card			1·00	3·50	☐	☐
Gutter Pair			2·50			☐

727 View of Earth from 'Apollo 11'

728 Navigational Chart of English Channel

729 Greenwich Observatory

730 Sir George Airey's Transit Telescope

Centenary of Greenwich Meridian

1984 (26 June) Phosphorised paper. Perf 14 × 14½

1254	**727**	16p multicoloured	50	25	☐	☐
1255	**728**	20½p multicoloured	75	80	☐	☐
1256	**729**	28p multicoloured	1·00	1·00	☐	☐
1257	**730**	31p multicoloured	1·00	1·10	☐	☐
Set of 4			3·00	3·00	☐	
First Day Cover				3·00	☐	
Presentation Pack			3·50		☐	
PHQ Cards (set of 4)			3·00	6·25	☐	☐
Set of 4 Gutter Pairs			6·50		☐	

731 Bath Mail Coach, 1784

732 Attack on Exeter Mail, 1816

733 Norwich Mail in Thunderstorm, 1827

734 Holyhead and Liverpool Mails leaving London, 1828

735 Edinburgh Mail Snowbound, 1831

T **731/5** were printed together, *se-tenant*, in horizontal strips of 5 throughout the sheet.

Bicentenary of First Mail Coach Run, Bath and Bristol to London

1984 (31 July) Phosphorised paper

1258	**731**	16p multicoloured	40	35	☐	☐
		a. Horiz strip of 5. Nos. 1258/62	2·50	2·75	☐	☐
1259	**732**	16p multicoloured	40	35	☐	☐
1260	**733**	16p multicoloured	40	35	☐	☐
1261	**734**	16p multicoloured	40	35	☐	☐
1262	**735**	16p multicoloured	40	35	☐	☐
Set of 5			2·50	2·75	☐	☐
First Day Cover				3·00		☐
Presentation Pack			3·00		☐	
Souvenir Book			7·50		☐	
PHQ Cards (set of 5)			3·00	6·50	☐	☐
Gutter Block of 10			6·50		☐	

736 Nigerian Clinic

737 Violinist and Acropolis, Athens

738 Building Project, Sri Lanka

739 British Council Library

50th Anniversary of The British Council

1984 (25 Sept.) Phosphorised paper

1263	**736**	17p multicoloured	50	25	☐	☐
1264	**737**	22p multicoloured	85	1·00	☐	☐
1265	**738**	31p multicoloured	85	1·00	☐	☐
1266	**739**	34p multicoloured	1·00	1·00	☐	☐
Set of 4			3·00	3·00	☐	☐
First Day Cover				3·00		☐
Presentation Pack			3·25		☐	
PHQ Cards (set of 4)			3·00	6·25	☐	☐
Set of 4 Gutter Pairs			6·50		☐	

740 The Holy Family

741 Arrival in Bethlehem

742 Shepherd and Lamb

743 Virgin and Child

744 Offering of Frankincense

Christmas

1984 (20 Nov.) One phosphor band (13p) or phosphorised paper (others)

1267	**740**	13p multicoloured	25	25	☐	☐
1268	**741**	17p multicoloured	50	50	☐	☐
1269	**742**	22p multicoloured	75	75	☐	☐
1270	**743**	31p multicoloured	1·00	1·00	☐	☐
1271	**744**	34p multicoloured	1·00	1·00	☐	☐
Set of 5			3·25	3·25	☐	☐
First Day Cover				3·25	☐	
Presentation Pack			3·75		☐	
PHQ Cards (set of 5)			3·00	6·25	☐	☐
Set of 5 Gutter Pairs			7·00		☐	

Collectors Pack 1984

1984 (20 Nov.) Comprises Nos. 1236/71

CP1271a	Collectors Pack	37·00	☐

Post Office Yearbook

1984 Comprises Nos. 1236/71 in hardbound book with slip case

YB1271a	Yearbook	85·00	☐

745 'Flying Scotsman'

746 'Golden Arrow'

747 'Cheltenham Flyer'

748 'Royal Scot'

749 'Cornish Riviera'

Famous Trains

1985 (22 Jan.) Phosphorised paper

1272	**745**	17p multicoloured	75	25	☐	☐
1273	**746**	22p multicoloured	75	1·00	☐	☐
1274	**747**	29p multicoloured	1·00	1·25	☐	☐
1275	**748**	31p multicoloured	1·25	1·50	☐	☐
1276	**749**	34p multicoloured	2·50	2·50	☐	☐
Set of 5			6·00	6·00	☐	☐

First Day Cover		6·00		☐	
Presentation Pack		6·00			☐
PHQ Cards (set of 5)		6·00	15·00	☐	☐
Set of 5 Gutter Pairs		12·00		☐	☐

Nos. 1272/6 were issued on the occasion of the 150th anniversary of the Great Western Railway Company.

750 *Bombus terrestris* (Bee)

751 *Coccinella septempunctata* (ladybird)

752 *Decticus verrucivorus* (bush-cricket)

753 *Lucanus cervus* (stag beetle)

754 *Anax imperator* (dragonfly)

Insects

1985 (12 Mar.) Phosphorised paper

1277	**750**	17p multicoloured	40	10	☐	☐
1278	**751**	22p multicoloured	60	55	☐	☐
1279	**752**	29p multicoloured	85	90	☐	☐
1280	**753**	31p multicoloured	1·00	1·00	☐	☐
1281	**754**	34p multicoloured	1·00	90	☐	☐
Set of 5			3·25	3·25	☐	☐
First Day Cover				3·50	☐	
Presentation Pack			4·50		☐	
PHQ Cards (set of 5)			3·00	7·50	☐	☐
Set of 5 Gutter Pairs			8·75		☐	

Nos. 1277/81 were issued on the occasion of the centenaries of the Royal Entomological Society of London's Royal Charter and of the Selborne Society.

755 'Water Music', by Handel

756 'The Planets', by Holst

757 'The First Cuckoo', by Delius

758 'Sea Pictures', by Elgar

Europa. European Music Year

1985 (14 May) Phosphorised paper. Perf 14½

1282	**755**	17p multicoloured	55	10	☐ ☐
1283	**756**	22p multicoloured	75	90	☐ ☐
1284	**757**	31p multicoloured	1·50	1·25	☐ ☐
1285	**758**	34p multicoloured	1·50	1·25	☐ ☐
Set of 4			4·00	3·25	☐ ☐
First Day Cover				4·00	☐
Presentation Pack			4·75		☐
PHQ Cards (set of 4)			3·00	6·50	☐ ☐
Set of 4 Gutter Pairs			10·00		☐

Nos. 1282/5 were issued on the occasion of the 300th birth anniversary of Handel.

759 R.N.L.I. Lifeboat and Signal Flags

760 Beachy Head Lighthouse and Chart

761 'Marecs A' Communications Satellite and Dish Aerials

762 Buoys

Safety at Sea

1985 (18 June) Phosphorised paper. Perf 14

1286	**759**	17p multicoloured	40	25	☐ ☐
1287	**760**	22p multicoloured	60	75	☐ ☐
1288	**761**	31p multicoloured	1·00	1·00	☐ ☐
1289	**762**	34p multicoloured	1·50	1·25	☐ ☐
Set of 4			3·00	3·00	☐ ☐
First Day Cover				3·00	☐
Presentation Pack			3·75		☐
PHQ Cards (set of 4)			3·00	6·50	☐ ☐
Set of 4 Gutter Pairs			7·00		☐

Nos. 1286/9 were issued to mark the bicentenary of the unimmersible lifeboat and the 50th anniversary of Radar.

763 Datapost Motorcyclist, City of London

764 Rural Postbus

765 Parcel Delivery in Winter

766 Town Letter Delivery

350 Years of Royal Mail Public Postal Service

1985 (30 July) Phosphorised paper

1290	**763**	17p multicoloured	50	10	☐ ☐
1291	**764**	22p multicoloured	75	70	☐ ☐
1292	**765**	31p multicoloured	1·00	1·00	☐ ☐
1293	**766**	34p multicoloured	1·50	1·50	☐ ☐
Set of 4			3·00	3·00	☐ ☐
First Day Cover				3·25	☐
Presentation Pack			3·75		☐
PHQ Cards (set of 4)			3·00	6·50	☐ ☐
Set of 4 Gutter Pairs			7·00		☐

767 King Arthur and Merlin

768 The Lady of the Lake

769 Queen Guinevere and Sir Lancelot

770 Sir Galahad

Arthurian Legends

1985 (3 Sept.) Phosphorised paper

1294	**767**	17p multicoloured	50	25	☐ ☐
1295	**768**	22p multicoloured	75	75	☐ ☐
1296	**769**	31p multicoloured	1·25	1·25	☐ ☐
1297	**770**	34p multicoloured	1·25	1·25	☐ ☐
Set of 4			3·50	3·00	☐ ☐
First Day Cover				3·50	☐
Presentation Pack			4·00		☐
PHQ Cards (set of 4)			3·00	6·50	☐ ☐
Set of 4 Gutter Pairs			7·00		☐

Nos. 1294/7 were issued to mark the 500th anniversary of the printing of Sir Thomas Malory's *Morte d'Arthur*.

780 Pantomime Cat

771 Peter Sellers (from
photo by Bill Brandt)

772 David Niven (from
photo by Cornell Lucas)

Christmas. Pantomime Characters

1985 (19 Nov.) One phosphor band (12p) or phosphorised
paper (others)

1303	**776**	12p multicoloured	50	15	☐	☐
1304	**777**	17p multicoloured	50	25	☐	☐
1305	**778**	22p multicoloured	75	1·10	☐	☐
1306	**779**	31p multicoloured	1·25	1·40	☐	☐
1307	**780**	34p multicoloured	1·25	1·40	☐	☐
Set of 5			4·00	4·00	☐	☐
First Day Cover				4·50		☐
Presentation Pack			4·25		☐	
PHQ Cards (*set of* 5)			3·00	6·50	☐	☐
Set of 5 Gutter Pairs			8·00		☐	

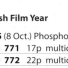

773 Charlie Chaplin (from
photo by Lord Snowdon)

774 Vivien Leigh (from
photo by Angus McBean)

Collectors Pack 1985

1985 (19 Nov.) Comprises Nos. 1272/1307
CP1307a Collectors Pack   35·00   ☐

Post Office Yearbook

1985 Comprises Nos. 1272/1307 in hardbound book with slip
case
YB1307a Yearbook   75·00   ☐

775 Alfred Hitchcock
(from photo by Howard Coster)

British Film Year

1985 (8 Oct.) Phosphorised paper. Perf 14½

1298	**771**	17p multicoloured	45	25	☐	☐
1299	**772**	22p multicoloured	60	75	☐	☐
1300	**773**	29p multicoloured	1·00	1·25	☐	☐
1301	**774**	31p multicoloured	1·10	1·50	☐	☐
1302	**775**	34p multicoloured	1·40	1·50	☐	☐
Set of 5			4·00	4·50	☐	☐
First Day Cover				5·00		☐
Presentation Pack			5·50		☐	
Souvenir Book			11·50		☐	
PHQ Cards (*set of* 5)			3·00	8·50	☐	☐
Set of 5 Gutter Pairs			10·50		☐	

781 Light Bulb and North
Sea Oil Drilling Rig (Energy)

17 PENCE · INDUSTRY YEAR 1986

22 PENCE · INDUSTRY YEAR 1986

782 Thermometer and
Pharmaceutical Laboratory
(Health)

31 PENCE · INDUSTRY YEAR 1986

34 PENCE · INDUSTRY YEAR 1986

783 Garden Hoe and Steel
Works (Steel)

784 Loaf of Bread and and
Cornfield (Agriculture)

Industry Year

1986 (14 Jan.) Phosphorised paper. Perf 14½ × 14

1308	**781**	17p multicoloured	75	25	☐	☐
1309	**782**	22p multicoloured	50	75	☐	☐
1310	**783**	31p multicoloured	1·25	1·40	☐	☐
1311	**784**	34p multicoloured	1·25	1·40	☐	☐
Set of 4			3·50	3·50	☐	☐
First Day Cover				3·50		☐
Presentation Pack			3·75		☐	
PHQ Cards (*set of* 4)			3·50	6·50	☐	☐
Set of 4 Gutter Pairs			7·00		☐	

776 Principal Boy

777 Genie

778 Dame

779 Good Fairy

785 Dr Edmond Halley as Comet

786 *Giotto* Spacecraft approaching Comet

791 Barn Owl

792 Pine Marten

793 Wild Cat

794 Natterjack Toad

787 'Twice in a Lifetime'

788 Comet orbiting Sun and Planets

Appearance of Halley's Comet

1986 (18 Feb.) Phosphorised paper

1312	**785**	17p multicoloured	50	25	☐	☐
1313	**786**	22p multicoloured	75	75	☐	☐
1314	**787**	31p multicoloured	1·25	1·25	☐	☐
1315	**788**	34p multicoloured	1·25	1·40	☐	☐
Set of 4			3·50	3·50	☐	☐
First Day Cover				3·50		☐
Presentation Pack			3·75		☐	
PHQ Cards (*set of 4*)			3·50	6·50	☐	☐
Set of 4 Gutter Pairs			7·00		☐	

789 Queen Elizabeth II in 1928, 1942 and 1952

790 Queen Elizabeth II in 1958, 1973 and 1982

Nos. 1316/17 and 1318/19 were each printed together, *se-tenant*, in horizontal pairs throughout the sheets.

60th Birthday of Queen Elizabeth II

1986 (21 Apr.) Phosphorised paper

1316	**789**	17p multicoloured	60	25	☐	☐
		a. Horiz pair.				
		Nos. 1316/17	1·50	1·50	☐	☐
1317	**790**	17p multicoloured	60	25	☐	☐
1318	**789**	34p multicoloured	70	50	☐	☐
		a. Horiz pair.				
		Nos. 1318/19	3·00	4·00	☐	☐
1319	**790**	34p multicoloured	70	50	☐	☐
Set of 4			4·50	5·00	☐	☐
First Day Cover				5·00		☐
Presentation Pack			5·50		☐	
Souvenir Book			8·50		☐	
PHQ Cards (*set of 4*)			5·00	6·50	☐	☐
Set of 2 Gutter Blocks of 4			11·00		☐	

Europa. Nature Conservation. Endangered Species

1986 (20 May) Phosphorised paper. Perf 14½ × 14

1320	**791**	17p multicoloured	40	10	☐	☐
1321	**792**	22p multicoloured	80	1·00	☐	☐
1322	**793**	31p multicoloured	1·50	1·25	☐	☐
1323	**794**	34p multicoloured	1·65	1·40	☐	☐
Set of 4			4·00	3·50	☐	☐
First Day Cover				4·00		☐
Presentation Pack			4·00		☐	
PHQ Cards (*set of 4*)			3·50	6·50	☐	☐
Set of 4 Gutter Pairs			10·00		☐	

795 Peasants Working in Fields

796 Freemen working at Town Trades

797 Knight and Retainers

798 Lord at Banquet

900th Anniversary of Domesday Book

1986 (17 June) Phosphorised paper

1324	**795**	17p multicoloured	40	10	☐	☐
1325	**796**	22p multicoloured	85	85	☐	☐
1326	**797**	31p multicoloured	1·25	1·40	☐	☐
1327	**798**	34p multicoloured	1·25	1·40	☐	☐
Set of 4			3·50	3·50	☐	☐
First Day Cover				4·00		☐
Presentation Pack			4·00		☐	
PHQ Cards (*set of 4*)			3·50	6·50	☐	☐
Set of 4 Gutter Pairs			7·00		☐	

799 Athletics

800 Rowing

801 Weightlifting

802 Rifle-shooting

803 Hockey

Thirteenth Commonwealth Games, Edinburgh (Nos. 1328/31) and World Men's Hockey Cup, London (No. 1332)

1986 (15 July) Phosphorised paper

1328	**799**	17p multicoloured	·40	25	☐	☐
1329	**800**	22p multicoloured	55	75	☐	☐
1330	**801**	29p multicoloured	75	1·00	☐	☐
1331	**802**	31p multicoloured	1·50	1·75	☐	☐
1332	**803**	34p multicoloured	1·75	1·75	☐	☐
Set of 5			4·00	4·00	☐	☐
First Day Cover				3·50		☐
Presentation Pack			4·00		☐	
PHQ Cards (*set of 5*)			3·50	7·50	☐	☐
Set of 5 Gutter Pairs			8·75		☐	

No. 1332 also marked the centenary of the Hockey Association.

804 Prince Andrew and Miss Sarah Ferguson

805 Prince Andrew and Miss Sarah Ferguson

Royal Wedding

1986 (22 July) One side band (12p) or phosphorised paper (17p)

1333	**804**	12p multicoloured	50	30	☐	☐
1334	**805**	17p multicoloured	1·00	1·25	☐	☐
Set of 2			1·50	1·50	☐	☐
First Day Cover				2·00		☐
Presentation Pack			1·75		☐	
PHQ Cards (*set of 2*)			2·25	5·00	☐	☐
Set of 2 Gutter Pairs			3·00		☐	

806 Stylised Cross on Ballot Paper

32nd Commonwealth Parliamentary Conference, London

1986 (19 Aug.) Phosphorised paper. Perf 14 × 14½

1335	**806**	34p multicoloured	1·25	1·25	☐	☐
First Day Cover				1·75		☐
PHQ Card			1·00	3·00	☐	☐
Gutter Pair			2·75		☐	

807 Lord Dowding and Hawker Hurricane Mk. I

808 Lord Tedder and Hawker Typhoon 1B

809 Lord Trenchard and de Havilland D.H.9A

810 Sir Arthur Harris and Avro Type 683 Lancaster

811 Lord Portal and de Havilland DH.98 Mosquito

History of the Royal Air Force

1986 (16th Sept.) Phosphorised paper. Perf 14½ × 14

1336	**807**	17p multicoloured	50	10	☐	☐
1337	**808**	22p multicoloured	75	95	☐	☐
1338	**809**	29p multicoloured	1·25	1·25	☐	☐
1339	**810**	31p multicoloured	1·75	1·60	☐	☐
1340	**811**	34p multicoloured	1·75	1·90	☐	☐
Set of 5			5·00	5·50	☐	☐
First Day Cover				5·50		☐
Presentation Pack			5·50		☐	
PHQ Cards (*set of 5*)			4·50	10·00	☐	☐
Set of 5 Gutter Pairs			12·00		☐	

Nos. 1336/40 were issued to celebrate the 50th anniversary of the first R.A.F. Commands.

812 The Glastonbury Thorn

813 The Tanad Valley Plygain

814 The Hebrides Tribute

815 The Dewsbury Church Knell

816 The Hereford Boy Bishop

Christmas. Folk Customs

1986 (18 Nov.–2 Dec.) One phosphor band (12p, 13p) or phosphorised paper (others)

1341	**812**	12p multicoloured (2 Dec.)	50	50
1342		13p multicoloured	25	15
1343	**813**	18p multicoloured	50	15
1344	**814**	22p multicoloured	1·00	1·00
1345	**815**	31p multicoloured	1·25	1·00
1346	**816**	34p multicoloured	1·25	1·10
Set of 6			3·75	3·50
First Day Covers (2)				3·75
Presentation Pack (Nos. 1342/6)			3·75	
PHQ Cards (set of 5) (Nos. 1342/6)			3·50	6·50
Set of 6 Gutter Pairs			9·00	

Collectors Pack 1986

1986 (18 Nov.) Comprises Nos. 1308/40, 1342/6

CP1346a	Collectors Pack	37·00	

Post Office Yearbook

1986 Comprises Nos. 1308/40, 1342/6 in hardbound book with slip case

YB1346a	Yearbook	70·00	

817 North American Blanket Flower

818 Globe Thistle

819 Echeveria

820 Autumn Crocus

Flower Photographs by Alfred Lammer

1987 (20 Jan.) Phosphorised paper. Perf 14½ × 14

1347	**817**	18p multicoloured	40	10
1348	**818**	22p multicoloured	70	85
1349	**819**	31p multicoloured	1·10	1·25
1350	**820**	34p multicoloured	1·10	1·25
Set of 4			3·25	3·25
First Day Cover				3·50
Presentation Pack			4·00	
PHQ Cards (set of 4)			3·00	7·00
Set of 4 Gutter Pairs			7·50	

821 The Principia Mathematica

822 Motion of Bodies in Ellipses

823 Optick Treatise

824 The System of the World

300th Anniversary of The Principia Mathematica by Sir Isaac Newton

1987 (24 Mar.) Phosphorised paper

1351	**821**	18p multicoloured	50	15
1352	**822**	22p multicoloured	75	75
1353	**823**	31p multicoloured	1·25	1·50
1354	**824**	34p multicoloured	1·25	1·25
Set of 4			3·50	3·25
First Day Cover				3·75
Presentation Pack			4·00	
PHQ Cards (set of 4)			3·00	6·50
Set of 4 Gutter Pairs			8·00	

825 Willis Faber and Dumas Building, Ipswich

826 Pompidou Centre, Paris

827 Staatsgalerie, Stuttgart

828 European Investment Bank, Luxembourg

Europa. British Architects in Europe

1987 (12 May) Phosphorised paper

1355	**825**	18p multicoloured	50	15	☐	☐
1356	**826**	22p multicoloured	75	75	☐	☐
1357	**827**	31p multicoloured	1·25	1·25	☐	☐
1358	**828**	34p multicoloured	1·75	1·25	☐	☐
Set of 4			4·00	3·25	☐	☐
First Day Cover				3·75		☐
Presentation Pack			4·00		☐	
PHQ Cards (*set of* 4)			3·00	6·50	☐	☐
Set of 4 Gutter Pairs			9·50		☐	

829 Brigade Members with Ashford Litter, 1887

830 Bandaging Blitz Victim, 1940

831 Volunteer with fainting Girl, 1965

832 Transport of Transplant Organ by Air Wing, 1987

Centenary of St John Ambulance Brigade

1987 (16 June) Phosphorised paper. Perf 14 × 14½

1359	**829**	18p multicoloured	40	25	☐	☐
1360	**830**	22p multicoloured	60	75	☐	☐
1361	**831**	31p multicoloured	1·25	1·25	☐	☐
1362	**832**	34p multicoloured	1·25	1·25	☐	☐
Set of 4			3·25	3·25	☐	☐
First Day Cover				3·75		☐
Presentation Pack			4·00		☐	
PHQ Cards (*set of* 4)			3·00	6·50	☐	☐
Set of 4 Gutter Pairs			7·50		☐	

833 Arms of the Lord Lyon King of Arms

834 Scottish Heraldic Banner of Prince Charles

835 Arms of Royal Scottish Academy of Painting, Sculpture and Architecture

836 Arms of Royal Society of Edinburgh

300th Anniversary of Revival of Order of the Thistle

1987 (21 July) Phosphorised paper. Perf 14½

1363	**833**	18p multicoloured	50	10	☐	☐
1364	**834**	22p multicoloured	75	90	☐	☐
1365	**835**	31p multicoloured	1·40	1·40	☐	☐
1366	**836**	34p multicoloured	1·50	1·40	☐	☐
Set of 4			3·75	3·50	☐	☐
First Day Cover				3·75		☐
Presentation Pack			4·00		☐	
PHQ Cards (*set of* 4)			3·00	6·50	☐	☐
Set of 4 Gutter Pairs			8·00		☐	

837 Crystal Palace, 'Monarch of the Glen' (Landseer) and Grace Darling

838 Great Eastern, Beeton's Book of Household Management and Prince Albert

839 Albert Memorial, Ballot Box and Disraeli

840 Diamond Jubilee Emblem, Morse Key and Newspaper Placard for Relief of Mafeking

150th Anniversary of Queen Victoria's Accession

1987 (8 Sept.) Phosphorised paper

1367	**837**	18p multicoloured	50	10	☐	☐
1368	**838**	22p multicoloured	80	75	☐	☐
1369	**839**	31p multicoloured	1·25	1·50	☐	☐
1370	**840**	34p multicoloured	1·35	1·60	☐	☐
Set of 4			3·50	3·50	☐	☐
First Day Cover				3·75		☐
Presentation Pack			4·25		☐	
PHQ Cards (*set of* 4)			3·00	6·50	☐	☐
Set of 4 Gutter Pairs			9·00		☐	

841 Pot by Bernard Leach

842 Pot by Elizabeth Fritsch

843 Pot by Lucie Rie

844 Pot by Hans Coper

Studio Pottery

1987 (13 Oct.) Phosphorised paper. Perf 14½ × 14

1371	**841**	18p multicoloured	50	25	☐	☐
1372	**842**	26p multicoloured	70	75	☐	☐
1373	**843**	31p multicoloured	1·25	1·25	☐	☐
1374	**844**	34p multicoloured	1·40	1·50	☐	☐
Set of 4			3·50	3·50	☐	☐
First Day Cover				3·75	☐	
Presentation Pack			3·50		☐	
PHQ Cards (set of 4)			3·00	6·50	☐	☐
Set of 4 Gutter Pairs			8·50		☐	

Nos. 1371/4 also mark the birth centenary of Bernard Leach, the potter.

845 Decorating the Christmas Tree

846 Waiting for Father Christmas

847 Sleeping Child and Father Christmas in Sleigh

848 Child reading

849 Child playing Flute and Snowman

Christmas

1987 (17 Nov.) One phosphor band (13p) or phosphorised paper (others)

1375	**845**	13p multicoloured	30	10	☐	☐
1376	**846**	18p multicoloured	40	20	☐	☐
1377	**847**	26p multicoloured	80	1·00	☐	☐
1378	**848**	31p multicoloured	1·10	1·25	☐	☐
1379	**849**	34p multicoloured	1·25	1·50	☐	☐
Set of 5			3·50	3·75	☐	☐
First Day Cover				3·75	☐	
Presentation Pack			3·50		☐	
PHQ Cards (set of 5)			3·00	6·50	☐	☐
Set of 5 Gutter Pairs			8·50		☐	

Collectors Pack 1987

1987 (17 Nov.) Comprises Nos. 1347/79
CP1379a   Collectors Pack   37·00   ☐

Post Office Yearbook

1987 Comprises Nos. 1347/79 in hardbound book with slip case
YB1379a   Yearbook   35·00   ☐

850 Short-spined Seascorpion ('Bull-rout') (Jonathan Couch)

851 Yellow Waterlily (Major Joshua Swatkin)

852 Whistling ('Bewick's') Swan (Edward Lear)

853 Morchella esculenta (James Sowerby)

Bicentenary of Linnean Society. Archive Illustrations

1988 (19 Jan.) Phosphorised paper

1380	**850**	18p multicoloured	55	10	☐	☐
1381	**851**	26p multicoloured	85	1·00	☐	☐
1382	**852**	31p multicoloured	1·10	1·25	☐	☐
1383	**853**	34p multicoloured	1·25	1·40	☐	☐
Set of 4			3·25	3·25	☐	☐
First Day Cover				3·75	☐	
Presentation Pack			4·00		☐	
PHQ Cards (set of 4)			3·00	6·50	☐	☐
Set of 4 Gutter Pairs			8·00		☐	

854 Revd William Morgan (Bible translator, 1588)

855 William Salesbury (New Testament translator, 1567)

864 Glasgow Tram No. 1173 and Pillar Box

865 Imperial Airways Handley Page H.P.45 *Horatius* and Airmail Van

856 Bishop Richard Davies (New Testament translator, 1567)

857 Bishop Richard Parry (editor of Revised Welsh Bible, 1620)

400th Anniversary of Welsh Bible

1988 (1 Mar.) Phosphorised paper. Perf 14½ × 14

1384	**854**	18p multicoloured	40	10	☐	☐
1385	**855**	26p multicoloured	70	95	☐	☐
1386	**856**	31p multicoloured	1·25	1·25	☐	☐
1387	**857**	34p multicoloured	1·40	1·25	☐	☐
Set of 4			3·25	3·25	☐	☐
First Day Cover				3·75	☐	
Presentation Pack			4·00		☐	
PHQ Cards (*set of 4*)			3·00	6·50	☐	☐
Set of 4 Gutter Pairs			8·00		☐	

Europa. Transport and Mail Services in 1930's

1988 (10 May) Phosphorised paper

1392	**862**	18p multicoloured	50	15	☐	☐
1393	**863**	26p multicoloured	1·00	1·00	☐	☐
1394	**864**	31p multicoloured	1·25	1·25	☐	☐
1395	**865**	34p multicoloured	1·60	1·50	☐	☐
Set of 4			4·00	3·50	☐	☐
First Day Cover				3·75	☐	
Presentation Pack			4·25		☐	
PHQ Cards (*set of 4*)			2·25	6·00	☐	☐
Set of 4 Gutter Pairs			11·00		☐	

858 Gymnastics (Centenary of British Amateur Gymnastics Association)

859 Downhill Skiing (Ski Club of Great Britain)

866 Early Settler and Sailing Clipper

867 Queen Elizabeth II with British and Australian Parliament Buildings

860 Tennis (Centenary of Lawn Tennis Association)

861 Football (Centenary of Football League)

868 W. G. Grace (cricketer) and Tennis Racquet

869 Shakespeare, John Lennon (entertainer) and Sydney Landmarks

Sports Organizations

1988 (22 Mar.) Phosphorised paper. Perf 14½

1388	**858**	18p multicoloured	40	15	☐	☐
1389	**859**	26p multicoloured	70	80	☐	☐
1390	**860**	31p multicoloured	1·10	1·25	☐	☐
1391	**861**	34p multicoloured	1·25	1·25	☐	☐
Set of 4			3·25	3·25	☐	☐
First Day Cover				3·50	☐	
Presentation Pack			4·00		☐	
PHQ Cards (*set of 4*)			2·50	6·00	☐	☐
Set of 4 Gutter Pairs			8·00		☐	

Nos. 1396/7 and 1398/9 were each printed together, *se-tenant*, in horizontal pairs throughout the sheets, each pair showing a background design of the Australian flag.

Bicentenary of Australian Settlement

1988 (21 June) Phosphorised paper. Perf 14½

1396	**866**	18p multicoloured	30	25	☐	☐
		a. Horiz pair. Nos. 1396/7	1·25	1·50	☐	☐
1397	**867**	18p multicoloured	30	25	☐	☐
1398	**868**	34p multicoloured	60	50	☐	☐
		a. Horiz pair. Nos. 1398/9	2·50	2·50	☐	☐
1399	**869**	34p multicoloured	60	50	☐	☐
Set of 4			3·50	3·50	☐	☐
First Day Cover				3·75	☐	
Presentation Pack			4·00		☐	
Souvenir Book			15·00		☐	
PHQ Cards (*set of 4*)			2·25	6·00	☐	☐
Set of 2 Gutter Blocks of 4			8·25		☐	

Stamps in similar designs were also issued by Australia. These are included in the Souvenir Book.

862 *Mallard* and Mailbags on Pick-up Arms

863 Loading Transatlantic Mail on Liner *Queen Elizabeth*

870 Spanish Galeasse off The Lizard

871 English Fleet leaving Plymouth

872 Engagement off Isle of Wight

873 Attack of English Fire-ships, Calais

874 Armada in Storm, North Sea

Nos. 1400/4 were printed together, *se-tenant*, in horizontal strips of 5 throughout the sheet, forming a composite design.

400th Anniversary of Spanish Armada

1988 (19 July) Phosphorised paper

1400	**870**	18p	multicoloured	30	25	☐	☐
		a.	Horiz strip of 5.				
			Nos. 1400/4	3·00	3·00	☐	☐
1401	**871**	18p	multicoloured	30	25	☐	☐
1402	**872**	18p	multicoloured	30	25	☐	☐
1403	**873**	18p	multicoloured	30	25	☐	☐
1404	**874**	18p	multicoloured	30	25	☐	☐
Set of 5				3·00	3·00	☐	☐
First Day Cover					3·75		☐
Presentation Pack				3·75		☐	
PHQ Cards (*set of 5*)				2·75	7·00	☐	☐
Gutter Block of 10				8·00		☐	

875 'The Owl and the pussy-cat'

876 'Edward Lear as a Bird' (self-portrait)

877 'Cat' (from alphabet book)

878 'There was a Young Lady whose Bonnet . . .' (limerick)

Death Centenary of Edward Lear (artist and author)

1988 (6–27 Sept.) Phosphorised paper

1405	**875**	19p	black, pale cream and carmine	65	20	☐	☐
1406	**876**	27p	black, pale cream and yellow	1·00	1·00	☐	☐
1407	**877**	32p	black, pale cream and emerald	1·25	1·40	☐	☐
1408	**878**	35p	black, pale cream and blue	1·40	1·40	☐	☐
Set of 4				4·00	3·50	☐	
First Day Cover					3·75		☐
Presentation Pack				4·25		☐	
PHQ Cards (*set of 4*)				2·25	6·00	☐	☐
Set of 4 Gutter Pairs				9·00		☐	
MS1409 122 × 90 mm. Nos. 1405/8				7·00	8·50	☐	☐
First Day Cover (27 Sept.)					8·50		☐

No. **MS**1409 was sold at £1·35, the premium being used for the 'Stamp World London 90' International Stamp Exhibition.

879 Carrickfergus Castle

880 Caernarvon Castle

881 Edinburgh Castle

882 Windsor Castle

1988 (18 Oct.) Ordinary paper

1410	**879**	£1 deep green	4·25	60	☐	☐
1411	**880**	£1·50 maroon	4·50	1·25	☐	☐
1412	**881**	£2 indigo	8·00	1·50	☐	☐
1413	**882**	£5 deep brown	21·00	5·50	☐	☐
Set of 4			35·00	8·00	☐	☐
First Day Cover				35·00		☐
Presentation Pack			35·00		☐	
Set of 4 Gutter pairs			70·00		☐	

For similar designs, but with silhouette of Queen's head see Nos. 1611/14 and 1993/6.

883 Journey to Bethlehem

884 Shepherds and Star

885 Three Wise Men

886 Nativity

887 The Annunciation

Christmas

1988 (15 Nov.) One phosphor band (14p) or phosphorised paper (others)

1414	**883**	14p multicoloured	45	25	☐	☐
1415	**884**	19p multicoloured	50	25	☐	☐
1416	**885**	27p multicoloured	90	1·00	☐	☐
1417	**886**	32p multicoloured	1·10	1·25	☐	☐
1418	**887**	35p multicoloured	1·40	1·25	☐	☐
Set of 5			4·00	3·75	☐	☐
First Day Cover				3·75	☐	
Presentation Pack			4·00		☐	
PHQ Cards (*set of* 5)			3·00	6·00	☐	☐
Set of 5 Gutter Pairs			9·50		☐	

Collectors Pack 1988

1988 (15 Nov.) Comprises Nos. 1380/1408, 1414/18

CP1418a	Collectors Pack	35·00	☐

Post Office Yearbook

1988 Comprises Nos. 1380/1404, MS1409, 1414/18 in hardbound book with slip case

YB1418a	Yearbook	37·00	☐

888 Atlantic Puffin

889 Avocet

890 Oystercatcher

891 Northern Gannet

Centenary of Royal Society for the Protection of Birds

1989 (17 Jan.) Phosphorised paper

1419	**888**	19p multicoloured	25	20	☐	☐
1420	**889**	27p multicoloured	1·25	1·25	☐	☐
1421	**890**	32p multicoloured	1·25	1·25	☐	☐
1422	**891**	35p multicoloured	1·25	1·25	☐	☐
Set of 4			3·50	3·50	☐	☐
First Day Cover				4·00	☐	
Presentation Pack			4·00		☐	
PHQ Cards (*set of* 4)			3·00	7·00	☐	☐
Set of 4 Gutter Pairs			9·50		☐	

892 Rose

893 Cupid

894 Yachts

895 Fruit

896 Teddy Bear

Nos. 1423/7 were printed together, *se-tenant*, in horizontal strips of five, two such strips forming the booklet pane with twelve half stamp-size labels.

Greetings Booklet Stamps

1989 (31 Jan.) Phosphorised paper

1423	**892**	19p multicoloured	60	50	☐	☐
		a. Booklet pane.				
		Nos. 1423/7 × 2	50·00		☐	
		b. Horiz strip of 5.				
		Nos. 1423/7	25·00	25·00	☐	☐
1424	**893**	19p multicoloured	60	50	☐	☐
1425	**894**	19p multicoloured	60	50	☐	☐
1426	**895**	19p multicoloured	60	50	☐	☐
1427	**896**	19p multicoloured	60	50	☐	☐
Set of 5			25·00	25·00	☐	☐
First Day Cover				25·00	☐	

897 Fruit and Vegetables

898 Meat Products

899 Dairy Produce

900 Cereal Products

Food and Farming Year

1989 (7 Mar.) Phosphorised paper. Perf 14 × 14½

1428	**897**	19p multicoloured	45	15	☐	☐
1429	**898**	27p multicoloured	90	85	☐	☐
1430	**899**	32p multicoloured	1·25	1·40	☐	☐
1431	**900**	35p multicoloured	1·40	1·50	☐	☐
Set of 4			3·50	3·50	☐	☐
First Day Cover				3·75		☐
Presentation Pack			4·00		☐	
PHQ Cards (*set of* 4)			2·25	6·50	☐	☐
Set of 4 Gutter Pairs			8·50		☐	

901 Mortar Board (150th Anniv of Public Education in England)

902 Cross on Ballot Paper (3rd Direct Elections to European Parliament)

903 Posthorn (26th Postal, Telegraph and Telephone International Congress, Brighton)

904 Globe (Inter - Parliamentry Union Centenary Conference, London)

Nos. 1432/3 and 1434/5 were each printed together, *se- tenant*, in horizontal pairs throughout the sheets

Anniversaries

1989 (11 Apr.) Phosphorised paper. Perf 14 × 14½

1432	**901**	19p multicoloured	50	25	☐	☐
		a. Horiz pair. Nos. 1432/3	1·50	1·50	☐	☐
1433	**902**	19p multicoloured	50	25	☐	☐
1434	**903**	35p multicoloured	75	50	☐	☐
		a. Horiz pair. Nos. 1434/5	2·50	2·50	☐	☐
1435	**904**	35p multicoloured	75	50	☐	☐
Set of 4			3·50	3·50	☐	☐
First Day Cover				4·50		☐
Presentation Pack			4·00		☐	
PHQ Cards (*set of* 4)			2·25	6·50	☐	☐
Set of 2 Gutter Strips of 4			9·00		☐	

905 Toy Train and Aeroplanes

906 Building Bricks

907 Dice and Board Games

908 Toy Robot, Boat and Doll's House

Europa. Games and Toys

1989 (16 May) Phosphorised paper

1436	**905**	19p multicoloured	65	25	☐	☐
1437	**906**	27p multicoloured	95	1·00	☐	☐
1438	**907**	32p multicoloured	1·40	1·25	☐	☐
1439	**908**	35p multicoloured	1·50	1·25	☐	☐
Set of 4			4·00	3·50	☐	☐
First Day Cover				3·75		☐
Presentation Pack			4·25		☐	
PHQ Cards (*set of* 4)			2·25	6·50	☐	☐
Set of 4 Gutter Pairs			10·50		☐	

909 Ironbridge, Shropshire

910 Tin Mine. St Agnes Head, Cornwall

911 Cotton Mills, New Lanark, Strathclyde

912 Pontcysylite Aqueduct, Clwyd

912a

Industrial Archaeology

1989 (4–25 July) Phosphorised paper

1440	**909**	19p multicoloured	60	15	☐	☐
1441	**910**	27p multicoloured	1·00	1·10	☐	☐
1442	**911**	32p multicoloured	1·10	1·25	☐	☐
1443	**912**	35p multicoloured	1·25	1·50	☐	☐
Set of 4			3·50	3·50	☐	
First Day Cover				3·75		☐
Presentation Pack			4·00		☐	
PHQ Cards (*set of* 4)			2·25	6·50	☐	☐
Set of 4 Gutter Pairs			8·50		☐	
MS1444 122 × 90 mm. 912a As						
Nos. 1440/3 but designs horizontal			6·00	6·50	☐	☐
First Day Cover (25 July)				6·50		☐

No. **MS**1444 was sold at £1·40, the premium being used for the 'Stamp World London 90' International Stamp Exhibition.

913

914

Booklet Stamps

1989 (22 Aug.)–**92**

(a) Printed in photogravure by Harrison and Sons. Perf 15 × 14

1445	**913**	(2nd) bright blue (1 centre band)	1·00	1·00	☐	☐
1446		(2nd) bright blue (1 side band) (20.3.90)	3·00	3·25	☐	☐
1447	**914**	(1st) black (phosphorised paper)	1·75	1·00	☐	☐
1448		(1st) brownish black (2 bands) (20.3.90)	3·25	3·00	☐	☐

(b) Printed in lithography by Walsall. Perf 14

1449	**913**	(2nd) bright blue (1 centre band)	1·00	90	☐	☐
1450	**914**	(1st) black (2 bands)	2·50	2·40	☐	☐

(c) Printed in lithography by Questa. Perf 15 × 14

1451	**913**	(2nd) bright blue (1 centre band) (19.9.89)	1·00	1·00	☐	☐
1451a		(2nd) bright blue (1 side band) (25.2.92)	3·00	3·00	☐	☐
1452	**914**	(1st) black (phosphorised paper) (19.9.89)	2·50	2·50	☐	☐
First Day Cover (Nos. 1445, 1447)				5·00		☐

For similar stamps showing changed colours see Nos. 1511/16, for those with elliptical perforations Nos. 1664/71 and for self-adhesive versions Nos. 2039/40.

No. 1451a exists with the phosphor band at the left or right of the stamp.

915 Snowflake (×10)

916 *Calliphora erythrocephala* (fly) (×5)

917 Blood Cells (×500) **918** Microchip (×600)

150th Anniversary of Royal Microscopical Society

1989 (5 Sept.) Phosphorised paper. Perf 14½ × 14

1453	**915**	19p multicoloured	45	25	☐	☐
1454	**916**	27p multicoloured	95	1·00	☐	☐
1455	**917**	32p multicoloured	1·10	1·25	☐	☐
1456	**918**	35p multicoloured	1·25	1·25	☐	☐
Set of 4			3·50	3·50	☐	☐
First Day Cover				3·50		☐
Presentation Pack			4·00		☐	
PHQ Cards (*set of* 4)			2·25	6·50	☐	☐
Set of 4 Gutter Pairs			8·50		☐	

919 Royal Mail Coach **920** Escort of Blues and Royals

921 Lord Mayor's Coach **922** Coach Team passing St Paul's

923 Blues and Royals Drum Horse

Nos. 1457/61 were printed together, *se-tenant*, in horizontal strips of 5 throughout the sheet, forming a composite design.

Lord Mayor's Show, London

1989 (17 Oct.) Phosphorised paper

1457	**919**	20p	multicoloured	40	30	☐	☐
		a.	Horiz strip of 5.				
			Nos. 1457/61	3·00	3·00	☐	☐
1458	**920**	20p	multicoloured	40	30	☐	☐
1459	**921**	20p	multicoloured	40	30	☐	☐
1460	**922**	20p	multicoloured	40	30	☐	☐
1461	**923**	20p	multicoloured	40	30	☐	☐
Set of 5				3·00	3·00	☐	☐
First Day Cover					3·50		☐
Presentation Pack				3·00		☐	
PHQ Cards (*set of* 5)				3·00	6·50	☐	☐
Gutter Strip of 10				8·00		☐	

Nos. 1457/61 commemorate the 800th anniversary of the installation of the first Lord Mayor of London.

924 14th-century Peasants from Stained-glass Window

925 Arches and Roundels, West Front

926 Octagon Tower

927 Arcade from West Transept

928 Triple Arch from West Front

Christmas. 800th Anniversary of Ely Cathedral

1989 (14 Nov.) One phosphor band (Nos. 1462/3) or phosphorised paper (others)

1462	**924**	15p	gold, silver and blue	40	15	☐	☐
1463	**925**	15p	+ 1p gold, silver and blue	50	40	☐	☐
1464	**926**	20p	+ 1p gold, silver and rosine	65	80	☐	☐
1465	**927**	34p	+ 1p gold, silver and emerald	1·25	1·75	☐	☐
1466	**928**	37p	+ 1p gold, silver and yellow-olive	1·40	1·90	☐	☐
Set of 5				3·75	4·50	☐	☐
First Day Cover					4·50		☐
Presentation Pack				4·50		☐	
PHQ Cards (*set of* 5)				3·00	6·00	☐	☐
Set of 5 Gutter Pairs				9·00			☐

Collectors Pack 1989

1989 (14 Nov.) Comprises Nos. 1419/22, 1428/43 and 1453/66

CP1466a	Collectors Pack		38·00	☐

Post Office Yearbook

1989 (14 Nov.) Comprises Nos. 1419/22, 1428/44 and 1453/66 in hardback book with slip case

YB1466a	Yearbook		42·00	☐

929 Queen Victoria and Queen Elizabeth II

150th Anniversary of the Penny Black

1990 (10 Jan.–17 Apr.)

(a) Printed in photogravure by Harrison and Sons (Nos. 1468, 1470, 1472 from booklets only). Perf 15 × 14

1467	**929**	15p	bright blue (1 centre band)	80	80	☐ ☐
1468		15p	bright blue (1 side band) (30 Jan.)	3·75	3·75	☐ ☐
1469		20p	brownish black and cream (phosphorised paper)	1·00	1·00	☐ ☐
1470		20p	brownish black and cream (2 bands) (30 Jan.)	2·75	2·75	☐ ☐
1471		29p	deep mauve (phosphorised paper)	1·75	1·75	☐ ☐
1472		29p	deep mauve (2 bands) (20 Mar.)	9·00	9·00	☐ ☐
1473		34p	deep bluish grey (phosphorised paper)	2·00	2·00	☐ ☐
1474		37p	rosine (phosphorised paper)	2·25	2·25	☐ ☐
Set of 5 (Nos. 1467, 1469, 1471, 1473/4)				7·00	7·00	☐ ☐
First Day Cover (Nos. 1467, 1469, 1471, 1473/4)					7·00	☐
Presentation Pack (Nos. 1467, 1469, 1471, 1473/4)				9·00		☐

(b) Litho Walsall (booklets). Perf 14 (30 Jan.)

1475	**929**	15p	bright blue (1 centre band)	1·50	1·75	☐ ☐
1476		20p	brownish black and cream (phosphorised paper)	1·60	1·75	☐ ☐

(c) Litho Questa (booklets). Perf 15 × 14 (17 Apr.)

1477	**929**	15p	bright blue (1 centre band)	2·25	2·25	☐ ☐
1478		20p	brownish black (phosphorised paper)	2·00	2·25	☐ ☐

No. 1468 exists with the phosphor band at the left or right of the stamp.

For Type 929 redrawn with "1st" face value see No. 2133.

930 Kitten

931 Rabbit

932 Duckling   **933** Puppy

150th Anniversary of Royal Society for Prevention of Cruelty to Animals

1990 (23 Jan.) Phosphorised paper. Perf 14 × 14½

1479	**930**	20p multicoloured	75	50	☐	☐
1480	**931**	29p multicoloured	1·25	1·25	☐	☐
1481	**932**	34p multicoloured	1·25	1·50	☐	☐
1482	**933**	37p multicoloured	1·50	1·50	☐	☐
	Set of 4		4·50	4·25	☐	☐
	First Day Cover			4·25		☐
	Presentation Pack		4·50		☐	
	PHQ Cards (*set of* 4)		3·00	7·50	☐	☐
	Set of 4 Gutter Pairs		9·50		☐	

934 Teddy Bear   **935** Dennis the Menace

936 Punch   **937** Cheshire Cat

938 The Man in the Moon   **939** The Laughing Policeman

940 Clown   **941** Mona Lisa

942 Queen of Hearts   **943** Stan Laurel (comedian)

T **934/43** were printed together, *se-tenant*, in booklet panes of 10.

Greetings Booklet Stamps. 'Smiles'

1990 (6 Feb.) Two phosphor bands

1483	**934**	20p multicoloured	70	60	☐	☐
		a. Booklet pane. Nos. 1483/92	30·00	26·00	☐	☐
1484	**935**	20p multicoloured	70	60	☐	☐
1485	**936**	20p multicoloured	70	60	☐	☐
1486	**937**	20p multicoloured	70	60	☐	☐
1487	**938**	20p multicoloured	70	60	☐	☐
1488	**939**	20p multicoloured	70	60	☐	☐
1489	**940**	20p multicoloured	70	60	☐	☐
1490	**941**	20p multicoloured	70	60	☐	☐
1491	**942**	20p multicoloured	70	60	☐	☐
1492	**943**	20p gold and grey-black	70	60	☐	☐
	Set of 10		30·00	26·00	☐	☐
	First Day Cover			28·00		☐

For these designs with the face value expressed as '1st' see Nos. 1550/9.

944 Alexandra Palace ('Stamp World London 90' Exhibition)   **945** Glasgow School of Art

946 British Philatelic Bureau, Edinburgh   **947** Templeton Carpet Factory, Glasgow

Europa (Nos. 1493 and 1495) and 'Glasgow 1990 European City of Culture' (Nos. 1494 and 1496)

1990 (6 Mar.) Phosphorised paper

1493	**944**	20p multicoloured	50	25	☐	☐
1494	**945**	20p multicoloured	50	25	☐	☐
1495	**946**	29p multicoloured	1·25	1·75	☐	☐
1496	**947**	37p multicoloured	1·50	1·75	☐	☐
	Set of 4		3·50	3·50	☐	☐
	First Day Cover			3·50		☐
	Presentation Pack		4·25		☐	
	PHQ Cards (*set of* 4)		3·00	6·00	☐	☐
	Set of 4 Gutter Pairs		10·00		☐	

948 Export
Achievement Award

949 Technological
Achievement Award

Nos. 1497/8 and 1499/500 were each printed together,
se-tenant, in horizontal pairs throughout the sheets.

25th Anniversary of Queen's Awards for Export and Technology

1990 (10 Apr.) Phosphorised paper. Perf 14 × 14½

1497	**948**	20p multicoloured	40	30	☐	☐
		a. Horiz pair. Nos. 1497/8	1·40	1·60	☐	☐
1498	**949**	20p multicoloured	40	30	☐	☐
1499	**948**	37p multicoloured	50	50	☐	☐
		a. Horiz pair. Nos. 1499/1500	3·00	3·00	☐	☐
1500	**949**	37p multicoloured	50	50	☐	☐
Set of 4			4·00	4·25	☐	☐
First Day Cover				4·50		☐
Presentation Pack			4·50		☐	
PHQ Cards (*set of* 4)			3·00	6·00	☐	☐
Set of 2 Gutter Strips of 4			8·50		☐	

949a

'Stamp World London 90' International Stamp Exhibition, London

1990 (3 May) Sheet 122 × 90 mm. Phosphorised paper

MS1501	**949a**	20p brownish black and cream	5·50	5·50	☐	☐
First Day Cover				5·75		☐
Souvenir Book (Nos. 1467, 1469, 1471, 1473/4 and **MS**1501			20·00		☐	

No. **MS**1501 was sold at £1, the premium being used for the exhibition.

950 Cycad and Sir
Joseph Banks Building

951 Stone Pine and
Princess of Wales
Conservatory

952 Willow Tree and
Palm House

953 Cedar Tree and
Pagoda

150th Anniversary of Kew Gardens

1990 (5 June) Phosphorised paper

1502	**950**	20p multicoloured	55	15	☐	☐
1503	**951**	29p multicoloured	75	1·00	☐	☐
1504	**952**	34p multicoloured	1·25	1·60	☐	☐
1505	**953**	37p multicoloured	1·50	1·50	☐	☐
Set of 4			3·50	3·75	☐	☐
First Day Cover				3·75		☐
Presentation Pack			4·00		☐	
PHQ Cards (*set of* 4)			3·00	6·00	☐	☐
Set of 4 Gutter Pairs			9·00		☐	

954 Thomas Hardy and Clyffe Clump, Dorset

150th Birth Anniversary of Thomas Hardy (author)

1990 (10 July) Phosphorised paper

1506	**954**	20p multicoloured	80	75	☐	☐
First Day Cover				1·50		☐
Presentation Pack			1·50		☐	
PHQ Card			1·00	2·25	☐	☐
Gutter Pair			1·75		☐	

955 Queen Elizabeth the Queen Mother

956 Queen Elizabeth

957 Elizabeth, Duchess of York

958 Lady Elizabeth Bowes-Lyon

959 Victoria Cross

960 George Cross

961 Distinguished Service Cross and Distinguished Service Medal

962 Military Cross and Military Medal

963 Distinguished Flying Cross and Distinguished Flying Medal

90th Birthday of Queen Elizabeth the Queen Mother

1990 (2 Aug.) Phosphorised paper

1507	**955**	20p multicoloured		95	25	☐ ☐
1508	**956**	29p silver, indigo and grey-blue		1·40	1·50	☐ ☐
1509	**957**	34p multicoloured		2·00	2·50	☐ ☐
1510	**958**	37p silver, sepia and stone		2·25	2·50	☐ ☐
Set of 4				6·00	6·25	☐ ☐
First Day Cover					6·25	☐
Presentation Pack				7·00		☐
PHQ Cards (set of 4)				5·50	8·00	☐ ☐
Set of 4 Gutter Pairs				15·00		☐

For these designs with Queen's head and frame in black see Nos. 2280/3.

Booklet Stamps

1990 (7 Aug.)–**92** As Types **913/14**, but colours changed

		(a) Photo Harrison. Perf 15 × 14			
1511	**913**	(2nd) deep blue (1 centre band)	1·50	1·50	☐ ☐
1512	**914**	(1st) bright orange-red (phosphorised paper)	1·50	1·50	☐ ☐
		(b) Litho Questa. Perf 15 × 14			
1513	**913**	(2nd) deep blue (1 centre band)	2·50	2·50	☐ ☐
1514	**914**	(1st) bright orange-red (phosphorised paper)	1·00	1·00	☐ ☐
1514a		(1st) bright orange-red (2 bands) (25.2.92)	2·25	2·25	☐ ☐
		(c) Litho Walsall. Perf 14			
1515	**913**	(2nd) deep blue (1 centre band)	1·00	1·00	☐ ☐
1516	**914**	(1st) bright orange-red (phosphorised paper)	1·25	1·25	☐ ☐
		c. Perf 13	2·75	3·00	☐ ☐
First Day Cover (Nos. 1515/16)				5·00	☐

For similar stamps with elliptical perforations see Nos. 1664/71.

Gallantry Awards

1990 (11 Sept.) Phosphorised paper

1517	**959**	20p multicoloured		80	75	☐ ☐
1518	**960**	20p multicoloured		80	75	☐ ☐
1519	**961**	20p multicoloured		80	75	☐ ☐
1520	**962**	20p multicoloured		80	75	☐ ☐
1521	**963**	20p multicoloured		80	75	☐ ☐
Set of 5				3·75	3·50	☐ ☐
First Day Cover					3·75	☐
Presentation Pack				4·00		☐
PHQ Cards (set of 5)				3·00	8·00	☐ ☐
Set of 5 Gutter Pairs				9·25		☐

For Type **959** with "all-over" phosphor and perf 14 × 14½ see No. 2666.

964 Armagh Observatory, Jodrell Bank Radio Telescope and La Palma Telescope

965 Newton's Moon and Tides Diagram with Early Telescopes

966 Greenwich Old
Observatory and Early
Astronomical Equipment

967 Stonehenge,
Gyroscope and Navigating
by Stars

Astronomy

1990 (16 Oct.) Phosphorised paper. Perf 14 × 14½

1522	**964**	22p multicoloured	65	15	☐ ☐
1523	**965**	26p multicoloured	1·00	1·10	☐ ☐
1524	**966**	31p multicoloured	1·25	1·40	☐ ☐
1525	**967**	37p multicoloured	1·50	1·40	☐ ☐
Set of 4			3·75	3·75	☐ ☐
First Day Cover				4·00	☐
Presentation Pack			4·50		☐
PHQ Cards (set of 4)			3·00	7·00	☐ ☐
Set of 4 Gutter Pairs			9·25		☐

Nos. 1522/5 commemorate the centenary of the British
Astronomical Association and the bicentenary of the Armagh
Observatory.

968 Building a Snowman

969 Fetching the Christmas
Tree

970 Carol Singing

971 Tobogganing

972 Ice-skating

Christmas

1990 (13 Nov.) One phosphor band (17p) or phosphorised
paper (others)

1526	**968**	17p multicoloured	50	15	☐ ☐
1527	**969**	22p multicoloured	70	20	☐ ☐
1528	**970**	26p multicoloured	70	1·10	☐ ☐
1529	**971**	31p multicoloured	1·25	1·50	☐ ☐
1530	**972**	37p multicoloured	1·25	1·50	☐ ☐
Set of 5			4·00	4·00	☐ ☐
First Day Cover				4·00	☐
Presentation Pack			4·50		☐
PHQ Cards (set of 5)			3·00	7·00	☐ ☐
Set of 5 Gutter Pairs			10·00		☐

Collectors Pack 1990

1990 (13 Nov.) Comprises Nos. 1479/82, 1493/1510 and
1517/30

CP1530a	Collectors Pack	40·00	☐

Post Office Yearbook

1990 Comprises Nos. 1479/82, 1493/1500, 1502/10 and
1517/30 in hardback book with slip case

YB1530a	Yearbook	45·00	☐

973 'King Charles Spaniel'

974 'A Pointer'

975 'Two Hounds in a
Landscape'

976 'A Rough Dog'

977 'Fino and Tiny'

Dogs. Paintings by George Stubbs

1991 (8 Jan.) Phosphorised paper. Perf 14 × 14½

1531	**973**	22p multicoloured	50	15	☐ ☐
1532	**974**	26p multicoloured	75	1·25	☐ ☐
1533	**975**	31p multicoloured	1·00	1·25	☐ ☐
1534	**976**	33p multicoloured	1·25	1·25	☐ ☐
1535	**977**	37p multicoloured	1·25	1·25	☐ ☐
Set of 5			4·50	4·50	☐ ☐
First Day Cover				5·00	☐
Presentation Pack			5·00		☐
PHQ Cards (set of 5)			3·50	7·00	☐ ☐
Set of 5 Gutter Pairs			11·00		☐

978 Thrush's Nest

979 Shooting Star and
Rainbow

980 Magpies and Charm Bracelet

981 Black Cat

Faraday – Electricity

988 Michael Faraday (inventor of electric motor) (Birth Bicentenary)

Babbage – Computer

989 Charles Babbage (computer science pioneer) (Birth Bicentenary)

982 Common Kingfisher with Key

983 Mallard and Frog

Radar – Watson·Watt

990 Radar Sweep of East Anglia (50th Anniv of Discovery by Sir Robert Watson-Watt)

Jet Engine – Whittle

991 Gloster Whittle E28/39 Aircraft over East Anglia (50th Anniv of First Flight of Sir Frank Whittle's Jet Engine)

984 Four-leaf Clover in Boot and Match Box

985 Pot of Gold at End of Rainbow

Scientific Achievements

1991 (5 Mar.) Phosphorised paper

1546 **988** 22p multicoloured	60	50	☐	☐
1547 **989** 22p multicoloured	60	50	☐	☐
1548 **990** 31p multicoloured	1·20	1·50	☐	☐
1549 **991** 37p multicoloured	1·35	1·75	☐	☐
Set of 4	3·50	4·00	☐	☐
First Day Cover		4·00		☐
Presentation Pack	4·25		☐	
PHQ Cards (*set of* 4)	3·50	7·00	☐	☐
Set of 4 Gutter Pairs	8·50		☐	

986 Heart-shaped Butterflies

987 Wishing Well and Sixpence

T **978/87** were printed together, *se-tenant*, in booklet panes of 10 stamps and 12 half stamp-size labels, the backgrounds of the stamps forming a composite design.

Greetings Booklet Stamps. 'Good Luck'

1991 (5 Feb.) Two phosphor bands

1536 **978** (1st) multicoloured	70	60	☐ ☐
a. Booklet pane. Nos. 1536/45	15·00	17·00	☐ ☐
1537 **979** (1st) multicoloured	70	60	☐ ☐
1538 **980** (1st) multicoloured	70	60	☐ ☐
1539 **981** (1st) multicoloured	70	60	☐ ☐
1540 **982** (1st) multicoloured	70	60	☐ ☐
1541 **983** (1st) multicoloured	70	60	☐ ☐
1542 **984** (1st) multicoloured	70	60	☐ ☐
1543 **985** (1st) multicoloured	70	60	☐ ☐
1544 **986** (1st) multicoloured	70	60	☐ ☐
1545 **987** (1st) multicoloured	70	60	☐ ☐
Set of 10	15·00	17·00	☐ ☐
First Day Cover		19·00	☐

992 Teddy Bear

Nos. 1550/9 were originally printed together, *se-tenant*, in booklet panes of 10 stamps and 12 half stamp-size labels.

Greetings Booklet Stamps. 'Smiles'

1991 (26 Mar.) As Nos. 1483/92, but inscribed '1st' as T **992**. Two phosphor bands. Perf 15 × 14

1550 **992** (1st) multicoloured	70	60	☐ ☐
a. Booklet pane. Nos. 1550/9	12·00	13·00	☐ ☐
1551 **935** (1st) multicoloured	70	60	☐ ☐
1552 **936** (1st) multicoloured	70	60	☐ ☐
1553 **937** (1st) multicoloured	70	60	☐ ☐
1554 **938** (1st) multicoloured	70	60	☐ ☐
1555 **939** (1st) multicoloured	70	60	☐ ☐
1556 **940** (1st) multicoloured	70	60	☐ ☐
1557 **941** (1st) multicoloured	70	60	☐ ☐

1558	**942**	(1st) multicoloured	70	60	☐	☐
1559	**943**	(1st) multicoloured	70	60	☐	☐
Set of 10			12·00	13·00	☐	☐
First Day Cover				13·00		☐

The stamps were re-issued in sheets of 10 each with *se-tenant* label on 22 May 2000 in connection with 'customised' stamps available at 'Stamp Show 2000'. The labels show either a pattern of ribbons or a personal photograph.

A similar sheet, but in lithography instead of photogravure, and perforated 14½ × 14, appeared on 3 July 2001 with the labels showing either greetings or a personal photograph. Three further sheets, also in lithography, appeared on 1 October 2002. One contained Nos. 1550/1 each × 10 with greetings labels. Both designs were also available in sheets of 20 with personal photographs.

993 Man looking at Space

994

995 Space looking at Man

996

Nos. 1560/1 and 1562/3 were each printed together, *se-tenant*, in horizontal pairs throughout the sheets, each pair forming a composite design.

Europa Europe in Space

1991 (23 Apr.) Phosphorised paper

1560	**993**	22p multicoloured	40	30	☐	☐
		a. Horiz pair. Nos. 1560/1	1·50	1·50	☐	☐
1561	**994**	22p multicoloured	40	30	☐	☐
1562	**995**	37p multicoloured	50	40	☐	☐
		a. Horiz pair. Nos. 1562/3	3·50	3·00	☐	☐
1563	**996**	37p multicoloured	50	40	☐	☐
Set of 4			4·00	3·50	☐	☐
First Day Cover				4·50		☐
Presentation Pack			5·00		☐	
PHQ Cards (*set of* 4)			3·00	7·00	☐	☐
Set of 2 Gutter Strips of 4			12·00		☐	

997 Fencing

998 Hurdling

999 Diving

1000 Rugby

World Student Games, Sheffield (Nos. 1564/6) and World Cup Rugby Championship, London (No. 1567)

1991 (11 June) Phosphorised paper. Perf 14½ × 14

1564	**997**	22p multicoloured	60	20	☐	☐
1565	**998**	26p multicoloured	1·00	1·00	☐	☐
1566	**999**	31p multicoloured	1·25	1·25	☐	☐
1567	**1000**	37p multicoloured	1·50	1·50	☐	☐
Set of 4			3·50	3·50	☐	☐
First Day Cover				4·00		☐
Presentation Pack			4·50		☐	
PHQ Cards (*set of* 4)			3·00	7·00	☐	☐
Set of 4 Gutter Pairs			9·00		☐	

1001 'Silver Jubilee'

1002 'Mme Alfred Carrière'

1003 Rosa moyesii

1004 'Harvest Fayre'

1005 'Mutabilis'

9th World Congress of Roses, Belfast

1991 (16 July) Phosphorised paper. Perf 14½ × 14

1568	**1001**	22p multicoloured	50	20	☐	☐
1569	**1002**	26p multicoloured	75	1·25	☐	☐
1570	**1003**	31p multicoloured	1·00	1·25	☐	☐
1571	**1004**	33p multicoloured	1·25	1·50	☐	☐
1572	**1005**	37p multicoloured	1·50	1·50	☐	☐
Set of 5			4·50	5·00	☐	☐
First Day Cover				5·00		☐
Presentation Pack			5·00		☐	
PHQ Cards (*set of* 5)			3·00	9·00	☐	☐
Set of 5 Gutter Pairs			11·00		☐	

1006 Iguanodon

1007 Stegosaurus

1008 Tyrannosaurus

1009 Protoceratops

1010 Triceratops

150th Anniversary of Dinosaurs' Identification by Owen

1991 (20 Aug.) Phosphorised paper. Perf 14½ × 14

1573	**1006**	22p multicoloured	60	20	☐	☐
1574	**1007**	26p multicoloured	1·10	1·25	☐	☐
1575	**1008**	31p multicoloured	1·25	1·25	☐	☐
1576	**1009**	33p multicoloured	1·50	1·50	☐	☐
1577	**1010**	37p multicoloured	1·60	1·50	☐	☐
Set of 5			5·75	5·00	☐	
First Day Cover				5·50	☐	
Presentation Pack			6·00		☐	
PHQ Cards (*set of* 5)			3·00	9·00	☐	☐
Set of 5 Gutter Pairs			12·00		☐	

1011 Map of 1816

1012 Map of 1906

1013 Map of 1959

1014 Map of 1991

Bicentenary of Ordnance Survey. Maps of Hamstreet, Kent

1991 (17 Sept.) Phosphorised paper. Perf 14½ × 14

1578	**1011**	24p multicoloured	60	20	☐	☐
1579	**1012**	28p multicoloured	1·00	95	☐	☐
1580	**1013**	33p multicoloured	1·25	1·40	☐	☐
1581	**1014**	39p multicoloured	1·50	1·40	☐	☐
Set of 4			3·50	3·50	☐	☐
First Day Cover				4·25		☐
Presentation Pack			4·50		☐	
PHQ Cards (*set of* 4)			3·00	7·00	☐	☐
Set of 4 Gutter Pairs			10·00		☐	

1015 Adoration of the Magi

1016 Mary and Baby Jesus in Stable

1017 Holy Family and Angel

1018 The Annunciation

1019 The Flight into Egypt

Christmas. Illuminated Manuscripts from the Bodleian Library, Oxford

1991 (12 Nov.) One phosphor band (18p) or phosphorised paper (others)

1582	**1015**	18p multicoloured	75	10	☐	☐
1583	**1016**	24p multicoloured	90	10	☐	☐
1584	**1017**	28p multicoloured	95	1·25	☐	☐
1585	**1018**	33p multicoloured	1·10	1·50	☐	☐
1586	**1019**	39p multicoloured	1·25	1·75	☐	☐
Set of 5			4·50	4·50	☐	☐
First Day Cover				4·50		☐
Presentation Pack			4·50		☐	
PHQ Cards (*set of* 5)			3·00	7·50	☐	☐
Set of 5 Gutter Pairs			11·00		☐	

Collectors Pack 1991

1991 (12 Nov.) Comprises Nos. 1531/5, 1546/9 and 1560/86
CP1586a	Collectors Pack	40·00	☐

Post Office Yearbook

1991 Comprises Nos. 1531/5, 1546/9 and 1560/86 in hardback book with slip case
YB1586a	Yearbook	45·00	☐

1020 Fallow Deer in Scottish Forest

1021 Hare on North Yorkshire Moors

1022 Fox in the Fens

1023 Redwing and Home Counties Village

1024 Welsh Mountain Sheep in Snowdonia

The Four Seasons. Wintertime

1992 (14 Jan.) One phosphor band (18p) or phosphorised paper (others)

1587	**1020**	18p multicoloured	55	25	☐	☐
1588	**1021**	24p multicoloured	75	25	☐	☐
1589	**1022**	28p multicoloured	1·00	1·25	☐	☐
1590	**1023**	33p multicoloured	1·25	1·50	☐	☐
1591	**1024**	39p multicoloured	1·40	1·75	☐	☐
Set of 5			4·50	4·50	☐	☐
First Day Cover				4·50		☐
Presentation Pack			4·50		☐	
PHQ Cards (*set of* 5)			3·00	8·00	☐	☐
Set of 5 Gutter Pairs			11·00		☐	

1025 Flower Spray

1026 Double Locket

1027 Key

1028 Model Car and Cigarette Cards

1029 Compass and Map

1030 Pocket Watch

1031 1854 1d. Red Stamp and Pen

1032 Pearl Necklace

1033 Marbles

1034 Bucket, Spade and Starfish

T **1025/34** were printed together, *se-tenant*, in booklet panes of 10 stamps and 12 half stamp-size labels, the backgrounds of the stamps forming a composite design.

Greetings Stamps. 'Memories'

1992 (28 Jan.) Two phosphor bands

1592	**1025**	(1st) multicoloured	70	60	☐	☐
		a. Booklet pane.				
		Nos. 1592/1601	13·00	13·00	☐	☐
1593	**1026**	(1st) multicoloured	70	60	☐	☐
1594	**1027**	(1st) multicoloured	70	60	☐	☐
1595	**1028**	(1st) multicoloured	70	60	☐	☐
1596	**1029**	(1st) multicoloured	70	60	☐	☐
1597	**1030**	(1st) multicoloured	70	60	☐	☐
1598	**1031**	(1st) multicoloured	70	60	☐	☐
1599	**1032**	(1st) multicoloured	70	60	☐	☐
1600	**1033**	(1st) multicoloured	70	60	☐	☐
1601	**1034**	(1st) multicoloured	70	60	☐	☐
Set of 10			13·00	13·00	☐	☐
First Day Cover				13·00		☐
Presentation Pack			17·00		☐	

1035 Queen Elizabeth in Coronation Robes and Parliamentary Emblem

1036 Queen Elizabeth in Garter Robes and Archiepiscopal Arms

1037 Queen Elizabeth with Baby Prince Andrew and Royal Arms

1038 Queen Elizabeth at Trooping the Colour and Service Emblems

1039 Queen Elizabeth and Commonwealth Emblem

Nos. 1602/6 were printed together, *se-tenant*, in horizontal strips of 5 throughout the sheet.

40th Anniversary of Accession

1992 (6 Feb.) Two phosphor bands. Perf 14½ × 14

1602	**1035**	24p multicoloured	50	50	☐	☐
		a. Horiz strip of 5.				
		Nos. 1602/6	6·00	6·50	☐	☐
1603	**1036**	24p multicoloured	50	50	☐	☐
1604	**1037**	24p multicoloured	50	50	☐	☐
1605	**1038**	24p multicoloured	50	50	☐	☐
1606	**1039**	24p multicoloured	50	50	☐	☐
Set of 5			6·00	6·50	☐	☐
First Day Cover				6·00		☐
Presentation Pack			7·00		☐	
PHQ Cards (*set of 5*)			3·00	7·50	☐	☐
Gutter Block of 10			15·00		☐	

1040 Tennyson in 1888 and 'The Beguiling of Merlin' (Sir Edward Burne-Jones)

1041 Tennyson in 1856 and 'April Love' of Merlin' (Arthur Hughes)

1042 Tennyson in 1864 and 'I am Sick of the Shadows' (John Waterhouse)

1043 Tennyson as a Young Man and 'Mariana' (Dante Gabriel Rossetti)

Death Centenary of Alfred, Lord Tennyson (poet)

1992 (10 Mar.) Phosphorised paper. Perf 14½ × 14

1607	**1040**	24p multicoloured	60	20	☐	☐
1608	**1041**	28p multicoloured	85	85	☐	☐
1609	**1042**	33p multicoloured	1·40	1·60	☐	☐
1610	**1043**	39p multicoloured	1·50	1·60	☐	☐
Set of 4			4·00	3·75	☐	☐
First Day Cover				4·25		☐
Presentation Pack			4·50		☐	
PHQ Cards (*set of 4*)			3·00	7·00	☐	☐
Set of 4 Gutter Pairs			10·00		☐	

CARRICKFERGUS CASTLE
1044 Carrickfergus Castle

1992 (24 Mar.)–**95**. Designs as Nos. 1410/13, but showing Queen's head in silhouette as T **1044**. Perf 15 × 14 (with one elliptical hole in each vertical side)

1611	**1044**	£1 bottle green and gold†	5·50	1·00	☐	☐
1612	**880**	£1·50 maroon and gold†	6·00	1·20	☐	☐
1613	**881**	£2 indigo and gold†	8·00	1·20	☐	☐
1613a	**1044**	£3 reddish violet and gold†	19·00	3·00	☐	☐
1614	**882**	£5 deep brown and gold†	18·00	3·00	☐	☐
Set of 5			50·00	8·00	☐	☐
First Day Cover (Nos. 1611/13, 1614)				35·00		☐
First Day Cover (22 Aug. 1995) (No. 1613a)				10·00		☐
Presentation Pack (P.O. Pack No. 27)						
(Nos. 1611/13, 1614)			38·00		☐	
Presentation Pack (P.O. Pack No 33)						
(No. 1613a)			30·00		☐	
PHQ Cards (Nos. 1611/14)			15·00	15·00	☐	
PHQ Card (No. 1613a)			10·00	25·00	☐	☐
Set of 5 Gutter Pairs			98·00		☐	

†The Queen's head on these stamps is printed in optically variable ink which changes colour from gold to green when viewed from different angles.

PHQ cards for Nos. 1611/13 and 1614 were not issued until 16 February 1993.

Nos. 1611/14 were printed by Harrison. For stamps with different lettering by Enschedé see Nos. 1993/6.

1045 British Olympic Association Logo (Olympic Games, Barcelona)

1046 British Paralympic Association Symbol (Paralympics '92, Barcelona)

1047 *Santa Maria* (500th Anniv of Discovery of America by Columbus)

1048 *Kaisei* (Japanese cadet brigantine) (Grand Regatta Columbus, 1992)

1049 British Pavilion, 'EXPO 92', Seville

Nos. 1615/16 were printed together, *se-tenant*, in horizontal pairs throughout the sheet.

Europa. International Events

1992 (7 Apr.) Phosphorised paper. Perf 14 × 14½

1615	**1045**	24p multicoloured	50	40	☐	☐
		a. Horiz pair.				
		Nos. 1615/16	2·25	1·75	☐	☐
1616	**1046**	24p multicoloured	50	40	☐	☐
1617	**1047**	24p multicoloured	1·00	75	☐	☐
1618	**1048**	39p multicoloured	1·40	1·50	☐	☐
1619	**1049**	39p multicoloured	1·40	1·50	☐	☐
Set of 5			4·50	4·50	☐	☐
First Day Cover				5·00		☐
Presentation Pack			5·25		☐	
PHQ Cards (set of 5)			3·00	7·00	☐	☐
Set of 3 Gutter Pairs and a Gutter						
	Strip of 4		13·00		☐	

1050 Pikeman

1051 Drummer

1052 Musketeer

1053 Standard Bearer

350th Anniversary of the Civil War

1992 (16 June) Phosphorised paper. Perf 14½ × 14

1620	**1050**	24p multicoloured	60	20	☐	☐
1621	**1051**	28p multicoloured	85	85	☐	☐
1622	**1052**	33p multicoloured	1·40	1·50	☐	☐
1623	**1053**	39p multicoloured	1·50	1·75	☐	☐
Set of 4			4·00	4·00	☐	☐
First Day Cover				4·00		☐
Presentation Pack			4·50		☐	
PHQ Cards (set of 4)			3·00	7·00	☐	☐
Set of 4 Gutter Pairs			10·50		☐	

1054 *The Yeomen of the Guard*

1055 *The Gondoliers*

1056 *The Mikado*

1057 *The Pirates of Penzance*

1058 *Iolanthe*

150th Birth Anniversary of Sir Arthur Sullivan (composer). Gilbert and Sullivan Operas

1992 (21 July) One phosphor band (18p) or phosphorised paper (others). Perf 14½ × 14

1624	**1054**	18p multicoloured	50	20	☐	☐
1625	**1055**	24p multicoloured	80	20	☐	☐
1626	**1056**	28p multicoloured	95	1·00	☐	☐
1627	**1057**	33p multicoloured	1·50	1·60	☐	☐
1628	**1058**	39p multicoloured	1·60	1·60	☐	☐
Set of 5			4·50	4·25	☐	☐
First Day Cover				4·50		☐
Presentation Pack			4·50		☐	
PHQ Cards (set of 5)			3·00	6·25	☐	☐
Set of 5 Gutter Pairs			10·50		☐	

1059 'Acid Rain Kills'

1060 'Ozone Layer'

1061 'Greenhouse Effect'

1062 'Bird of Hope'

Protection of the Environment. Children's Paintings

1992 (15 Sept.) Phosphorised paper. Perf 14 × 14½

1629	**1059**	24p multicoloured	70	25	☐	☐
1630	**1060**	28p multicoloured	1·10	1·25	☐	☐
1631	**1061**	33p multicoloured	1·25	1·50	☐	☐
1632	**1062**	39p multicoloured	1·40	1·50	☐	☐
Set of 4			4·00	4·00	☐	☐
First Day Cover				4·00	☐	
Presentation Pack			4·50		☐	
PHQ Cards (set of 4)			3·00	6·25	☐	☐
Set of 4 Gutter Pairs			10·00		☐	

1063 European Star

Single European Market

1992 (13 Oct.) Phosphorised paper

1633	**1063**	24p multicoloured	1·00	1·00	☐	☐
First Day Cover				1·50		☐
Presentation Pack			1·50		☐	
PHQ Card			1·50	4·00	☐	☐
Gutter Pair			2·25		☐	

1064 'Angel Gabriel', St. James's, Pangbourne

1065 'Madonna and Child', St. Mary's, Bibury

1066 'King with Gold', Our Lady and St. Peter, Leatherhead

1067 'Shepherds', All Saints, Porthcawl

1068 'Kings with Frankincense and Myrrh', Our Lady and St. Peter, Leatherhead

Christmas. Stained Glass Windows

1992 (10 Nov.) One phosphor band (18p) or phosphorised paper (others)

1634	**1064**	18p multicoloured	50	15	☐	☐
1635	**1065**	24p multicoloured	75	15	☐	☐
1636	**1066**	28p multicoloured	1·00	1·10	☐	☐
1637	**1067**	33p multicoloured	1·25	1·50	☐	☐
1638	**1068**	39p multicoloured	1·25	1·50	☐	☐
Set of 5			4·25	4·00	☐	☐
First Day Cover				4·50		☐
Presentation Pack			4·50		☐	
PHQ Cards (set of 5)			3·00	7·50	☐	☐
Set of 5 Gutter Pairs			10·00		☐	

Collectors Pack 1992

1992 (10 Nov.) Comprises Nos. 1587/91, 1602/10 and 1615/38

CP1638a	Collectors Pack	45·00	☐

Post Office Yearbook

1992 (11 Nov.) Comprises Nos. 1587/91, 1602/10 and 1615/38 in hardback book with slip case

YB1638a	Yearbook	55·00	☐

1069 Mute Swan Cob and St. Catherine's, Abbotsbury

1070 Cygnet and Decoy

1071 Swans and Cygnet

1072 Eggs in Nest and Tithe Barn, Abbotsbury

1073 Young Swan and the Fleet

600th Anniversary of Abbotsbury Swannery

1993 (19 Jan.) One phosphor band (18p) or phosphorised paper (others)

1639	**1069**	18p multicoloured	1·25	25	☐	☐
1640	**1070**	24p multicoloured	1·10	25	☐	☐
1641	**1071**	28p multicoloured	1·40	2·25	☐	☐
1642	**1072**	33p multicoloured	1·75	2·50	☐	☐
1643	**1073**	39p multicoloured	1·90	2·50	☐	☐
Set of 5			6·50	7·50	☐	☐
First Day Cover				7·50		☐
Presentation Pack			7·00		☐	
PHQ Cards (*set of 5*)			4·25	8·50	☐	☐
Set of 5 Gutter Pairs			15·00		☐	

1074 Long John Silver and Parrot (*Treasure Island*)

1075 Tweedledum and Tweedledee (*Alice Through the Looking-Glass*)

1076 William (*William* books)

1077 Mole and Toad (*The Wind in the Willows*)

1078 Teacher and Wilfrid ('The Bash Street Kids')

1079 Peter Rabbit and Mrs Rabbit (*The Tale of Peter Rabbit*)

1080 Snowman (*The Snowman*) and Father Christmas (*Father Christmas*)

1081 The Big Friendly Giant and Sophie (*The BFG*)

1082 Bill Badger and Rupert Bear

1083 Aladdin and the Genie

T **1074/83** were printed together, *se-tenant*, in booklet panes of 10 stamps and 20 half stamp-size labels.

Greetings Stamps. 'Gift Giving'

1993 (2 Feb.) Two phosphor bands. Perf 15 × 14 (with one elliptical hole in each vertical side)

1644	**1074**	(1st) multicoloured	60	50	☐	☐
		a. Booklet pane. Nos. 1644/53	11·00	12·00	☐	☐
1645	**1075**	(1st) gold, cream and black	60	50	☐	☐
1646	**1076**	(1st) multicoloured	60	50	☐	☐
1647	**1077**	(1st) multicoloured	60	50	☐	☐
1648	**1078**	(1st) multicoloured	60	50	☐	☐
1649	**1079**	(1st) multicoloured	60	50	☐	☐
1650	**1080**	(1st) multicoloured	60	50	☐	☐
1651	**1081**	(1st) multicoloured	60	50	☐	☐
1652	**1082**	(1st) multicoloured	60	50	☐	☐
1653	**1083**	(1st) multicoloured	60	50	☐	☐
Set of 10			11·00	12·00	☐	☐
First Day Cover				12·00		☐
Presentation Pack			16·00		☐	
PHQ Cards (*set of 10*)			16·00	30·00	☐	☐

1084 Decorated Enamel Dial

1085 Escapement, Remontoire and Fusee

1086 Balance, Spring and Temperature Compensator

1087 Back of Movement

300th Birth Anniversary of John Harrison (inventor of the marine chronometer). Details of 'H4' Clock

1993 (16 Feb.) Phosphorised paper. Perf 14½ × 14

1654	**1084**	24p multicoloured	60	25	☐	☐
1655	**1085**	28p multicoloured	1·00	1·25	☐	☐
1656	**1086**	33p multicoloured	1·40	1·25	☐	☐
1657	**1087**	39p multicoloured	1·50	1·50	☐	☐
Set of 4			4·00	4·00	☐	☐
First Day Cover				4·00		☐

Presentation Pack	4·25		☐
PHQ Cards (set of 4)	4·25	7·00	☐ ☐
Set of 4 Gutter Pairs	10·00		☐

1088 Britannia

1993 (2 Mar.) Granite paper. Perf 14 × 14½ (with two elliptical holes in each horizontal side)

1658	**1088**	£10 multicoloured	40·00	12·00	☐ ☐
First Day Cover				25·00	☐
Presentation Pack			45·00		☐
PHQ Card			8·00	60·00	☐ ☐

1089 *Dendrobium hellwigianum*

1090 *Paphiopedilum Maudiae* 'Magnifcum'

1091 *Cymbidium lowianum*

1092 *Vanda* Rothschildiana

1093 *Dendrobium vexillarius* var *albiviride*

1093a

14th World Orchid Conference, Glasgow

1993 (16 Mar.) One phosphor band (18p) or phosphorised paper (others)

1659	**1089**	18p multicoloured	45	25	☐ ☐
1660	**1090**	24p multicoloured	75	25	☐ ☐
1661	**1091**	28p multicoloured	1·00	1·25	☐ ☐
1662	**1092**	33p multicoloured	1·25	1·50	☐ ☐
1663	**1093**	39p multicoloured	1·60	1·50	☐ ☐
Set of 5			4·50	4·50	☐ ☐
First Day Cover				4·50	☐
Presentation Pack			5·00		☐
PHQ Cards (set of 5)			4·50	7·00	☐ ☐
Set of 5 Gutter Pairs			10·00		☐

1993 (6 Apr.)–**2008**. As T **913/14** and **1093a**, but Perf 14 (No. 1665) or 15 × 14 (others) (both with one elliptical hole In each vertical side)

(a) Photo

Harrison (No. 1666)
Questa (Nos. 1664a, 1667a)
Walsall (No. 1665)
Harrison (later De La Rue), Questa or Walsall (No. 1667)
Harrison (later De La Rue), Enschedé, Questa or Walsall (Nos. 1664, 1668, 1669)

1664	**913**	(2nd) bright blue			
		(1 centre band)	1·00	1·00	☐ ☐
		a. Perf 14	1·10	1·10	☐ ☐
1665		(2nd) bright blue			
		(1 side band)	1·10	1·10	☐ ☐
1666	**914**	(1st) bright orange-red			
		(phosphorised paper)	1·50	1·25	☐ ☐
1667		(1st) bright orange-red			
		(2 phosphor bands)	1·10	1·10	☐ ☐
		a. Perf 14	1·50	1·50	☐ ☐
1668		(1st) gold			
		(2 phosphor bands)	1·00	1·00	☐ ☐
1669	**1093a**	(E) deep blue			
		(2 phosphor bands)	1·25	1·25	☐ ☐

(b) Litho Questa or Walsall (No. 1670), Questa Enschedé or Walsall (No. 1671), De La Rue or Walsall (No. 1672)

1670	**913**	(2nd) bright blue			
		(1 centre band)	90	90	☐ ☐
1671	**914**	(1st) bright orange-red			
		(2 phosphor bands)	1·00	1·00	☐ ☐
1672		(1st) gold			
		(2 phosphor bands)	1·00	1·00	☐ ☐
First Day Covers					
21 Apr. 1997 (1st), 26p (Nos 1668, Y1686)				3·50	☐
19 Jan. 1999 (E) (No 1669)				3·50	☐

Nos. 1664, 1667, 1669 and 1670/1 also come from sheets.

No. 1665 exists with the phosphor band at the left or right of the stamp and was only issued in booklets.

No. 1668 was issued by Harrison in booklets and Walsall in sheets and booklets for the Queen's Golden Wedding on 21 April 1997. The gold colour was later adopted for the (1st) class rate, replacing bright orange-red.

For No. 1668 in presentation pack see Pack No. 38 listed below, No. Y1667 etc.

No. 1669 was valid for the basic European airmail rate, initially 30p.

No. 1672 was only issued in £7.40 or £7.15 stamp booklets.

For self-adhesive versions in these colours see Nos. 2039/40 and 2295/8.

I Normal figures of face value   **II** Open '4' and open lower curve of '5'

1993–2010 As Nos. X841 etc, but perf 14 (No. Y1678) or 15 × 14 (others) (both with one elliptical hole In each vertical side)

(a) Photo

Enschedé:— 20p (Y1679), 29p, 35p (Y1692), 36p, 38p (Y1700), 41p (Y1706), 43p (Y1710)

Harrison:— 20p (Y1681), 25p (Y1683), 26p (Y1686), 35p (Y1693), 41p (Y1707), 43p (Y1711)

Walsall:— 10p (Y1676a), 19p (Y1678), 38p (Y1701a), 43p (Y1711a)

Enschedé or Harrison (later De La Rue):— 4p, 5p, 6p, 10p (Y1676), 25p (Y1684), 31p, 39p (Y1702), £1 (Y1725)

Enschedé, Harrison (later De La Rue) or Questa:— 1p, 2p

Enschedé, Harrison (later De La Rue) or Walsall:— 30p, 37p (Y1697), 42p, 50p (Y1719), 63p

Harrison (later De La Rue) or Questa:— 19p (Y1677), 20p (Y1680), 26p (Y1685)

De La Rue or Walsall:— 38p (Y1701), 39p (Y1703), 40p (Y1704), 64p, 65p, 68p

De La Rue:— 7p, 8p, 9p, 12p, 14p, 15p, 16p, 17p, 20p (Y1682), 22p, 33p, 34p, 35p (Y1694), 37p (Y1698/9), 41p (Y1708), 43p (Y1712), 44p, 45p, 48p, 49p, 50p (Y1719b), 56p, 60p, 62p, 67p, 72p, 78p, 81p, 88p, 90p, 97p, £1 (Y1725b), £1·46, £1·50, £2, £3, £5

Enschedé or De La Rue:— 35p (Y1695), 40p (Y1705), 46p, 47p, 54p

Y1667	**367**	1p crimson (2 bands)	25	25	☐	☐
Y1668		2p deep green (2 bands)	25	25	☐	☐
Y1669		4p new blue (2 bands)	25	25	☐	☐
Y1670		5p dull red-brown (2 bands)	25	25	☐	☐
Y1671		6p yellow-olive (2 bands)	25	30	☐	☐
Y1672		7p grey (2 bands)	35	35	☐	☐
Y1673		7p bright magenta (2 bands)	25	25	☐	☐
Y1674		8p yellow (2 bands)	35	35	☐	☐
Y1675		9p yellow-orange (2 bands)	15	20	☐	☐
Y1676		10p dull orange (2 bands)	35	35	☐	☐
		a. Perf 14	2·00	2·00	☐	☐
Y1676b		12p greenish blue (2 bands)	20	25	☐	☐
Y1676c		14p rose-red (2 bands)	20	25	☐	☐
Y1676d		15p bright magenta (2 bands)	35	35	☐	☐
Y1676e		16p pale cerise (2 bands)	35	35	☐	☐
Y1676f		17p brown-olive (2 bands)	50	50	☐	☐
Y1677		19p bistre (1 centre band)	75	75	☐	☐
Y1678		19p bistre (1 side band)	2·00	2·00	☐	☐
Y1679		20p turquoise-green (2 bands)	90	90	☐	☐
Y1680		20p bright green (1 centre band)	70	70	☐	☐
Y1681		20p bright green (1 side band)	1·50	1·50	☐	☐
Y1682		20p bright green (2 bands)	75	75	☐	☐
Y1682b		22p drab (2 bands)	50	50	☐	☐
Y1683		25p rose-red (phosphorised paper)	1·10	1·10	☐	☐
Y1684		25p rose-red (2 bands)	1·10	1·10	☐	☐
Y1685		26p red-brown (2 bands)	1·10	1·10	☐	☐
Y1686		26p gold (2 bands)	1·10	1·10	☐	☐
Y1687		29p grey (2 bands)	1·25	1·25	☐	☐
Y1688		30p deep olive-grey (2 bands)	1·10	1·10	☐	☐
Y1689		31p deep mauve (2 bands)	1·20	1·20	☐	☐
Y1690		33p grey-green (2 bands)	1·50	1·50	☐	☐
Y1691		34p yellow-olive (2 bands)	1·25	1·00	☐	☐
Y1692		35p yellow (2 bands)	1·50	1·50	☐	☐
Y1693		35p yellow (phosphorised paper)	12·00	12·00	☐	☐
Y1694		35p sepia (2 bands)	1·10	1·10	☐	☐
Y1695		35p yellow-olive (1 centre band)	50	55	☐	☐
Y1696		36p bright ultramarine (2 bands)	1·50	1·50	☐	☐
Y1697		37p bright mauve (2 bands)	1·40	1·40	☐	☐
Y1698		37p grey-black (2 bands)	1·40	1·40	☐	☐
Y1699		37p brown-olive (1 centre band)	90	90	☐	☐
Y1700		38p rosine (2 bands)	1·50	1·50	☐	☐
Y1701		38p ultramarine (2 bands)	2·00	2·00	☐	☐
		a. Perf 14	7·50	7·50	☐	☐
Y1702		39p bright magenta (2 bands)	1·50	1·50	☐	☐
Y1703		39p grey (2 bands)	1·20	1·20	☐	☐
Y1704		40p deep azure (2 bands)	1·40	1·40	☐	☐
Y1705		40p turquoise-blue (2 bands)	1·30	1·30	☐	☐
Y1706		41p grey-brown (2 bands)	1·75	1·75	☐	☐
Y1707		41p drab (phosphorised paper)	12·00	12·00	☐	☐
Y1708		41p rosine (2 bands)	1·40	1·40	☐	☐
Y1709		42p deep olive-grey (2 bands)	1·40	1·40	☐	☐
Y1710		43p deep olive-brown (2 bands)	1·75	1·75	☐	☐
Y1711		43p sepia (2 bands)	2·50	2·50	☐	☐
		a. Perf 14	2·50	2·50	☐	☐
Y1712		43p emerald (2 bands)	1·40	1·40	☐	☐
Y1713		44p grey-brown (2 bands)	5·00	5·00	☐	☐
Y1714		44p deep bright blue (2 bands)	1·00	1·00	☐	☐
Y1715		45p bright mauve (2 bands)	1·50	1·50	☐	☐
Y1716		46p yellow (2 bands)	1·00	1·00	☐	☐
Y1717		47p turquoise-green (2bands)	1·75	1·75	☐	☐
Y1717a		48p bright mauve (2 bands)	1·00	1·00	☐	☐
Y1718		49p red-brown (2 bands)	1·00	1·00	☐	☐
Y1719		50p ochre (2 bands)	1·75	1·75	☐	☐
Y1719b		50p grey (2 bands)	1·00	1·00	☐	☐
Y1719c		54p red-brown (2 bands)	1·10	1·10	☐	☐
Y1719d		56p yellow-olive (2 bands)	1·10	1·10	☐	☐
Y1719e		60p light emerald (2 bands)	1·40	1·40	☐	☐
Y1719f		62p rosine (2 bands)	1·40	1·40	☐	☐
Y1720		63p light emerald (2 bands)	2·00	2·00	☐	☐
Y1721		64p turquoise-green (2 bands)	2·25	2·25	☐	☐
Y1722		65p greenish blue (2 bands)	2·10	2·10	☐	☐
Y1722a		67p bright mauve (2 bands)	1·50	1·50	☐	☐
Y1723		68p grey-brown (2 bands)	2·10	2·10	☐	☐
Y1724		72p rosine (2 bands)	1·50	1·50	☐	☐
Y1724a		78p emerald (2 bands)	1·50	1·50	☐	☐
Y1724b		81p turquoise-green (2 bands)	1·50	1·50	☐	☐
Y1724c		88p bright magenta (2 bands)	2·00	2·00	☐	☐
Y1724d		90p ultramarine (2 bands)	2·00	2·00	☐	☐
Y1724e		97p violet (2 bands)	2·25	2·25	☐	☐
Y1725		£1 bluish violet (2 bands)	3·25	3·00	☐	☐
Y1725b		£1 magenta (2 bands)	2·00	2·00	☐	☐
Y1725c		£1·46 greenish-blue (2 bands)	3·25	3·25	☐	☐
Y1726		£1·50 brown-red (2 bands)	4·00	4·00	☐	☐
Y1727		£2 deep blue-green (2 bands)	5·50	5·50	☐	☐
Y1728		£3 deep mauve (2 bands)	8·00	8·00	☐	☐
Y1729		£5 azure (2 bands)	14·00	14·00	☐	☐

(b) Litho Cartor (1p (Y1743n), 5p (Y1743t), 10p (Y1749a) 16p, 17p, 20p, 22p, 50p, 54p, 60p (Y1758a), 62p, 90p), De La Rue (5p, (Y1743s) 48p), Questa or De La Rue (10p), (Y1749) Questa or Walsall (25p, 35p, 41p), Walsall (37p, 60p (Y1758), 63p), Questa (others)

Y1743	**367**	1p lake (2 bands)	40	40	☐	☐
Y1743n		1p reddish purple (2 bands)	1·00	1·00	☐	☐
Y1743s		5p dull red-brown (2 bands)	70	70	☐	☐
Y1743t		5p red-brown (2 bands) (Type III)	1·00	1·00	☐	☐
Y1748		6p yellow-olive (2 bands)	12·00	13·00	☐	☐
Y1749		10p dull orange (2 bands)	5·00	5·00	☐	☐
Y1749a		10p pale orange (2 bands)	1·00	1·00	☐	☐
Y1749m		16p pale cerise (2 bands)	70	70	☐	☐
Y1749n		17p bistre (2 bands)	1·00	1·00	☐	☐
Y1750		19p bistre (1 side band)	1·90	1·75	☐	☐
Y1751		20p bright yellow-green (1 centre band)	2·25	2·25	☐	☐
Y1751m		20p light green (2 bands)	2·50	2·50	☐	☐
Y1751n		22p olive-brown (2 bands)	2·50	2·50	☐	☐
Y1752		25p red (2 bands)	1·10	1·10	☐	☐
Y1753		26p chestnut (2 bands)	1·00	1·00	☐	☐
Y1754		30p olive-grey (2 bands)	4·25	4·25	☐	☐
Y1755		35p yellow (2 bands)	1·60	1·60	☐	☐
Y1756		37p bright mauve (2 bands)	3·50	3·50	☐	☐
Y1757		41p drab (2 bands)	1·75	1·75	☐	☐
Y1757f		48p bright mauve (2 bands)	2·25	2·25	☐	☐
Y1757g		50p grey (2 bands)	2·25	2·25	☐	☐
Y1757j		54p chestnut (2 bands) (Type III)	1·50	1·50	☐	☐
Y1758		60p dull blue-grey (2 bands)	2·50	2·50	☐	☐
Y1758a		60p emerald (2 bands)	1·40	1·40	☐	☐
Y1758e		62p rosine (2 bands)	1·75	1·75	☐	☐
Y1759		63p light emerald (2 bands)	3·50	3·50	☐	☐
Y1760		90p bright blue (2 bands)	2·25	2·25	☐	☐

(c) Recess Enschedé or De La Rue

Y1800	**367**	£1·50 red	4·50	2·00	☐	☐
Y1801		£2 dull blue	6·00	2·25	☐	☐
Y1802		£3 dull violet	9·00	3·00	☐	☐
Y1803		£5 brown	15·50	5·00	☐	☐
PHQ Card (No· Y1725)			3·00	15·00	☐	☐

PHQ Cards (Nos. 1664, 1668, Y1667/8, Y1670,
  Y1675/6, Y1676d/e, Y1682, Y1717a, Y1719b,
  Y1719d, Y1724b, Y1725b, Y1726/9,
  2357a/9, 2652/3)   7·00   ☐

Presentation Pack (P.O. Pack No. 30) (contains
  19p (Y1677), 25p (Y1683), 29p (Y1687), 36p
  (Y1696), 38p (Y1700), 41p (Y1706))   7·00   ☐

Presentation Pack (P.O. Pack No. 34) (contains
  1p (Y1667), 2p (Y1668), 4p (Y1669), 5p
  (Y1670), 6p (Y1671), 10p (Y1676), 19p
  (Y1677), 20p (Y1679), 25p (Y1684), 29p
  (Y1687), 30p (Y1688), 35p (Y1692), 36p
  (Y1696), 38p (Y1700), 41p (Y1706), 50p
  (Y1719), 60p (Y1758), £1 (Y1725))   30·00   ☐

Presentation Pack (P.O. Pack No. 35)
  (contains 20p (Y1680), 26p (Y1685),
  31p (Y1689), 37p (Y1697), 39p (Y1702),
  43p (Y1710), 63p (Y1720))   9·50   ☐

Presentation Pack (P.O. Pack No. 38)
  (contains 1st (Y1668), 26p (Y1686))   7·50   ☐

Presentation Pack (P.O. Pack No. 41)
  (contains 2nd (1664), 1st (1667),

1p (Y1667), 2p (Y1668), 4p (Y1669),
5p (Y1670), 6p (Y1671), 10p (Y1676),
20p (Y1680), 26p (Y1685), 30p (Y1688),
31p (Y1689), 37p (Y1697), 39p (Y1702),
43p (Y1711), 50p (Y1719), 63p (Y1720),
£1 (Y1725))   16·00   ☐

Presentation Pack (P.O. Pack No. 43 or 43A)
  (contains £1·50 (Y1800), £2 (Y1801),
  £3 (Y1802), £5 (Y1803))   55·00   ☐

Presentation Pack (P.O. Pack No. 44) contains 7p
  (Y1672), 19p (Y1677), 38p (Y1701), 44p (Y1713),
  64p (Y1721))   11·00   ☐

Presentation Pack (P.O. Pack No. 49)
  (contains 8p (Y1674), 33p (Y1690),
  40p (Y1704), 41p (Y1708), 45p (Y1715),
  65p (Y1722))   10·00   ☐

Presentation Pack (P.O. Pack No.57) (contains
  2nd (1664), 1st (1667), E (1669), 1p (Y1667),
  2p (Y1668), 4p (Y1669), 5p (Y1670), 8p
  (Y1674), 10p (Y1676), 20p (Y1682), 33p
  (Y1690), 40p (Y1704), 41p (Y1708), 45p
  (Y1715), 50p (Y1719), 65p (Y1722),
  £1(Y1725))   16·00   ☐

Presentation Pack (P.O. Pack No. 58) (contains
  37p (Y1698), 42p (Y1709), 47p (Y1716), 68p
  (Y1723)   7·50   ☐

Presentation Pack (P.O. Pack No. 62) (contains
  £1·50 (Y1726), £2 (Y1727), £3 (Y1728),
  £5(Y1729)   23·00   ☐

Presentation Pack (P.O. Pack No. 67) (contains
  7p (No. Y1673), 1st (1668), 35p (Y1694),
  39p(Y1703), 40p (Y1705), 43p (Y1712),
  Worldwide postcard (2357a)   6·00   ☐

Presentation Pack (P.O. Pack No. 71) (contains
  1p (Y1667), 2p (Y1668), 5p (Y1670), 9p
  (Y1675), 10p (Y1676), 20p (Y1682), 35p
  (Y1695), 40p(Y1705), 42p (Y1709), 46p
  (Y1716), 47p (Y1717), 50p (Y1719), 68p
  (Y1723), £1 (Y1725), 2nd (2039), 1st(2295),
  Worldwide postcard (2357a), Europe (2358),
  Worldwide (2359)   11·50   ☐

Presentation Pack (P.O. Pack No. 72) (contains
  37p (Y1699), 44p (Y1714), 49p (Y1718), 72p
  (Y1724)   3·50   ☐

Presentation Pack (P.O. Pack No.75) (contains
  16p (Y1676e), 48p (Y1717a), 50p (Y1719b),
  54p (Y1719c), 78p (Y1724a)   6·75   ☐

Presentation Pack (P.O. Pack No.77) (contains
  1p (Y1667), 2p (Y1668), 5p (Y1670), 10p
  (Y1676), 14p (Y1676c), 16p (Y1676d), 20p
  (Y1682), 46p (Y1716), 48p (Y1717a), 50p
  (Y1719b), 54p (Y1719c), 78p (Y1724a), £1
  (Y1725b), 2nd (1664), 1st (1668), 2nd Large
  (2652), 1st Large (2653), Worldwide postcard
  (2357a), Europe (2358), Worldwide (2359) 20·00   ☐

Presentation Pack (P.O. Pack No.78) (contains
  15p (Y1676d), 56p (Y1719d), 81p (Y1724b) 4·00   ☐

Presentation Pack (P.O. Pack No. 84) (contains
  17p (Y1676f), 22p (Y1682b), 62p (Y1719f),
  90p (Y1724d)   5·25   ☐

Presentation Pack (P.O. Pack No. 86) (contains
  60p (Y1719e), 67p (Y1722a), 88p (Y1724c),
  97p (Y1724e), £1.46 (Y1725c), Europe (2358a),
  Worldwide (2359a), Recorded Signed for
  1st (U2916a), Recorded Signed for 1st Large
  (U2916b)   20.00   ☐

Presentation Pack (P.O. Pack No. 88) (contains
  1p (Y1667), 2p (Y1668), 5p (Y1670), 9p (Y1675),
  10p (Y1676), 20p (Y1682), 50p (Y1719b),
  60p (Y1719e), 67p (Y1722a), 88p (Y1724c),
  97p (Y1724e), £1 (Y1725b), £1.46 (Y1725c),
  Worldwide postcard (2357a), Europe (2358),
  Europe (2358a), Worldwide (2359), Worldwide
  (2359a), 2nd (1664), 1st (1668), 2nd Large
  (2652), 1st Large (2653), Recorded Signed for
  1st (U2940), Recorded Signed for 1st Large
  (U2941)   35.00   ☐

For P.O. Pack No. 37 see below No. 1977.
For P.O. Pack No. 74 containing Nos. Y1676b/c see below No.
2657.

First Day Covers

26 Oct. 1993	19p, 25p, 29p, 36p, 38p, 41p (Nos. Y1677, Y1683, Y1687, Y1696, Y1700, Y1706)	6·00	☐
9 Aug. 1994	60p (No. Y1758)	4·00	☐
22 Aug. 1995	£1 (No. Y1725)	3·50	☐
25 June 1996	20p, 26p, 31p, 37p, 39p, 43p, 63p (Nos. Y1680, Y1685, Y1689, Y1697, Y1702, Y1710, Y1720)	8·00	☐
9 Mar. 1999	£1·50, £2, £3, £5 (Nos. Y1800/3)	27·00	☐
20 Apr. 1999	7p, 38p, 44p, 64p (Nos. Y1672, Y1701, Y1713, Y1721)	5·00	☐
25 Apr. 2000	8p, 33p, 40p, 41p, 45p, 65p (Nos. Y1674, Y1690, Y1704, Y1708, Y1715, Y1722)	5·00	☐
4 July 2002	37p, 42p, 47p, 68p, (Nos. Y1698, Y1709, Y1716, Y1723)	4·00	☐
6 May 2003	34p (No. Y1691)	1·20	☐
1 July 2003	£1·50, £2, £3, £5 (Nos. Y1726/9)	21·00	☐
1 April 2004	7p, 35p, 39p, 40p, 43p, World-wide postcard (Nos. Y1673, Y1694, Y1703, Y1705, Y1712, 2357a)	9·00	☐
5 April 2005	9p, 35p, 46p (Nos. Y1675, Y1695, Y1716)	2·20	☐
28 March 2006	37p, 44p, 49p, 72p (Nos. Y1699, Y1714, Y1718, Y1724)	4·25	☐
27 March 2007	16p, 48p, 50p, 54p, 78p (Nos. Y1676e, Y1717a, Y1719b/c, Y1724a)	6·00	☐
1 April 2008	15p, 56p, 81p (Nos. Y1676d, Y1719d, Y1724b)	4·50	☐
31 March 2009	17p, 22p, 62p, 90p, (Nos. Y1676f, Y1682b, Y1719f, Y1724d)	6·00	☐
30 March 2010	60p, 67p, 88p, 97p, £1.46, Europe, Worldwide (Nos. Y1719e, 1722a, Y1724c, Y1724e, Y1725c, 2358a, 2359a)	14·00	☐

For Nos. Y1676b/c on first day cover see under Nos. 2650/7.
Nos. Y1725/9 are printed in Iriodin ink which gives a shiny effect
to the solid part of the background behind the Queen's head.
Nos. Y1693 and Y1707 were only issued in coils and Nos.
Y1676a, Y1678, Y1681, Y1701a, Y1711a and Y1743/60 only in
booklets.
No. Y1750 exists with the phosphor band at the left or right
of the stamp, but Nos. Y1678 and Y1681 exist with band at
right only.

For self-adhesive versions of the 42p and 68p see Nos.
2297/8.

1094 'Family Group' (bronze sculpture) (Henry Moore)   **1095** 'Kew Gardens' (lithograph) (Edward Bawden)

1096 'St Francis and the Birds' (Stanley Spencer)   **1097** 'Still Life: Odyssey I' (Ben Nicholson)

Europa. Contemporary Art

1993 (11 May) Phosphorised paper. Perf 14 × 14½

1767	**1094**	24p multicoloured	60	20	☐	☐
1768	**1095**	28p multicoloured	90	1·00	☐	☐
1769	**1096**	33p multicoloured	1·25	1·40	☐	☐
1770	**1097**	39p multicoloured	1·75	1·75	☐	☐
Set of 4			4·00	4·00	☐	
First Day Cover				4·50		☐
Presentation Pack			4·50		☐	
PHQ Cards (*set of 4*)			4·00	7·00	☐	☐
Set of 4 Gutter Pairs			10·00		☐	

1098 Emperor Claudius (from gold coin)   **1099** Emperor Hadrian (bronze head)

1100 Goddess Roma (from gemstone)   **1101** Christ (Hinton St. Mary mosaic)

Roman Britain

1993 (15 June) Phosphorised paper with two phosphor
bands. Perf 14 × 14½

1771	**1098**	24p multicoloured	60	20	☐	☐
1772	**1099**	28p multicoloured	90	1·00	☐	☐
1773	**1100**	33p multicoloured	1·30	1·50	☐	☐
1774	**1101**	39p multicoloured	1·50	1·60	☐	☐
Set of 4			4·00	4·00	☐	
First Day Cover				4·00		☐

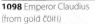

Presentation Pack	4·50		☐
PHQ Cards (*set of* 4)	4·25	7·00	☐ ☐
Set of 4 Gutter Pairs	10·00		☐

1102 Midland Maid and other Narrow Boats, Grand Junction Canal

1103 Yorkshire Maid and other Humber Keels, Stainforth and Keadby Canal

1104 Valley Princess and other Horse-drawn Barges, Brecknock and Abergavenny Canal

1105 Steam Barges including Pride of Scotland and Fishing Boats, Crinan Canal

Inland Waterways

1993 (20 July) Two phosphor bands. Perf 14½ × 14

1775	**1102**	24p multicoloured	50	20	☐ ☐
1776	**1103**	28p multicoloured	1·00	1·00	☐ ☐
1777	**1104**	33p multicoloured	1·25	1·25	☐ ☐
1778	**1105**	39p multicoloured	1·50	1·40	☐ ☐
Set of 4			3·75	3·50	☐ ☐
First Day Cover				3·75	☐
Presentation Pack			4·50		☐
PHQ Cards (*set of* 4)			4·25	7·00	☐ ☐
Set of 4 Gutter Pairs			9·00		☐

Nos. 1775/8 commemorate the bicentenaries of the Acts of Parliament authorising the canals depicted.

1106 Horse Chestnut

1107 Blackberry

1108 Hazel

1109 Rowan

1110 Pear

The Four Seasons. Autumn. Fruits and Leaves

1993 (14 Sept.) One phosphor band (18p) or phosphorised paper (others)

1779	**1106**	18p multicoloured	50	20	☐ ☐
1780	**1107**	24p multicoloured	75	20	☐ ☐
1781	**1108**	28p multicoloured	1·10	1·25	☐ ☐
1782	**1109**	33p multicoloured	1·40	1·50	☐ ☐
1783	**1110**	39p multicoloured	1·50	1·50	☐ ☐
Set of 5			4·75	4·50	☐ ☐
First Day Cover				4·50	☐
Presentation Pack			4·75		☐
PHQ Cards (*set of* 5)			4·50	· 7·00	☐ ☐
Set of 5 Gutter Pairs			10·50		☐

1111 The Reigate Square

1112 The Hound of the Baskervilles

1113 The Six Napoleons

1114 The Greek Interpreter

1115 The Final Problem

T **1111/15** were printed together, *se-tenant*, in horizontal strips of 5 throughout the sheet.

Sherlock Holmes. Centenary of the Publication of The Final Problem

1993 (12 Oct.) Phosphorised paper. Perf 14 × 14½

1784	**1111**	24p multicoloured	50	40	☐ ☐
		a. Horiz strip of 5.			
		Nos. 1784/8	5·00	5·25	☐ ☐
1785	**1112**	24p multicoloured	50	40	☐ ☐
1786	**1113**	24p multicoloured	50	40	☐ ☐
1787	**1114**	24p multicoloured	50	40	☐ ☐
1788	**1115**	24p multicoloured	50	40	☐ ☐
Set of 5			5·00	5·25	☐ ☐
First Day Cover				5·50	☐

Presentation Pack	5·00		☐
PHQ Cards (set of 5)	4·50	8·00	☐ ☐
Gutter Strip of 10	11·00		☐

1116

Self-adhesive Booklet Stamp

1993 (19 Oct.) Litho Walsall. Two phosphor bands. Die-cut perf 14 × 15 (with one elliptical hole in each vertical side)

1789 **1116**	(1st) orange-red	1·25	1·40	☐ ☐
First Day Cover			4·50	☐
Presentation Pack (booklet pane of 20)		25·00		☐
PHQ Card		4·00	8·00	☐ ☐

For similar 2nd and 1st designs printed in photogravure by Enschedé see Nos. 1976/7.

1117 Bob Cratchit and Tiny Tim   **1118** Mr and Mrs Fezziwig

1119 Scrooge   **1120** The Prize Turkey

1121 Mr Scrooge's Nephew

Christmas. 150th Anniversary of Publication of A Christmas Carol

1993 (9 Nov.) One phosphor band (19p) or phosphorised paper (others)

1790 **1117**	19p multicoloured	60	15	☐ ☐
1791 **1118**	25p multicoloured	90	15	☐ ☐
1792 **1119**	30p multicoloured	1·25	1·50	☐ ☐
1793 **1120**	35p multicoloured	1·40	1·60	☐ ☐
1794 **1121**	41p multicoloured	1·40	1·60	☐ ☐
Set of 5		4·50	4·50	☐ ☐
First Day Cover			5·00	☐
Presentation Pack		5·00		☐
PHQ Cards (set of 5)		4·50	8·00	☐ ☐
Set of 5 Gutter Pairs		11·00		☐

Collectors Pack 1993

1993 (9 Nov.) Comprises Nos. 1639/43, 1654/7, 1659/63, 1767/88 and 1790/4

| CP1794a | Collectors Pack | 45·00 | | ☐ |

Post Office Yearbook

1993 (9 Nov.) Comprises Nos. 1639/43, 1654/7, 1659/63, 1767/88 and 1790/4 in hardback book with slip case

| YB1794a | Yearbook | 65·00 | ☐ |

1122 Class 5 No. 44957 and Class B1 No. 61342 on West Highland Line   **1123** Class A1 No. 60149 Amadis at Kings Cross

1124 Class 4 No. 43000 on Turntable at Blythe North   **1125** Class 4 No. 42455 near Wigan Central

1126 Class Castle No. 7002 Devizes Castle on Bridge crossing Worcester and Birmingham Canal

The Age of Steam. Railway Photographs by Colin Gifford

1994 (18 Jan.) One phosphor band (19p) or phosphorised paper with two bands (others). Perf 14½

1795 **1122**	19p deep blue-green, grey-black and black	55	25	☐ ☐
1796 **1123**	25p slate-lilac, grey-black and black	90	95	☐ ☐
1797 **1124**	30p lake brown, grey-black and black	1·40	1·50	☐ ☐
1798 **1125**	35p deep claret, grey-black and black	1·75	1·80	☐ ☐
1799 **1126**	41p indigo, grey-black and black	1·80	1·90	☐ ☐
Set of 5		6·00	6·00	☐ ☐
First Day Cover			6·00	☐
Presentation Pack		5·75		☐
PHQ Cards (set of 5)		5·75	11·00	☐ ☐
Set of 5 Gutter Pairs		12·00		☐

1127 Dan Dare and the Mekon   **1128** The Three Bears

1129 Rupert Bear

1130 Alice
(*Alice in Wonderland*)

1131 Noggin and the Ice
Dragon

1132 Peter Rabbit posting
Letter

1133 Red Riding Hood
and Wolf

1134 Orlando the Marmalade
Cat

1135 Biggles

1136 Paddington Bear on
Station

T **1127/36** were printed together, *se-tenant*, in booklet panes
of 10 stamps and 20 half stamp-size labels.

Greeting Stamps. 'Messages'

1994 (1 Feb.) Two phosphor bands. Perf 15 × 14 (with one
elliptical hole in each vertical side)

1800	**1127**	(1st) multicoloured	60	50	☐	☐
		a. Booklet pane.				
		Nos. 1800/9	13·00	12·00	☐	☐
1801	**1128**	(1st) multicoloured	60	50	☐	☐
1802	**1129**	(1st) multicoloured	60	50	☐	☐
1803	**1130**	(1st) gold, bistre-yellow				
		and black	60	50	☐	☐
1804	**1131**	(1st) multicoloured	60	50	☐	☐
1805	**1132**	(1st) multicoloured	60	50	☐	☐
1806	**1133**	(1st) multicoloured	60	50	☐	☐
1807	**1134**	(1st) multicoloured	60	50	☐	☐
1808	**1135**	(1st) multicoloured	60	50	☐	☐
1809	**1136**	(1st) multicoloured	60	50	☐	☐
Set of 10			13·00	12·00	☐	☐
First Day Cover				12·00		☐
Presentation Pack			18·00		☐	
PHQ Cards (*set of* 10)			16·00	30·00	☐	☐

1137 Castell Y Waun (Chirk
Castle), Clwyd, Wales

1138 Ben Arkle, Sutherland,
Scotland

1139 Mourne Mountains,
County Down, Northern Ireland

1140 Dersingham, Norfolk,
England

1141 Dolwyddelan, Gwynedd, Wales

**25th Anniversary of Investiture of the Prince of
Wales. Paintings by Prince Charles**

1994 (1 Mar.) One phosphor band (19p) or phosphorised
paper (others)

1810	**1137**	19p multicoloured	55	20	☐	☐
1811	**1138**	25p multicoloured	1·00	20	☐	☐
1812	**1139**	30p multicoloured	1·10	1·50	☐	☐
1813	**1140**	35p multicoloured	1·40	1·75	☐	☐
1814	**1141**	41p multicoloured	1·50	1·75	☐	☐
Set of 5			5·00	5·00	☐	☐
First Day Cover				5·00		☐
Presentation Pack			5·00		☐	
PHQ Cards (*set of* 5)			5·75	11·50	☐	☐
Set of 5 Gutter Pairs			11·00		☐	

1142 Bather at
Blackpool

1143 'Where's my
Little Lad?'

1144 'Wish You were
Here!

1145 Punch and
Judy Show

1146 'The Tower Crane' Machine

Centenary of Picture Postcards

1994 (12 Apr.) One side band (19p) or two phosphor bands (others). Perf 14 × 14½

1815	**1142**	19p multicoloured	60	20		
1816	**1143**	25p multicoloured	90	20		
1817	**1144**	30p multicoloured	1·10	1·50		
1818	**1145**	35p multicoloured	1·40	1·75		
1819	**1146**	41p multicoloured	1·50	1·75		
Set of 5			5·00	5·00		
First Day Cover				5·00		
Presentation Pack			5·00			
PHQ Cards (*set of* 5)			5·75	11·50		
Set of 5 Gutter Pairs			11·00			

1147 British Lion and French Cockerel over Tunnel

1148 Symbolic Hands over Train

Nos. 1820/1 and 1822/3 were printed together, *se-tenant*, in horizontal pairs throughout the sheets.

Opening of Channel Tunnel

1994 (3 May) Phosphorised paper. Perf 14 × 14½

1820	**1147**	25p multicoloured	50	40		
		a. Horiz pair.				
		Nos. 1820/1	1·75	2·00		
1821	**1148**	25p multicoloured	50	40		
1822	**1147**	41p multicoloured	60	50		
		a. Horiz pair.				
		Nos. 1822/3	3·25	2·50		
1823	**1148**	41p multicoloured	60	50		
Set of 4			4·50	4·50		
First Day Cover				5·25		
First Day Covers (2) (UK and						
		French stamps)		20·00		
Presentation Pack			5·00			
Presentation Pack (UK and						
		French stamps)	25·00			

Souvenir Book		50·00			
PHQ Cards (*set of* 4)		5·75	9·00		

Stamps in similar designs were also issued by France and these are included in the joint Presentation Pack and Souvenir Book.

1149 Groundcrew replacing Smoke Canisters on Douglas Boston of 88 Sqn

1150 H.M.S. *Warspite* (battleship) shelling Enemy Positions

1151 Commandos Landing on Gold Beach

1152 Infantry regrouping on Sword Beach

1153 Tank and Infantry advancing, Ouistreham

Nos. 1824/8 were printed together, *se-tenant*, in horizontal strips of 5 throughout the sheet.

50th Anniversary of D-Day

1994 (6 June) Two phosphor bands. Perf 14½ × 14

1824	**1149**	25p multicoloured	50	40		
		a. Horiz strip of 5.				
		Nos. 1824/8	4·25	5·00		
1825	**1150**	25p multicoloured	50	40		
1826	**1151**	25p multicoloured	50	40		
1827	**1152**	25p multicoloured	50	40		
1828	**1153**	25p multicoloured	50	40		
Set of 5			4·25	5·00		
First Day Cover				5·50		
Presentation Pack			5·50			
PHQ Cards (*set of* 5)			5·00	11·50		
Gutter Block of 10			11·00			

1154 The Old Course, St Andrews

1155 The 18th Hole, Muirfield

1156 The 15th Hole ('Luckyslap'), Carnoustie

1157 The 8th Hole ('The Postage Stamp'), Royal Troon

1158 The 9th Hole, Turnberry

Scottish Golf Courses

1994 (5 July) One phosphor band (19p) or phosphorised paper (others). Perf 14½ × 14

1829	**1154**	19p multicoloured	50	20	☐	☐
1830	**1155**	25p multicoloured	75	20	☐	☐
1831	**1156**	30p multicoloured	1·10	1·40	☐	☐
1832	**1157**	35p multicoloured	1·25	1·40	☐	☐
1833	**1158**	41p multicoloured	1·40	1·40	☐	☐
Set of 5			4·50	4·25	☐	☐
First Day Cover				4·75	☐	
Presentation Pack			4·75		☐	
PHQ Cards (*set of 5*)			5·75	11·50	☐	☐
Set of 5 Gutter Pairs			11·50		☐	

Nos. 1829/33 commemorate the 250th anniversary of golf's first set of rules produced by the Honourable Company of Edinburgh Golfers.

1159 Royal Welsh Show, Llanelwedd

1160 All England Tennis Championships, Wimbledon

1161 Cowes Week

1162 Test Match, Lord's

1163 Braemar Gathering

The Four Seasons. Summertime. Events

1994 (2 Aug.) One phosphor band (19p) or phosphorised paper (others)

1834	**1159**	19p multicoloured	50	20	☐	☐
1835	**1160**	25p multicoloured	75	20	☐	☐
1836	**1161**	30p multicoloured	1·10	1·25	☐	☐
1837	**1162**	35p multicoloured	1·25	1·60	☐	☐
1838	**1163**	41p multicoloured	1·40	1·60	☐	☐
Set of 5			4·50	4·25	☐	☐
First Day Cover				4·75	☐	
Presentation Pack			4·75		☐	
PHQ Cards (*set of 5*)			5·75	11·50	☐	☐
Set of 5 Gutter Pairs			11·50		☐	

1164 Ultrasonic Imaging

1165 Scanning Electron Microscopy

1166 Magnetic Resonance Imaging

1167 Computed Tomography

Europa. Medical Discoveries

1994 (27 Sept.) Phosphorised paper. Perf 14 × 14½

1839	**1164**	25p multicoloured	75	25	☐	☐
1840	**1165**	30p multicoloured	1·00	1·25	☐	☐
1841	**1166**	35p multicoloured	1·50	1·75	☐	☐
1842	**1167**	41p multicoloured	1·75	1·75	☐	☐
Set of 4			4·50	4·50	☐	☐
First Day Cover				4·75	☐	
Presentation Pack			4·75		☐	
PHQ Cards (*set of 4*)			5·75	10·00	☐	☐
Set of 4 Gutter Pairs			11·00		☐	

1168 Virgin Mary and Joseph

1169 Three Wise Men

1170 Virgin and Child

1171 Shepherds

1172 Angels

Christmas. Children's Nativity Plays

1994 (1 Nov.) One phosphor band (19p) or phosphorised paper (others)

1843	**1168**	19p multicoloured	50	15	☐	☐
1844	**1169**	25p multicoloured	75	15	☐	☐
1845	**1170**	30p multicoloured	1·00	1·50	☐	☐
1846	**1171**	35p multicoloured	1·25	1·50	☐	☐
1847	**1172**	41p multicoloured	1·50	1·75	☐	☐
Set of 5			4·50	4·75	☐	☐
First Day Cover				4·75		☐
Presentation Pack			4·75		☐	
PHQ Cards (*set of 5*)			5·75	11·50	☐	☐
Set of 5 Gutter Pairs			10·50		☐	

Collectors Pack 1994

1994 (14 Nov.) Comprises Nos. 1795/1847

CP1847a	Collectors Pack	55·00	☐

Post Office Yearbook

1994 (14 Nov.) Comprises Nos. 1795/9 and 1810/47 in hardback book with slip case

YB1847a	Yearbook	55·00	☐

1173 Sophie (black cat)

1174 Puskas (Siamese) and Tigger (tabby)

1175 Chloe (ginger cat)

1176 Kikko (tortoiseshell) and Rosie (Abyssinian)

1177 Fred (black and white cat)

Cats

1995 (17 Jan.) One phosphor band (19p) or two phosphor bands (others). Perf 14½ × 14

1848	**1173**	19p multicoloured	75	20	☐	☐
1849	**1174**	25p multicoloured	75	25	☐	☐
1850	**1175**	30p multicoloured	1·00	1·50	☐	☐
1851	**1176**	35p multicoloured	1·25	1·50	☐	☐
1852	**1177**	41p multicoloured	1·50	1·50	☐	☐
Set of 5			4·75	4·75	☐	☐
First Day Cover				4·75		☐
Presentation Pack			5·50		☐	
PHQ Cards (*set of 5*)			6·00	11·50	☐	☐
Set of 5 Gutter Pairs			11·00		☐	

1178 Dandelions

1179 Sweet Chestnut Leaves

1180 Garlic Leaves

1181 Hazel Leaves

1182 Spring Grass

The Four Seasons. Springtime. Plant Sculptures by Andy Goldsworthy

1995 (14 Mar.) One phosphor band (19p) or two phosphor bands (others)

1853	**1178**	19p multicoloured	75	15	☐	☐
1854	**1179**	25p multicoloured	75	15	☐	☐
1855	**1180**	30p multicoloured	1·00	1·50	☐	☐
1856	**1181**	35p multicoloured	1·25	1·50	☐	☐
1857	**1182**	41p multicoloured	1·50	1·75	☐	☐
Set of 5			4·75	4·75	☐	☐
First Day Cover				4·75		☐
Presentation Pack			5·00		☐	
PHQ Cards (*set of 5*)			6·00	11·50	☐	☐
Set of 5 Gutter Pairs			11·50		☐	

1183 'La Llanse a la Campagne' (Renoir)

1184 'Troilus and Criseyde' (Peter Brookes)

1185 'The Kiss' (Rodin)

1186 'Girls on the Town' (Beryl Cook)

1187 'Jazz' (Andrew Mockett)

1188 'Girls performing a Kathal Dance' (Aurangzeb period)

1189 'Alice Keppel with her Daughter' (Alice Hughes)

1190 'Children Playing' (L. S. Lowry)

1191 'Circus Clowns' (Emily Firmin and Justin Mitchell)

1192 Decoration from 'All the Love Poems of Shakespeare' (Eric Gill)

T **1183/92** were printed together, *se-tenant*, in booklet panes of 10 stamps and 20 half stamp-size labels.

Greetings Stamp. 'Greetings in Art'

1995 (21 Mar.) Two phosphor bands. Perf 14½ × 14 (with one elliptical hole in each vertical side)

1858	**1183**	(1st) multicoloured	60	50	☐	☐
	a. Booklet pane. Nos. 1858/67	11·00	11·00	☐	☐
1859	**1184**	(1st) multicoloured	60	50	☐	☐
1860	**1185**	(1st) multicoloured	60	50	☐	☐
1861	**1186**	(1st) multicoloured	60	50	☐	☐
1862	**1187**	(1st) multicoloured	60	50	☐	☐
1863	**1188**	(1st) multicoloured	60	50	☐	☐
1864	**1189**	(1st) purple-brown and silver	60	50	☐	☐
1865	**1190**	(1st) multicoloured	60	50	☐	☐
1866	**1191**	(1st) multicoloured	60	50	☐	☐
1867	**1192**	(1st) black, greenish yellow and silver	60	50	☐	☐
Set of 10			11·50	11·00	☐	☐
First Day Cover				11·50		☐
Presentation Pack			12·00		☐	
PHQ Cards (*set of* 10)			16·00	30·00	☐	☐

1193 Fireplace Decoration, Attingham Park, Shropshire

1194 Oak Seedling

1195 Carved Table Leg, Attingham Park

1196 St. David's Head, Dyfed, Wales

1197 Elizabethan Window, Little Moreton Hall, Cheshire

Centenary of The National Trust

1995 (11 Apr.) One phosphor band (19p), two phosphor bands (25p, 35p) or phosphorised paper (30p, 41p)

1868	**1193**	19p multicoloured	60	20	☐	☐
1869	**1194**	25p multicoloured	80	20	☐	☐
1870	**1195**	30p multicoloured	1·00	1·50	☐	☐
1871	**1196**	35p multicoloured	1·25	1·50	☐	☐
1872	**1197**	41p multicoloured	1·40	1·75	☐	☐
Set of 5			4·50	4·75	☐	
First Day Cover				4·75		☐
Presentation Pack			4·75		☐	
PHQ Cards (*set of* 5)			6·00	11·50	☐	☐
Set of 5 Gutter Pairs			11·00		☐	

1198 British Troops and French Civilians celebrating

1199 Symbolic Hands and Red Cross

1200 St. Paul's Cathedral and Searchlights

1201 Symbolic Hand releasing Peace Dove

1202 Symbolic Hands

Europa. Peace and Freedom

1995 (2 May) One phosphor band (Nos. 1873/4) or two phosphor bands (others). Perf 14½ × 14

1873	**1198**	19p silver, bistre-brown and grey-black	70	40	☐	☐
1874	**1199**	19p multicoloured	70	40	☐	☐
1875	**1200**	25p silver, blue and grey-black	1·00	1·00	☐	☐
1876	**1201**	25p multicoloured	1·00	1·00	☐	☐

1877 **1202**	30p multicoloured	1·25	2·25	☐ ☐
Set of 5		4·25	4·25	☐ ☐
First Day Cover			4·75	☐
Presentation Pack		5·00		☐
PHQ Cards (*set of* 5)		6·00	11·50	☐ ☐
Set of 5 Gutter Pairs		10·50		☐

Nos. 1873 and 1875 commemorate the 50th anniversary of the end of the Second World War, No. 1874 the 125th anniversary of the British Red Cross Society and Nos. 1876/7 the 50th anniversary of the United Nations.
Nos. 1876/7 include the 'EUROPA' emblem.
For No. 1875 with the face value expressed as '1st' see No. **MS**2547.

1203 *The Time Machine*

1204 *The First Men in the Moon*

1205 *The War of the Worlds*

1206 *The Shape of Things to Come*

Science Fiction. Novels by H. G. Wells

1995 (6 June) Two phosphor bands. Perf 14½ × 14

1878 **1203**	25p multicoloured	75	25	☐ ☐
1879 **1204**	30p multicoloured	1·25	1·50	☐ ☐
1880 **1205**	35p multicoloured	1·25	1·60	☐ ☐
1881 **1206**	41p multicoloured	1·50	1·60	☐ ☐
Set of 4		4·25	4·50	☐ ☐
First Day Cover			4·75	☐
Presentation Pack		5·00		☐
PHQ Cards (*set of* 4)		6·00	11·50	☐ ☐
Set of 4 Gutter Pairs		10·00		☐

Nos. 1878/81 commemorate the centenary of publication of Wells's *The Time Machine*.

1207 *The Swan, 1595*

1208 *The Rose, 1592*

1209 *The Globe, 1599*

1210 *The Hope, 1613*

1211 *The Globe, 1614*

T **1207/11** were printed together, *se-tenant*, in horizontal strips of 5 throughout the sheet, the backgrounds forming a composite design.

Reconstruction of Shakespeare's Globe Theatre

1995 (8 Aug.) Two phosphor bands. Perf 14½

1882 **1207**	25p multicoloured	50	40	☐ ☐
	a. Horiz strip of 5.			
	Nos. 1882/6	4·50	4·75	☐ ☐
1883 **1208**	25p multicoloured	50	40	☐ ☐
1884 **1209**	25p multicoloured	50	40	☐ ☐
1885 **1210**	25p multicoloured	50	40	☐ ☐
1886 **1211**	25p multicoloured	50	40	☐ ☐
Set of 5		4·50	4·75	☐ ☐
First Day Cover			5·50	☐
Presentation Pack		5·00		☐
PHQ Cards (*set of* 5)		6·00	11·50	☐ ☐
Gutter Strip of 10		10·50		☐

1212 *Sir Rowland Hill and Uniform Penny Postage Petition*

1213 *Hill and Penny Black*

1214 *Guglielmo Marconi and Early Wireless*

1215 *Marconi and Sinking of Titanic (liner)*

Pioneers of Communications

1995 (5 Sept.) One phosphor band (19p) or phosphorised paper (others). Perf 14½ × 14

1887 **1212**	19p silver, red and black	75	30	☐ ☐
1888 **1213**	25p silver, brown and			

	black	1·00	50	☐ ☐
1889 **1214**	41p silver, grey-green and black	1·50	1·75	☐ ☐
1890 **1215**	60p silver, deep ultramarine and black	1·75	2·25	☐ ☐
Set of 4		4·50	4·50	☐ ☐
First Day Cover			4·75	☐
Presentation Pack		5·00		☐
PHQ Cards (*set of* 4)		5·75	11·50	☐ ☐
Set of 4 Gutter Pairs		11·00		☐

Nos. 1887/8 mark the birth bicentenary of Sir Rowland Hill and Nos. 1889/90 the centenary of the first radio transmissions.

1216 Harold Wagstaff

1217 Gus Risman

1218 Jim Sullivan

1219 Billy Batten

1220 Brian Bevan

Centenary of Rugby League

1995 (3 Oct.) One phosphor band (19p) or two phosphor bands (others). Perf 14 × 14½

1891 **1216**	19p multicoloured	75	25	☐ ☐
1892 **1217**	25p multicoloured	75	30	☐ ☐
1893 **1218**	30p multicoloured	1·00	1·50	☐ ☐
1894 **1219**	35p multicoloured	1·00	1·60	☐ ☐
1895 **1220**	41p multicoloured	1·50	1·60	☐ ☐
Set of 5		4·75	4·75	☐ ☐
First Day Cover			4·75	☐
Presentation Pack		5·50		☐
PHQ Cards (*set of* 5)		6·00	11·50	☐ ☐
Set of 5 Gutter Pairs		11·00		☐

1221 European Robin in Mouth of Pillar Box

1222 European Robin on Railings and Holly

1223 European Robin on Snow-covered Milk Bottles

1224 European Robin on Road Sign

1225 European Robin on Door Knob and Christmas Wreath

Christmas. Christmas Robins

1995 (30 Oct.) One phosphor band (19p) or two phosphor bands (others)

1896 **1221**	19p multicoloured	60	20	☐ ☐
1897 **1222**	25p multicoloured	85	30	☐ ☐
1898 **1223**	30p multicoloured	1·25	1·50	☐ ☐
1899 **1224**	41p multicoloured	1·60	1·75	☐ ☐
1900 **1225**	60p multicoloured	1·75	1·90	☐ ☐
Set of 5		5·50	5·50	☐ ☐
First Day Cover			5·50	☐
Presentation Pack		5·75		☐
PHQ Cards (*set of* 5)		6·00	11·50	☐ ☐
Set of 5 Gutter Pairs		12·00		☐

The 19p value was re-issued on 3 October 2000 and 9 October 2001 in sheets of 20 each with *se-tenant* label, in connection with 'customised' stamps available from the Philatelic Bureau. The labels show either Christmas greetings or a personal photograph.

Collectors Pack 1995

1995 (30 Oct.) Comprises Nos. 1848/1900

CP1900a	Collectors Pack	60·00	☐

Post Office Yearbook

1995 (30 Oct.) Comprises Nos. 1848/57 and 1868/1900 in hardback book with slip case

YB1900a	Yearbook	55·00	☐

1226 Opening Lines of 'To a Mouse' and Fieldmouse

1227 'O my Luve's like a red, red rose' and Wild Rose

1228 'Scots, wha hae wi Wallace bled' and Sir William Wallace

1229 'Auld Lang Syne' and Highland Dancers

Death Bicentenary of Robert Burns (Scottish poet)

1996 (25 Jan.) One phosphor band (19p) or two phosphor bands (others). Perf 14½

1901	**1226**	19p cream, bistre-brown and black	75	25	☐	☐
1902	**1227**	25p multicoloured	1·00	30	☐	☐
1903	**1228**	41p multicoloured	1·50	2·00	☐	☐
1904	**1229**	60p multicoloured	1·75	2·50	☐	☐
Set of 4			4·50	4·50	☐	☐
First Day Cover				4·75		☐
Presentation Pack			5·00		☐	
PHQ Cards (*set of 4*)			6·00	11·50	☐	☐
Set of 4 Gutter Pairs			10·50		☐	

1230 'MORE! LOVE' (Mel Calman)

1231 'Sincerely' (Charles Barsotti)

1232 'Do you have something for the HUMAN CONDITION? (Mel Calman)

1233 'MENTAL FLOSS' (Leo Cullum)

1234 '4.55 P.M.' (Charles Barsotti)

1235 'Dear lottery prize winner (Larry)

1236 'I'm writing to you because...' (Mel Calman)

1237 'FETCH THIS, FETCH THAT' (Charles Barsotti)

1238 'My day starts before I'm ready for it' (Mel Calman)

1239 'THE CHEQUE IN THE POST' (Jack Ziegler)

T **1230/9** were printed together, *se-tenant*, in booklet panes of 10 stamps and 20 half stamp-size labels.

Greetings Stamps. Cartoons

1996 (26 Feb.–11 Nov.) 'All-over' phosphor. Perf 14½ × 14 (with one elliptical hole in each vertical side)

1905	**1230**	(1st) black and bright mauve	50	40	☐	☐
		a. Booklet pane. Nos. 1905/14	10·00	11·00	☐	☐
		p. Two phosphor bands	1·00	60	☐	☐
		pa. Booklet pane. Nos. 1905p/14p (11 Nov.)	38·00	36·00	☐	☐
1906	**1231**	(1st) black and blue-green	50	40	☐	☐
		p. Two phosphor bands	1·00	60	☐	☐
1907	**1232**	(1st) black and new blue	50	40	☐	☐
		p. Two phosphor bands	1·00	60	☐	☐
1908	**1233**	(1st) black and bright violet	50	40	☐	☐
		p. Two phosphor bands	1·00	60	☐	☐
1909	**1234**	(1st) black and vermilion	50	40	☐	☐
		p. Two phosphor bands	1·00	60	☐	☐
1910	**1235**	(1st) black and new blue	50	40	☐	☐
		p. Two phosphor bands	1·00	60	☐	☐
1911	**1236**	(1st) black and vermilion	50	40	☐	☐
		p. Two phosphor bands	1·00	60	☐	☐
1912	**1237**	(1st) black and bright violet	50	40	☐	☐
		p. Two phosphor bands	1·00	60	☐	☐
1913	**1238**	(1st) black and blue-green	50	40	☐	☐
		p. Two phosphor bands	1·00	60	☐	☐
1914	**1239**	(1st) black and bright mauve	50	40	☐	☐
		p. Two phosphor bands	1·00	60	☐	☐
Set of 10 (Nos. 1905/14)			10·00	11·00	☐	☐
Set of 10 (Nos. 1905p/14p)			38·00	36·00	☐	☐
First Day Cover (Nos. 1905/14)				11·00		☐
Presentation Pack (Nos. 1905/14)			16·00		☐	
PHQ Cards (*set of 10*)			16·00	30·00	☐	☐

Nos. 1905/14 were re-issued on 18 December 2001 in sheets of 10, each stamp with a *se-tenant* label showing cartoon titles. They were again issued on 29 July 2003 in sheets of 20 containing two of each design, each stamp accompanied by a half stamp size label showing a crossword grid or personal photograph. Such sheets are perforated without elliptical holes.

1240 'Muscovy Duck'

1241 'Lapwing'

1242 'White-fronted Goose'

1243 'Bittern'

1244 'Whooper Swan'

50th Anniversary of the Wildfowl and Wetlands Trust. Bird Paintings by C. F. Tunnicliffe

1996 (12 Mar.) One phosphor band (19p) or phosphorised paper (others). Perf 14 × 14½

1915	**1240**	19p multicoloured	70	25	☐	☐
1916	**1241**	25p multicoloured	90	30	☐	☐
1917	**1242**	30p multicoloured	1·00	1·25	☐	☐
1918	**1243**	35p multicoloured	1·10	1·50	☐	☐
1919	**1244**	41p multicoloured	1·50	1·60	☐	☐
Set of 5			4·75	4·50	☐	☐
First Day Cover				5·75		☐
Presentation Pack			5·00		☐	
PHQ Cards (set of 5)			6·00	11·50	☐	☐
Set of 5 Gutter Pairs			10·50		☐	

1245 The Odeon, Harrogate

1246 Laurence Olivier and Vivien Leigh in Lady Hamilton (film)

1247 Old Cinema Ticket

1248 Pathé News Still

1249 Cinema Sign, The Odeon, Manchester

Centenary of Cinema

1996 (16 Apr.) One phosphor band (19p) or two phosphor bands (others). Perf 14 × 14½

1920	**1245**	19p multicoloured	50	25	☐	☐
1921	**1246**	25p multicoloured	70	30	☐	☐
1922	**1247**	30p multicoloured	1·00	1·75	☐	☐
1923	**1248**	35p black, red and silver	1·25	2·00	☐	☐
1924	**1249**	41p multicoloured	1·50	2·25	☐	☐
Set of 5			4·75	4·75	☐	☐
First Day Cover				5·75		☐
Presentation Pack			5·50		☐	
PHQ Cards (set of 5)			6·00	11·50	☐	☐
Set of 5 Gutter Pairs			11·00		☐	

1250 Dixie Dean

1251 Bobby Moore

1252 Duncan Edwards

1253 Billy Wright

1254 Danny Blanchflower

European Football Championship

1996 (14 May) One phosphor band (19p) or two phosphor bands (others). Perf 14½ × 14

1925	**1250**	19p multicoloured	50	20	☐	☐
1926	**1251**	25p multicoloured	75	20	☐	☐
1927	**1252**	35p multicoloured	1·25	1·75	☐	☐
1928	**1253**	41p multicoloured	1·50	1·75	☐	☐
1929	**1254**	60p multicoloured	1·75	2·00	☐	☐
Set of 5			5·50	5·75	☐	☐
First Day Cover				5·75		☐
Presentation Pack			5·75		☐	
PHQ Cards (set of 5)			6·00	11·50	☐	☐
Set of 5 Gutter Pairs			12·00		☐	

1255 Athlete on Starting Blocks

1256 Throwing the Javelin

1257 Basketball

1258 Swimming

1259 Athlete celebrating and Olympic Rings

T **1255/9** were printed together, se-tenant, in horizontal strips of 5 throughout the sheet.

Olympic and Paralympic Games, Atlanta

1996 (9 July) Two phosphor bands. Perf 14½ × 14

1930	**1255**	26p multicoloured	50	40	☐	☐
		a. Horiz strip of 5.				
		Nos. 1930/4	4·50	4·50	☐	☐
1931	**1256**	26p multicoloured	50	40	☐	☐
1932	**1257**	26p multicoloured	50	40	☐	☐
1933	**1258**	26p multicoloured	50	40	☐	☐
1934	**1259**	26p multicoloured	50	40	☐	☐
Set of 5			4·50	4·50	☐	☐
First Day Cover				5·00		☐
Presentation Pack			4·50		☐	
PHQ Cards (set of 5)			6·00	11·50	☐	☐
Gutter Strip of 10			11·00		☐	

For these designs with the face value expressed as '1st' see **MS**2554.

1260 Prof. Dorothy Hodgkin (scientist)

1261 Dame Margot Fonteyn (ballerina)

1262 Dame Elisabeth Frink (sculptress)

1263 Dame Daphne du Maurier (novelist)

1264 Dame Marea Hartman (sports administrator)

Europa. Famous Women

1996 (6 Aug.) One phosphor band (20p) or two phosphor bands (others). Perf 14½

1935	**1260**	20p dull blue-green, brownish grey and black	60	25	☐	☐
1936	**1261**	26p dull mauve, brownish grey and black	75	25	☐	☐
1937	**1262**	31p bronze, brownish grey and black	1·10	1·10	☐	☐
1938	**1263**	37p silver, brownish grey and black	1·25	1·40	☐	☐
1939	**1264**	43p gold, brownish grey and black	1·50	1·50	☐	☐
Set of 5			4·75	4·50	☐	☐
First Day Cover				5·00		☐
Presentation Pack			4·75		☐	
PHQ Cards (set of 5)			6·00	11·50	☐	☐
Set of 5 Gutter Pairs			12·00		☐	

Nos. 1936/7 include the 'EUROPA' emblem.

1265 Muffin the Mule

1266 Sooty

1267 Stingray

1268 The Clangers

1269 Dangermouse

50th Anniversary of Children's Television

1996 (3 Sept.)–**97** One phosphor band (20p) or two phosphor bands (others). Perf 14½ × 14

1940	**1265**	20p multicoloured	55	20	☐	☐
		a. Perf 15 × 14 (23.9.97)	2·00	2·00	☐	☐
1941	**1266**	26p multicoloured	80	20	☐	☐
1942	**1267**	31p multicoloured	1·00	1·50	☐	☐
1943	**1268**	37p multicoloured	1·40	1·75	☐	☐
1944	**1269**	43p multicoloured	1·60	2·00	☐	☐
Set of 5			4·75	4·75	☐	☐
First Day Cover				4·75		☐
Presentation Pack			4·75		☐	
PHQ Cards (set of 5)			6·00	11·50	☐	☐
Set of 5 Gutter Pairs			10·50		☐	

No. 1940a comes from stamp booklets.

1270 Triumph TR3

1271 MG TD

1272 Austin-Healey 100

1273 Jaguar XK120

1274 Morgan Plus 4

Classic Sports Cars

1996 (1 Oct.) One phosphor band (20p) or two phosphor bands (others). Perf 14½

1945	**1270**	20p multicoloured	55	20	☐	☐
1946	**1271**	26p multicoloured	1·10	20	☐	☐
1947	**1272**	37p multicoloured	1·40	1·90	☐	☐
1948	**1273**	43p multicoloured	1·60	1·90	☐	☐
1949	**1274**	63p multicoloured	1·75	2·00	☐	☐
Set of 5			5·75	6·00	☐	☐
First Day Cover				6·00		☐
Presentation Pack			6·00		☐	
PHQ Cards (*set of* 5)			6·00	11·50	☐	☐
Set of 5 Gutter Pairs			13·00		☐	

1275 The Three Kings   **1276** The Annunciation

1277 The Journey to   **1278** The Nativity
Bethlehem

1279 The Shepherds

Christmas

1996 (28 Oct.) One phosphor band (2nd) or two phosphor bands (others)

1950	**1275**	(2nd) multicoloured	75	20	☐	☐
1951	**1276**	(1st) multicoloured	1·00	35	☐	☐
1952	**1277**	31p multicoloured	1·25	1·75	☐	☐
1953	**1278**	43p multicoloured	1·25	1·75	☐	☐
1954	**1279**	63p multicoloured	1·50	2·00	☐	☐
Set of 5			5·50	5·50	☐	☐
First Day Cover				6·00		☐
Presentation Pack			5·75		☐	
PHQ Cards (*set of* 5)			6·00	11·50	☐	☐
Set of 5 Gutter Pairs			13·00		☐	

Collectors Pack 1996

1996 (28 Oct.) Comprises Nos. 1901/54
CP1954a   Collectors Pack   65·00   ☐

Post Office Yearbook

1996 (28 Oct.) Comprises Nos. 1901/4 and 1915/54 in hardback book with slip case
YB1954a   Yearbook   60·00   ☐

1280 *Gentiana acaulis*   **1281** *Magnolia grandiflora*
(Georg Ehret)   (Ehret)

1282 *Camellia japonica*   **1283** *Tulipa* (Ehret)
(Alfred Chandler)

1284 *Fuchsia* 'Princess of   **1285** *Tulipa gesneriana* (Ehret)
Wales' (Augusta Sowerby)

1286 *Gazania splendens*   **1287** *Iris latifolia* (Ehret)
(Charlotte Sowerby)

1288 *Hippeastrum rutilum*   **1289** *Passiflora coerulea*
(Pierre-Joseph Redoute)   (Ehret)

T **1280/9** were printed together, *se-tenant*, in booklet panes of 10 stamps and 20 half stamp-size labels.

Greeting Stamps. 19th-century Flower Paintings

1997 (6 Jan.) Two phosphor bands. Perf 14½ × 14 (with one elliptical hole in each vertical side)

1955	**1280**	(1st) multicoloured	50	40	☐	☐
		a. Booklet pane.				
		Nos. 1955/64	11·00	11·00	☐	☐
1956	**1281**	(1st) multicoloured	50	40	☐	☐
1957	**1282**	(1st) multicoloured	50	40	☐	☐
1958	**1283**	(1st) multicoloured	50	40	☐	☐
1959	**1284**	(1st) multicoloured	50	40	☐	☐
1960	**1285**	(1st) multicoloured	50	40	☐	☐

1961 **1286**	(1st) multicoloured	50	40	☐ ☐
1962 **1287**	(1st) multicoloured	50	40	☐ ☐
1963 **1288**	(1st) multicoloured	50	40	☐ ☐
1964 **1289**	(1st) multicoloured	50	40	☐ ☐
Set of 10		11·00	11·00	☐ ☐
First Day Cover			11·50	☐
Presentation Pack		16·00		☐
PHQ Cards (set of 10)		16·00	30·00	☐ ☐

Nos. 1955/64 were re-issued on 21 January 2003 in *se-tenant* sheets of 20, each accompanied by a label showing flowers or personal photograph. Such sheets are perforated without elliptical holes.

For Nos. 1955, 1958 and 1962 perf 15 × 14 see Nos. 2463/5.

1290 'King Henry VIII'

1291 'Catherine of Aragon'   **1292** 'Anne Boleyn'

1293 'Jane Seymour'   **1294** 'Anne of Cleves'

1295 'Catherine Howard'   **1296** 'Catherine Parr'

T **1290/6** were printed together, *se-tenant*, in horizontal strips of 6 throughout the sheet.

450th Death Anniversary of King Henry VIII

1997 (21 Jan.) Two phosphor bands. Perf 15 (No. 1965) or 14 × 15 (others)

| 1965 **1290** | 26p multicoloured | 50 | 40 | ☐ ☐ |
| 1966 **1291** | 26p multicoloured | 50 | 40 | ☐ ☐ |

	a. Horiz strip of 6.			
	Nos. 1966/71	8·00	8·50	☐ ☐
1967 **1292**	26p multicoloured	50	40	☐ ☐
1968 **1293**	26p multicoloured	50	40	☐ ☐
1969 **1294**	26p multicoloured	50	40	☐ ☐
1970 **1295**	26p multicoloured	50	40	☐ ☐
1971 **1296**	26p multicoloured	50	40	☐ ☐
Set of 7		8·00	8·50	☐ ☐
First Day Cover			9·50	☐
Presentation Pack		10·00		☐
PHQ Cards (set of 7)		10·00	18·00	☐ ☐
Gutter Pair and Gutter Block of 12		17·00		☐

1297 St. Columba in Boat   **1298** St. Columba on Iona

1299 St. Augustine with King Ethelbert   **1300** St. Augustine with Model of Cathedral

Religious Anniversaries

1997 (11 Mar.) Two phosphor bands. Perf 14½

1972 **1297**	26p multicoloured	75	35	☐ ☐
1973 **1298**	37p multicoloured	1·10	1·50	☐ ☐
1974 **1299**	43p multicoloured	1·50	1·50	☐ ☐
1975 **1300**	63p multicoloured	2·00	2·10	☐ ☐
Set of 4		4·75	5·00	☐ ☐
First Day Cover			5·75	☐
Presentation Pack		5·25		☐
PHQ Cards (set of 4)		5·75	11·50	☐ ☐
Set of 4 Gutter Pairs		11·50		☐

Nos. 1972/3 commemorate the 1400th death anniversary of St Columba and Nos. 1974/5 the 1400th anniversary of the arrival of St Augustine of Canterbury in Kent.

1301   **1302**

Self-adhesive Coil Stamps

1997 (18 Mar.) Photo Enschedé. One centre phosphor band (2nd) or two phosphor bands (1st). Perf 14 × 15 die-cut (with one elliptical hole in each vertical side)

1976 **1301**	(2nd) bright blue	2·75	2·50	☐ ☐
1977 **1302**	(1st) bright orange-red	2·75	2·75	☐ ☐
Set of 2		5·00	4·75	☐ ☐
First Day Cover			5·50	☐
Presentation Pack		7·00		☐

Nos. 1976/7, which were priced at 20p and 26p, were each sold in rolls of 100 with the stamps separate on the backing paper.

Machin stamps printed in gold were issued on 21 April 1997 for the Royal Golden Wedding. These are listed as definitives under Nos. 1668 (1st) and Y1686 26p.

1303 *Dracula*

1304 *Frankenstein*

1305 *Dr Jekyll and Mr Hyde*

1306 *The Hound of the Baskervilles*

Europa. Tales and Legends. Horror Stories

1997 (13 May) Two phosphor bands. Perf 14 × 15

1980	**1303**	26p multicoloured	1·00	40	☐	☐
1981	**1304**	31p multicoloured	1·10	1·50	☐	☐
1982	**1305**	37p multicoloured	1·30	1·75	☐	☐
1983	**1306**	43p multicoloured	2·00	1·95	☐	☐
Set of 4			5·00	5·50	☐	☐
First Day Cover				5·50	☐	
Presentation Pack			5·25		☐	
PHQ Cards (*set of 4*)			5·75	11·50	☐	☐
Set of 4 Gutter Pairs			12·00		☐	

Nos. 1980/3 commemorate the birth bicentenary of Mary Shelley (creator of Frankenstein) with the 26p and 31p values incorporating the 'EUROPA' emblem.

1307 Reginald Mitchell and Supermarine Spitfire MkIIA

1308 Roy Chadwick and Avro Lancaster MkI

1309 Ronald Bishop and de Havilland Mosquito B MkXVI

1310 George Carter and Gloster Meteor T Mk7

1311 Sir Sidney Camm and Hawker Hunter FGA Mk9

British Aircraft Designers

1997 (10 June) One phosphor band (20p) or two phosphor bands (others)

1984	**1307**	20p multicoloured	75	40	☐	☐
1985	**1308**	26p multicoloured	1·10	1·25	☐	☐
1986	**1309**	37p multicoloured	1·40	1·25	☐	☐
1987	**1310**	43p multicoloured	1·50	1·60	☐	☐
1988	**1311**	63p multicoloured	2·00	2·00	☐	☐
Set of 5			6·00	6·50	☐	☐
First Day Cover				6·50		☐
Presentation Pack			6·50		☐	
PHQ Cards			6·00	13·00	☐	☐
Set of 5 Gutter Pairs			15·00		☐	

1312 Carriage Horse and Coachman

1313 Lifeguards Horse and Trooper

1314 Household Cavalry Drum Horse and Drummer

1315 Duke of Edinburgh's Horse and Groom

'All The Queen's Horses'. 50th Anniv of the British Horse Society

1997 (8 July) One phosphor band (20p) or two phosphor bands (others). Perf 14½

1989	**1312**	20p multicoloured	80	45	☐	☐
1990	**1313**	26p multicoloured	1·10	1·50	☐	☐
1991	**1314**	43p multicoloured	1·50	1·50	☐	☐
1992	**1315**	63p multicoloured	2·00	2·00	☐	☐
Set of 4			5·00	5·25	☐	☐
First Day Cover				5·75		☐
Presentation Pack			5·50		☐	
PHQ Cards (*set of 4*)			5·75	11·50	☐	☐
Set of 4 Gutter Pairs			12·00		☐	

CASTLE
Harrison printing (Nos. 1611/14)

CASTLE
Enschedé printing (Nos. 1993/6)

Differences between Harrison and Enschedé printings:

Harrison – 'C' has top serif and tail of letter points to right. 'A' has flat top. 'S' has top and bottom serifs.

Enschedé – 'C' has no top serif and tail of letter points upwards. 'A' has pointed top. 'S' has no serifs.

1997 (29 July) Designs as Nos. 1611/14 with Queen's head in silhouette as T 1044, but re-engraved as above. Perf 15 × 14 (with one elliptical hole in each vertical side)

1993	**880**	£1·50 deep claret and gold†	12·00	6·00	☐	☐
1994	**881**	£2 indigo and gold†	14·00	2·25	☐	☐
1995	**1044**	£3 violet and gold†	30·00	3·50	☐	☐
1996	**882**	£5 deep brown and gold†	36·00	10·00	☐	☐
Set of 4			80·00	18·00	☐	☐
Set of 4 Gutter Pairs			£175		☐	
Presentation Pack (P.O Pack No. 40)			£150		☐	

† The Queen's head on these stamps is printed in optically variable ink which changes colour from gold to green when viewed from different angles.

1316 Haroldswick, Shetland

1318 Beddgelert, Gwynedd

1319 Ballyroney, County Down

Sub-Post Offices

1997 (12 Aug.) One phosphor band (20p) or two phosphor bands (others). Perf 14½

1997	**1316**	20p multicoloured	75	50	☐	☐
1998	**1317**	26p multicoloured	1·00	1·00	☐	☐
1999	**1318**	43p multicoloured	1·50	1·50	☐	☐
2000	**1319**	63p multicoloured	2·25	2·25	☐	☐
Set of 4			5·50	5·00	☐	☐
First Day Cover				5·75		☐
Presentation Pack			5·00		☐	
PHQ Cards (*set of* 4)			5·75	11·50	☐	☐
Set of 4 Gutter Pairs			12·00		☐	

Nos. 1997/2000 also mark the centenary of the National Federation of Sub-Postmasters.

1320 *Noddy*

1321 *Famous Five*

1322 *Secret Seven*

1323 *Faraway Tree*

1324 *Malory Towers*

Birth Centenary of Enid Blyton (children's author)

1997 (9 Sept.) One phosphor band (20p) or two phosphor bands (others). Perf 14 × 14½

2001	**1320**	20p multicoloured	50	45	☐	☐
2002	**1321**	26p multicoloured	1·00	1·25	☐	☐
2003	**1322**	37p multicoloured	1·25	1·25	☐	☐
2004	**1323**	43p multicoloured	1·50	2·00	☐	☐
2005	**1324**	63p multicoloured	1·75	2·00	☐	☐
Set of 5			5·50	6·00	☐	☐
First Day Cover				6·00		☐
Presentation Pack			5·75		☐	
PHQ Cards (*set of* 5)			6·00	13·00	☐	☐
Set of 5 Gutter Pairs			12·00		☐	

1325 Children and Father Christmas pulling Cracker

1326 Father Christmas with Traditional Cracker

1327 Father Christmas riding Cracker

1328 Father Christmas on Snowball

1329 Father Christmas and Chimney

Christmas. 150th Anniversary of the Christmas Cracker

1997 (27 Oct.) One phosphor band (2nd) or two phosphor bands (others)

2006 **1325**	(2nd) multicoloured	75	20	☐	☐
2007 **1326**	(1st) multicoloured	90	30	☐	☐
2008 **1327**	31p multicoloured	1·00	1·50	☐	☐
2009 **1328**	43p multicoloured	1·25	1·75	☐	☐
2010 **1329**	63p multicoloured	1·60	2·00	☐	☐
Set of 5		5·50	5·00	☐	☐
First Day Cover			6·00		☐
Presentation Pack		5·75		☐	
PHQ Cards (*set of* 5)		6·00	13·00	☐	☐
Set of 5 Gutter Pairs		12·00		☐	

The 1st value was re-issued on 3 October 2000 and 9 October 2001, in sheets of 10 in photogravure, each stamp with a *se-tenant* label, in connection with 'customised' service available from the Philatelic Bureau. On 1 October 2002 in sheet size of 20 in lithography the 1st value was again issued but perforated 14½ × 14. The labels show either Christmas greetings or a personal photograph.

1330 Wedding Photograph, 1947

1331 Queen Elizabeth II and Prince Philip, 1997

Royal Golden Wedding

1997 (13 Nov.) One phosphor band (20p) or two phosphor bands (others). Perf 15

2011 **1330**	20p gold, yellow-brown and grey-black	85	45	☐	☐
2012 **1331**	26p multicoloured	1·10	70	☐	☐
2013 **1330**	43p gold, bluish green and grey-black	1·90	2·25	☐	☐
2014 **1331**	63p multicoloured	2·50	3·00	☐	☐
Set of 4		5·75	5·75	☐	☐
First Day Cover			8·25		☐
Presentation Pack		6·25		☐	
Souvenir Book (contains Nos. 1668, 1989/92 and 2011/14)		50·00		☐	
PHQ Cards (*set of* 4)		5·75	11·50	☐	☐
Set of 4 Gutter Pairs		12·00		☐	

Collectors Pack 1997

1997 (13 Nov.) Comprises Nos. 1965/75, 1980/92 and 1997/2014

CP2014a	Collectors Pack	65·00	☐

Post Office Yearbook

1997 (13 Nov.) Comprises Nos. 1965/75, 1980/92 and 1997/2014 in hardback book with slip case

YB2014a	Yearbook	65·00	☐

1332 Common Doormouse

1333 Lady's Slipper Orchid

1334 Song Thrush

1335 Shining Ram's-horn Snail

1336 Mole Cricket

1337 Devil's Bolete

Endangered Species

1998 (20 Jan.) One side phosphor band (20p) or two phosphor bands (others). Perf 14 × 14½

2015 **1332**	20p multicoloured	60	40	☐	☐
2016 **1333**	26p multicoloured	75	40	☐	☐
2017 **1334**	31p multicoloured	1·00	2·00	☐	☐
2018 **1335**	37p multicoloured	1·25	1·25	☐	☐
2019 **1336**	43p multicoloured	1·40	1·75	☐	☐
2020 **1337**	63p multicoloured	1·90	2·25	☐	☐
Set of 6		6·25	6·50	☐	☐
First Day Cover			6·50		☐
Presentation Pack		6·75		☐	
PHQ Cards (*Set of* 6)		6·00	14·00	☐	☐
Set of 6 Gutter Pairs		15·00		☐	

1338 Diana, Princess of Wales (photo by Lord Snowdon)

1339 At British Lung Foundation Function, April 1997 (photo by John Stillwell)

1340 Wearing Tiara, 1991 (photo by Lord Snowdon)

1341 On Visit to Birmingham, October 1995 (photo by Tim Graham)

1342 In Evening Dress, 1987 (photo by Terence Donovan)

T **1338/42** were printed together, *se-tenant*, in horizontal strips of 5 throughout the sheet.

Diana, Princess of Wales Commemoration

1998 (3 Feb.) Two phosphor bands

2021	**1338**	26p multicoloured	50	40	☐	☐
		a. Horiz strip of 5.				
		Nos. 2021/5	4·50	4·50	☐	☐
2022	**1339**	26p multicoloured	50	40	☐	☐
2023	**1340**	26p multicoloured	50	40	☐	☐
2024	**1341**	26p multicoloured	50	40	☐	☐
2025	**1342**	26p multicoloured	50	40	☐	☐
Set of 5			4·50	4·50	☐	☐
First Day Cover				5·50		☐
Presentation Pack			16·00		☐	
Presentation Pack (Welsh)			£150		☐	
Gutter Strip of 10			10·00		☐	

1343 Lion of England and Griffin of Edward III

1344 Falcon of Plantagenet and Bull of Clarence

1345 Lion of Mortimer and Yale of Beaufort

1346 Greyhound of Richmond and Dragon of Wales

1347 Unicorn of Scotland and Horse of Hanover

T **1343/7** were printed together, *se-tenant*, in horizontal strips of 5 throughout the sheet.

650th Anniversary of the Order of the Garter. The Queen's Beasts

1998 (24 Feb.) Two phosphor bands

2026	**1343**	26p multicoloured	90	90	☐	☐
		a. Horiz strip of 5.				
		Nos. 2026/30	4·50	4·50	☐	☐
2027	**1344**	26p multicoloured	90	90	☐	☐
2028	**1345**	26p multicoloured	90	90	☐	☐
2029	**1346**	26p multicoloured	90	90	☐	☐
2030	**1347**	26p multicoloured	90	90	☐	☐
Set of 5			4·00	4·00	☐	☐
First Day Cover				5·25		☐
Presentation Pack			5·00		☐	
PHQ Cards (*set of 5*)			6·00	13·00	☐	☐
Gutter Block of 10			10·00		☐	

The phosphor bands on Nos. 2026/30 are only half the height of the stamps and do not cover the silver parts of the designs.

1348

Booklet Stamps

1998 (10 Mar.) Design as T **157** (issued 1952–54), but with face values in decimal currency as T **1348**. One side phosphor band (20p) or two phosphor bands (others). Perf 14 (with one elliptical hole in each vertical side)

2031	**1348**	20p light green	70	75	☐	☐
2032		26p red-brown	90	95	☐	☐
2033		37p light purple	2·75	2·75	☐	☐
Set of 3			4·00	4·00	☐	☐

For further Wilding designs see Nos. 2258/9, **MS**2326, **MS**2367 and 2378/80.

1349 St. John's Point Lighthouse, County Down

1350 Smalls Lighthouse, Pembrokeshire

1351 Needles Rock Lighthouse, Isle of Wight, c 1900

1352 Bell Rock Lighthouse, Arbroath, mid-19th-century

1353 Eddystone Lighthouse, Plymouth, 1698

Lighthouses

1998 (24 Mar.) One side phosphor band (20p) or two phosphor bands (others). Perf 14½ × 14

2034 **1349**	20p multicoloured	50	40	☐ ☐
2035 **1350**	26p multicoloured	75	50	☐ ☐
2036 **1351**	37p multicoloured	1·10	1·50	☐ ☐
2037 **1352**	43p multicoloured	1·50	1·75	☐ ☐
2038 **1353**	63p multicoloured	2·10	2·50	☐ ☐
Set of 5		5·50	6·00	☐ ☐
First Day Cover			6·00	☐
Presentation Pack		6·00		☐
PHQ Cards (set of 5)		6·00	13·00	☐ ☐
Set of 5 Gutter Pairs		13·50		☐

Nos. 2034/8 commemorate the 300th anniversary of the first Eddystone Lighthouse and the final year of manned lighthouses.

Self-adhesive stamps

1998 (6 Apr.) Photo Enschedé, Questa or Walsall. Designs as T 913/14. One centre phosphor band (2nd) or two phosphor bands (1st). Perf 15 × 14 die-cut (with one elliptical hole in each vertical side)

2039	(2nd) bright blue	1·00	1·00	☐ ☐
	b. Perf 14½ × 14 die-cut	£150		☐ ☐
2040	(1st) bright orange-red	1·50	1·50	☐ ☐
	b. Perf 14½ × 14 die-cut	£150		☐ ☐
Set of 2		2·50	2·50	☐ ☐

Nos. 2039/40 were initially priced at 20p and 26p, and were available in coils of 200 (Enschedé), sheets of 100 (Enschedé, Questa or Walsall) or self-adhesive booklets (Questa or Walsall).

See also Nos. 2295/8.

1354 Tommy Cooper

1355 Eric Morecambe

1356 Joyce Grenfell

1357 Les Dawson

1358 Peter Cook

Comedians

1998 (23 Apr.) One phosphor band (20p) or two phosphor bands (others). Perf 14½ × 14

2041 **1354**	20p multicoloured	50	50	☐ ☐
2042 **1355**	26p multicoloured	75	85	☐ ☐
2043 **1356**	37p multicoloured	1·25	1·25	☐ ☐
2044 **1357**	43p multicoloured	1·50	1·50	☐ ☐
2045 **1358**	63p multicoloured	1·75	2·10	☐ ☐
Set of 5		5·25	5·50	☐ ☐
First Day Cover			6·00	☐
Presentation Pack		6·00		☐
PHQ Cards (set of 5)		6·00	13·00	☐ ☐
Set of 5 Gutter Pairs		13·50		☐

1359 Hands forming Heart

1360 Adult and Child holding Hands

1361 Hands forming Cradle

1362 Hands taking Pulse

50th Anniversary of National Health Service

1998 (23 June) One side phosphor band (20p) or two phosphor bands (others). Perf 14 × 14½

2046	**1359**	20p multicoloured	50	50	☐	☐
2047	**1360**	26p multicoloured	90	90	☐	☐
2048	**1361**	43p multicoloured	1·50	1·50	☐	☐
2049	**1362**	63p multicoloured	2·10	2·10	☐	☐
Set of 4			4·50	4·50	☐	☐
First Day Cover				5·75		☐
Presentation Pack			5·50		☐	
PHQ Cards (*set of* 4)			5·75	11·50	☐	☐
Set of 4 Gutter Pairs			11·00		☐	

1363 *The Hobbit* (J.R.R. Tolkien)

1364 *The Lion, The Witch and the Wardrobe* (C. S. Lewis)

1365 *The Phoenix and the Carpet* (E. Nesbit)

1366 *The Borrowers* (Mary Norton)

1367 *Through the Looking Glass* (Lewis Carroll)

Famous Children's Fantasy Novels

1998 (21 July) One phosphor band (20p) or two phosphor bands (others)

2050	**1363**	20p multicoloured	50	45	☐	☐
2051	**1364**	26p multicoloured	75	55	☐	☐
2052	**1365**	37p multicoloured	1·25	1·50	☐	☐
2053	**1366**	43p multicoloured	1·50	1·50	☐	☐
2054	**1367**	63p multicoloured	2·10	2·00	☐	☐
Set of 5			5·75	5·75	☐	☐
First Day Cover				5·75		☐
Presentation Pack			6·00		☐	
PHQ Cards (*set of* 5)			6·00	13·00	☐	☐
Set of 5 Gutter Pairs			13·00		☐	

Nos. 2050/4 commemorate the birth centenary of C. S. Lewis and the death centenary of Lewis Carroll.

1368 Woman in Yellow Feathered Costume

1369 Woman in Blue Costume and Headdress

1370 Group of Children in White and Gold Robes

1371 Child in 'Tree' Costume

Europa. Festivals. Notting Hill Carnival

1998 (25 Aug.) One centre phosphor band (20p) or two phosphor bands (others). Perf 14 × 14½

2055	**1368**	20p multicoloured	75	45	☐	☐
2056	**1369**	26p multicoloured	95	55	☐	☐
2057	**1370**	43p multicoloured	1·50	2·00	☐	☐
2058	**1371**	63p multicoloured	2·00	2·75	☐	☐
Set of 4			4·75	4·75	☐	☐
First Day Cover				5·75		☐
Presentation Pack			5·25		☐	
PHQ Cards (*set of* 4)			5·75	11·50	☐	☐
Set of 4 Gutter Pairs			12·50		☐	

Nos. 2055/6 include the 'EUROPA' emblem.

1372 Sir Malcolm Campbell's *Bluebird*, 1925

1373 Sir Henry Segrave's *Sunbeam*, 1926

1374 John G. Parry Thomas's *Babs*, 1926

1375 John R. Cobb's *Railton Mobil Special*, 1947

1376 Donald Campbell's *Bluebird CN7*, 1964

British Land Speed Record Holders

1998 (29 Sept.–13 Oct.) One phosphor band (20p) or two phosphor bands (others). Perf 15 × 14

2059	**1372**	20p multicoloured (centre band)	50	25	☐	☐
		a. Perf 14½ × 13½ (side band) (13 Oct.)	1·40	1·20	☐	☐
2060	**1373**	26p multicoloured	75	30	☐	☐
2061	**1374**	30p multicoloured	1·25	1·50	☐	☐
2062	**1375**	43p multicoloured	1·50	1·60	☐	☐
2063	**1376**	63p multicoloured	2·00	2·40	☐	☐
Set of 5			5·50	5·50	☐	☐
First Day Cover				6·00		☐

Presentation Pack	6·25	☐	
PHQ Cards (*set of* 5)	6·00	13·00	☐ ☐
Set of 5 Gutter Pairs	13·00	☐	

No. 2059a, which occurs with the phosphor band at the left or right of the stamp, comes from stamp booklets. There are minor differences of design between No. 2059 and No. 2059a, which also omits the copyright symbol and date.

Nos. 2059/63 commemorate the 50th death anniversary of Sir Malcolm Campbell.

1377 Angel with Hands raised in Blessing

1378 Angel praying

1379 Angel playing Flute

1380 Angel playing Lute

1381 Angel praying

Christmas. Angels

1998 (2 Nov.) One phosphor band (20p) or two phosphor bands (others)

2064 **1377**	20p multicoloured	50	50	☐ ☐
2065 **1378**	26p multicoloured	75	60	☐ ☐
2066 **1379**	30p multicoloured	1·25	1·50	☐ ☐
2067 **1380**	43p multicoloured	1·50	1·60	☐ ☐
2068 **1381**	63p multicoloured	2·00	2·25	☐ ☐
Set of 5		5·75	5·75	☐ ☐
First Day Cover			6·00	☐
Presentation Pack		6·50		☐
PHQ Cards (*set of* 5)		6·00	13·00	☐ ☐
Set of 5 Gutter Pairs		13·00		☐

Collectors Pack 1998

1998 (2 Nov.) Comprises Nos. 2015/30, 2034/8 and 2041/68

CP2068a	Collectors Pack	95·00	☐

Post Office Yearbook

1998 (2 Nov.) Comprises Nos. 2015/30, 2034/8 and 2041/68 in hardback book with slip case

YB2068a	Yearbook	85·00	☐

1382 Greenwich Meridian and Clock (John Harrison's Chronometer)

1383 Industrial Worker and Blast Furnace (James Watt's discovery of steam power)

1384 Early Photos of Leaves (Henry Fox-Talbot's photographic experiments)

1385 Computer inside Human Head (Alan Turing's work on computers)

Millennium Series. The Inventors' Tale

1999 (12 Jan.–21 Sept.) One centre phosphor band (20p) or two phosphor bands (others). Perf 14 × 14½

2069 **1382**	20p multicoloured	75	70	☐ ☐
2070 **1383**	26p multicoloured	95	1·00	☐ ☐
2071 **1384**	43p multicoloured	1·50	1·60	☐ ☐
2072 **1385**	63p multicoloured	2·25	2·40	☐ ☐
	a. Perf 13½ × 14			
	(21 Sept.)	3·50	3·50	☐ ☐
Set of 4		5·25	5·25	☐ ☐
First Day Cover			14·00	☐
Presentation Pack		7·50		☐
PHQ Cards (*set of* 4)		8·50	13·00	☐ ☐
Set of 4 Gutter Pairs		13·00		☐

1386 Airliner hugging Globe (International air travel)

1387 Woman on Bicycle (Development of the bicycle)

1388 Victorian Railway Station (Growth of public transport)

1389 Captain Cook and Maori (Captain James Cook's voyages)

Millennium Series. The Travellers' Tale

1999 (2 Feb.) One centre phosphor band (20p) or two phosphor bands (others). Perf 14 × 14½

2073 **1386**	20p multicoloured	75	70	☐ ☐
2074 **1387**	26p multicoloured	95	1·00	☐ ☐

2075 **1388**	43p grey-black, stone and bronze	1·50	1·60	☐ ☐
2076 **1389**	63p multicoloured	2·25	2·40	☐ ☐
Set of 4		5·25	5·25	☐ ☐
First Day Cover			8·00	☐
Presentation Pack		7·50		☐
PHQ Cards (*set of* 4)		8·50	13·00	☐ ☐
Set of 4 Gutter Pairs		13·00		☐

1390

Booklet Stamps

1999 (16 Feb.)

(a) Embossed and litho Walsall. Self-adhesive.
Die-cut perf 14 × 15

2077 **1390**	(1st) grey (face value) (Queen's head in colourless relief) (phosphor background around head)	3·00	2·50	☐ ☐
	(b) Recess Enschedé. Perf 14 × 14½			
2078 **1390**	(1st) grey-black (2 phosphor bands)	3·00	2·50	☐ ☐
	(c) Typo Harrison. Perf 14 × 15			
2079 **1390**	(1st) black (2 phosphor bands)	3·00	2·50	☐ ☐
Set of 3		8·00	7·00	☐ ☐

Nos. 2077/9 were only issued in £7·54 stamp booklets.

1391 Vaccinating Child
(pattern in cow markings)
(Jenner's development of
smallpox vaccine)

1392 Patient on Trolley
(nursing care)

1393 Penicillin Mould
(Fleming's discovery of
Penicillin)

1394 Sculpture of Test-tube
Baby (development of in
vitro fertilization)

Millennium Series. The Patients' Tale

1999 (2 Mar.) One centre phosphor band (20p) or two
phosphor bands (others). Perf 13½ × 14

| 2080 **1391** | 20p multicoloured | 75 | 70 | ☐ ☐ |

2081 **1392**	26p multicoloured	95	1·00	☐ ☐
2082 **1393**	43p multicoloured	1·50	1·60	☐ ☐
2083 **1394**	63p multicoloured	2·25	2·40	☐ ☐
Set of 4		5·25	5·25	☐ ☐
First Day Cover			8·00	☐
Presentation Pack		7·50		☐
PHQ Cards (*set of* 4)		8·50	13·00	☐ ☐
Set of 4 Gutter Pairs		13·00		☐

1395 Dove and Norman
Settler (medieval migration
to Scotland)

1396 Pilgrim Fathers and
Red Indian (17th-century
migration to America)

1397 Sailing Ship and
Aspects of Settlement
(19th-century migration
to Australia)

1398 Hummingbird and
Superimposed Stylised
Face (20th-century
migration to Great Britain)

Millennium Series. The Settlers' Tale

1999 (6 Apr.) One centre phosphor band (20p) or two
phosphor bands (others). Perf 14 × 14½

2084 **1395**	20p multicoloured	75	70	☐ ☐
2085 **1396**	26p multicoloured	95	1·00	☐ ☐
2086 **1397**	43p multicoloured	2·00	1·75	☐ ☐
2087 **1398**	63p multicoloured	3·00	3·00	☐ ☐
Set of 4		5·75	5·75	☐ ☐
First Day Cover			8·00	☐
Presentation Pack		7·50		☐
PHQ Cards (*set of* 4)		8·50	13·00	☐ ☐
Set of 4 Gutter Pairs		13·00		☐

1399 Woven Threads
(wollen industry)

1400 Salts Mill, Saltaire
(worsted cloth industry)

1401 Hull on Slipway
(shipbuilding)

1402 Lloyd's Building (City
of London finance centre)

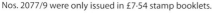

Millennium Series. The Workers' Tale

1999 (4 May) One centre phosphor band (19p) or two phosphor bands (others). Perf 14 × 14½

2088	**1399**	19p multicoloured	75	70	☐	☐
2089	**1400**	26p multicoloured	95	1·00	☐	☐
2090	**1401**	44p multicoloured	1·75	1·60	☐	☐
2091	**1402**	64p multicoloured	2·25	2·40	☐	☐
Set of 4			5·25	5·25	☐	☐
First Day Cover				8·00	☐	
Presentation Pack			7·50		☐	
PHQ Cards (*set of* 4)			8·50	13·00	☐	☐
Set of 4 Gutter Pairs			13·00		☐	

1403 Freddie Mercury (lead singer of Queen) ('Popular Music')

1404 Bobby Moore with World Cup, 1966 ('Sport')

1405 Dalek from *Dr Who* (science-fiction series) ('Television')

1406 Charlie Chaplin (film star) ('Cinema')

Millennium Series. The Entertainers' Tale

1999 (1 June) One centre phosphor band (19p) or two phosphor bands (others). Perf 14 × 14½

2092	**1403**	19p multicoloured	75	70	☐	☐
2093	**1404**	26p multicoloured	95	1·00	☐	☐
2094	**1405**	44p multicoloured	1·50	1·60	☐	☐
2095	**1406**	64p multicoloured	2·25	2·40	☐	☐
Set of 4			5·25	5·25	☐	☐
First Day Cover				8·00	☐	
Presentation Pack			7·50		☐	
PHQ Cards (*set of* 4)			8·50	13·00	☐	☐
Set of 4 Gutter Pairs			13·00		☐	

1407 Prince Edward and Miss Sophie Rhys-Jones (from photos by John Swannell)

1408 Prince Edward and Miss Sophie Rhys-Jones (from photos by John Swannell)

Royal Wedding

1999 (15 June) Two phosphor bands

2096	**1407**	26p multicoloured	85	85	☐	☐
2097	**1408**	64p multicoloured	2·50	2·50	☐	☐
Set of 2			3·00	3·00	☐	☐
First Day Cover				4·75	☐	
Presentation Pack			4·00		☐	
PHQ Cards (*set of* 2)			8·50	6·75	☐	☐

Set of 2 Gutter Pairs	7·00	☐

1409 Suffragette behind Prison Window ('Equal Rights for Women')

1410 Water Tap ('Right to Health')

1411 Generations of School Children ('Right to Education')

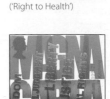

1412 'MAGNA CARTA' ('Human Rights')

Millennium Series. The Citizens' Tale

1999 (6 July) One centre phosphor band (19p) or two phosphor bands (others). Perf 14 × 14½

2098	**1409**	19p multicoloured	75	70	☐	☐
2099	**1410**	26p multicoloured	95	1·00	☐	☐
2100	**1411**	44p multicoloured	1·75	1·60	☐	☐
2101	**1412**	64p multicoloured	2·50	2·40	☐	☐
Set of 4			5·75	5·25	☐	☐
First Day Cover				8·00	☐	
Presentation Pack			7·50		☐	
PHQ Cards (*set of* 4)			8·50	13·00	☐	☐
Set of 4 Gutter Pairs			13·00		☐	

1413 Molecular Structures ('DNA decoding')

1414 Galapagos Finch and Fossilized Skeleton ('Darwin's theory of evolution')

1415 Rotation of Polarized Light by Magnetism (Faraday's work on electricity)

1416 Saturn (development of astronomical telescopes)

Millennium Series. The Scientists' Tale

1999 (3 Aug.–21 Sept.) One centre phosphor band (19p) or two phosphor bands (others). Perf 13½ × 14 (19p, 64p) or 14 × 14½ (26p, 44p)

2102	**1413**	19p multicoloured	75	70	☐	☐
2103	**1414**	26p multicoloured	1·50	1·00	☐	☐

	b. Perf 14½ × 14				
	(21 Sept.)	2·50	2·50	☐	☐
2104 **1415**	44p multicoloured	1·50	1·60	☐	☐
	a. Perf 14½ × 14				
	(21 Sept.)	2·75	2·75	☐	☐
2105 **1416**	64p multicoloured	2·25	2·40	☐	☐
Set of 4		5·25	5·25	☐	☐
First Day Cover			8·00	☐	
Presentation Pack		7·50		☐	
PHQ Cards (*set of* 4)		8·50	13·00	☐	☐
Set of 4 Gutter Pairs		13·00		☐	

Nos. 2103b and 2104a come from stamp booklets.

1416a

Solar Eclipse

1999 (11 Aug.) Sheet 89 × 121 mm. Two phosphor bands. Perf 14 × 14½

MS2106 1416a 64p × 4 multicoloured	22·00	22·00	☐	☐
First Day Cover		22·00		☐

1417 Upland Landscape (Strip farming)

1418 Horse-drawn Rotary Seed Drill (Mechanical farming)

1419 Man peeling Potato (Food imports)

1420 Aerial View of Combine Harvester (Satellite agriculture)

Millennium Series. The Farmers' Tale

1999 (7 Sept.) One centre phosphor band (19p) or two

---

phosphor bands (others). Perf 14 × 14½

2107 **1417**	19p multicoloured	75	70	☐	☐
2108 **1418**	26p multicoloured	95	1·00	☐	☐
2109 **1419**	44p multicoloured	2·00	1·60	☐	☐
2110 **1420**	64p multicoloured	2·50	2·40	☐	☐
Set of 4		5·75	5·25	☐	☐
First Day Cover			8·00	☐	
Presentation Pack		7·50		☐	
PHQ Cards (*set of* 4)		8·50	13·00	☐	☐
Set of 4 Gutter Pairs		13·00		☐	

No. 2107 includes the 'EUROPA' emblem.

1421 Robert the Bruce (Battle of Bannockburn, 1314)

1422 Cavalier and Horse (English Civil War)

1423 War Graves Cemetery, The Somme (World Wars)

1424 Soldiers with Boy (Peace-keeping)

Millennium Series. The Soldiers' Tale

1999 (5 Oct.) One centre phosphor band (19p) or two phosphor bands (others). Perf 14 × 14½

2111 **1421**	19p black, stone and silver	75	70	☐	☐
2112 **1422**	26p multicoloured	95	1·00	☐	☐
2113 **1423**	44p grey-black, black and silver	2·00	1·60	☐	☐
2114 **1424**	64p multicoloured	2·50	2·40	☐	☐
Set of 4		5·75	5·25	☐	☐
First Day Cover			8·00	☐	
Presentation Pack		7·50		☐	
PHQ Cards (*set of* 4)		8·50	13·00	☐	☐
Set of 4 Gutter Pairs		13·00		☐	

1425 'Hark the herald angels sing' and Hymn book (John Wesley)

1426 King James I and Bible (Authorised Version of Bible)

1427 St. Andrews Cathedral, Fife ('Pilgrimage')

1428 Nativity ('First Christmas')

Millennium Series. The Christians' Tale

1999 (2 Nov.) One centre phosphor band (19p) or two phosphor bands (others). Perf 14 × 14½

2115	**1425**	19p multicoloured	75	70	☐	☐
2116	**1426**	26p multicoloured	95	1·00	☐	☐
2117	**1427**	44p multicoloured	1·50	1·60	☐	☐
2118	**1428**	64p multicoloured	2·25	2·40	☐	☐
	Set of 4		5·25	5·25	☐	☐
	First Day Cover			8·00	☐	
	Presentation Pack		7·50		☐	
	PHQ Cards (set of 4)		8·50	13·00	☐	☐
	Set of 4 Gutter Pairs		13·00		☐	

1429 'World of the Stage' (Allen Jones)

1430 'World of Music' (Bridget Riley)

1431 'World of Literature' (Lisa Milroy)

1432 'New Worlds' (Sir Howard Hodgkin)

Millennium Series. The Artists' Tale

1999 (7 Dec.) One centre phosphor band (19p) or two phosphor bands (others). Perf 14 × 14½

2119	**1429**	19p multicoloured	75	70	☐	☐
2120	**1430**	26p multicoloured	95	1·00	☐	☐
2121	**1431**	44p multicoloured	1·50	1·60	☐	☐
2122	**1432**	64p multicoloured	2·25	2·40	☐	☐
	Set of 4		5·25	5·25	☐	☐
	First Day Cover			8·00	☐	
	Presentation Pack		7·50		☐	
	PHQ Cards (set of 4)		8·50	13·00	☐	☐
	Set of 4 Gutter Pairs		13·00		☐	

Collectors Pack 1999

1999 (7 Dec.) Comprises Nos. 2069/76, 2080/105 and 2107/22

CP2122a	Collectors Pack	£135	☐

Post Office Yearbook

1999 (7 Dec.) Comprises Nos. 2069/76, 2080/105 and 2107/22

in hardback book with slip case

YB2122a	Yearbook	£130	☐

1433a

Millennium Series. 'Millennium Timekeeper'

1999 (14 Dec.) Sheet 120 × 89 mm. Multicoloured. Two phosphor bands. Perf 14 × 14½

MS2123	**1433a**	64p Clock face and map of North America; 64p Clock face and map of Asia; 64p Clock face and map of Middle East; 64p Clock face and map of Europe	26·00	26·00	☐	☐
	First Day Cover			26·00		☐
	Presentation Pack		30·00		☐	
	PHQ Cards (set of 5)		14·00	32·00	☐	☐

No. **MS**2123 also exists overprinted 'EARLS COURT, LONDON 22–28 MAY 2000 THE STAMP SHOW 2000' from Exhibition Premium Passes, costing £10, available from 1 March 2000.

1437 Queen Elizabeth II

New Millennium

2000 (6 Jan.) Photo De La Rue, Questa or Walsall (No. 2124); Questa or Walsall (No. 2124d). Two phosphor bands. Perf 15 × 14 (with one elliptical hole in each vertical side)

2124	**1437**	(1st) olive-brown	1·00	1·00	☐	☐
		d. Perf 14	1·00	1·00	☐	☐
	First Day Cover			3·00		☐
	Presentation Pack		9·00		☐	
	PHQ Card (23 May)		5·00	16·00	☐	☐

No. 2124 comes from sheets or stamp booklets and No. 2124d from booklets only.

1438 Barn Owl (World Owl Trust, Muncaster)

1439 Night Sky (National Space Science Centre, Leicester)

1440 River Goyt and Textile Mills (Torrs Walkaway, New Mills)

1441 Cape Gannets (Seabird Centre, North Berwick)

Millennium Projects (1st series). 'Above and Beyond'

2000 (18 Jan.–26 May) One centre phosphor band (19p) or two phosphor bands (others). Perf 14 × 14½ (1st, 44p) or 13½ × 14 (others)

2125	**1438**	19p multicoloured	1·25	70	☐	☐
2126	**1439**	26p multicoloured	95	1·00	☐	☐
2126a		(1st) multicoloured				
		(26 May)	5·25	4·50	☐	☐
2127	**1440**	44p multicoloured	1·75	1·75	☐	☐
2128	**1441**	64p multicoloured	2·75	2·75	☐	☐
Set of 4 (ex No. 2126a)			6·00	6·00		
00					☐	☐
First Day Cover				8·00		☐
Presentation Pack			7·00		☐	
PHQ Cards (set of 4)			8·50	13·00	☐	☐
Set of 4 Gutter Pairs			13·00		☐	

No. 2126a was only issued in £2·70 and £6·83 stamp booklets.

1442 Millennium Beacon (Beacons across the Land)

1443 Garratt Steam Locomotive No. 143 pulling Train (Rheilffordd Eryri, Welsh Highland Railway)

 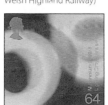

1444 Lightning (Dynamic Earth Centre, Edinburgh)

1445 Multicoloured Lights (Lighting Croydon's Skyline)

Millennium Projects (2nd series). 'Fire and Light'

2000 (1 Feb.) One centre phosphor band (19p) or two phosphor bands (others). Perf 14 × 14½

2129	**1442**	19p multicoloured	75	70	☐	☐
2130	**1443**	26p multicoloured	1·25	1·00	☐	☐
2131	**1444**	44p multicoloured	1·50	1·50	☐	☐
2132	**1445**	64p multicoloured	2·25	2·50	☐	☐
Set of 4			5·50	5·50	☐	☐
First Day Cover				8·00		☐
Presentation Pack			7·00		☐	
PHQ Cards (set of 4)			8·50	13·00	☐	☐
Set of 4 Gutter Pairs			13·00		☐	

1446 Queen Victoria and Queen Elizabeth II

Booklet Stamp

2000 (15 Feb.) Design T **929**, but redrawn with '1st' face value as T **1446**. Two phosphor bands. Perf 14 (with one elliptical hole in each vertical side)

2133	**1446**	(1st) brownish black and cream	1·50	1·25	☐	☐

1447 Beach Pebbles (Turning the Tide, Durham Coast)

1448 Frog's Legs and Water Lilies (National Pondlife Centre, Merseyside)

1449 Cliff Boardwalk (Parc Ardfordirol, Llanelli Coast)

1450 Reflections in Water (Portsmouth Harbour Development)

Millennium Projects (3rd series). 'Water and Coast'

2000 (7 Mar.) One centre phosphor band (19p) or two phosphor bands (others). Perf 14 × 14½

2134	**1447**	19p multicoloured	75	70	☐	☐
2135	**1448**	26p multicoloured	1·25	1·00	☐	☐
2136	**1449**	44p black, grey and silver	1·50	1·50	☐	☐
2137	**1450**	64p multicoloured	2·25	2·50	☐	☐
Set of 4			5·50	5·50	☐	☐
First Day Cover				8·00		☐
Presentation Pack			7·00		☐	
PHQ Cards (set of 4)			8·50	13·00	☐	☐
Set of 4 Gutter Pairs			13·00		☐	

1451 Reed Beds, River Braid (ECOS, Ballymena)

1452 South American Leaf-cutter Ants ('Web of Life' Exhibition, London Zoo)

1453 Solar Sensors
(Earth Centre, Doncaster)

1454 Hydroponic Leaves
(Project SUZY, Teesside)

Millennium Projects (4th series). 'Life and Earth'

2000 (4 Apr.) One centre phosphor band (2nd) or two phosphor bands (others). Perf 14 × 14½

2138	**1451**	(2nd) multicoloured	75	70	☐	☐
2139	**1452**	(1st) multicoloured	1·25	1·00	☐	☐
2140	**1453**	44p multicoloured	1·50	1·50	☐	☐
2141	**1454**	64p multicoloured	2·25	1·50	☐	☐
Set of 4			5·50	5·50	☐	☐
First Day Cover				8·00	☐	
Presentation Pack			7·00		☐	
PHQ Cards (set of 4)			8·50	13·00	☐	☐
Set of 4 Gutter Pairs			13·00		☐	

1455 Pottery Glaze (Ceramic Mesuem, stoke-on-trent)

1456 Bankside Galleries (Tate Modern, London)

1457 Road Marking (Cycle Network Artworks)

1458 People of Salford (Lowry Centre, Salford)

Millennium Projects (5th series). 'Art and Craft'

2000 (2 May) One centre phosphor band (2nd) or two phosphor bands (others). Perf 14 × 14½

2142	**1455**	(2nd) multicoloured	75	70	☐	☐
2143	**1456**	(1st) multicoloured	1·25	1·00	☐	☐
2144	**1457**	45p multicoloured	1·50	1·50	☐	☐
2145	**1458**	65p multicoloured	2·25	2·50	☐	☐
Set of 4			5·50	5·50	☐	☐
First Day Cover				8·00	☐	
Presentation Pack			7·50		☐	
PHQ Cards (set of 4)			8·50	13·00	☐	☐
Set of 4 Gutter Pairs			13·00		☐	

'Stamp Show 2000' International Stamp Exhibition, London. Jeffrey Matthews Colour Palette

2000 (22 May) Sheet, 124 × 70 mm, containing stamps as T **367** with two labels. Phosphorised paper. Perf 15 × 14 (with one elliptical hole in each vertical side)
MS2146   4p new blue; 5p dull red-brown;

6p yellow-olive; 10p dull orange; 31p dp mauve; 39p brt magenta; 64p turq-green; £1 bluish violet

		30·00	30·00	☐ ☐
First Day Cover			30·00	☐
Exhibition Card (wallet, sold at £4.99, containing one mint sheet and one cancelled on postcard)		75·00		☐

The £1 value is printed in Iriodin ink which gives a shiny effect to the solid part of the background behind the Queen's head.

1459

'Stamp Show 2000' International Stamp Exhibition, London. 'Her Majesty's Stamps'

2000 (23 May) Sheet 121 × 89 mm. Phosphorised paper. Perf 15 × 14 (with one elliptical hole in each vertical side of stamps as T **1437**)

MS2147	**1459** (1st) olive-brown (Type **1437**) × 4; £1 slate-green (as Type **163**)	21·00	21·00	☐	☐
First Day Cover			22·00		☐
Presentation Pack		£100		☐	
PHQ Cards (set of 2)		16·00	34·00	☐	☐

The £1 value is an adaptation of the 1953 Coronation 1s. 3d. stamp. It is shown on one of the PHQ cards with the other depicting the complete miniature sheet.
See also No. 2380 for T **163** from £7·46 stamp booklet.

1460 Children playing (Millenium Greens Project)

1461 Millennium Bridge, Gateshead

1462 Daisies (Mile End Park, London)

1463 African Hut and Thatched Cottage ('On the Meridian Line' Project)

Millennium Projects (6th series). 'People and Places'

2000 (6 June) One centre phosphor band (2nd) or two phosphor bands (others). Perf 14 × 14½

2148	**1460**	(2nd) multicoloured	75	70	☐	☐
2149	**1461**	(1st) multicoloured	1·25	1·00	☐	☐
2150	**1462**	45p multicoloured	1·50	1·50	☐	☐
2151	**1463**	65p multicoloured	2·25	2·50	☐	☐
Set of 4			5·50	5·50	☐	☐
First Day Cover				8·00		☐
Presentation Pack			7·50		☐	
PHQ Cards (*set of* 4)			8·50	13·00	☐	☐
Set of 4 Gutter Pairs			13·00		☐	

1464 Raising the Stone (Strangford Stone, Killyleagh)

1465 Horse's Hooves (Trans Pennine Trail, Derbyshire)

1466 Cyclist (Kingdom of Fife Cycle Ways, Scotland)

1467 Bluebell Wood (Groundwork's 'Changing Places' Project)

Millennium Projects (7th series). 'Stone and Soil'

2000 (4 July) One centre phosphor band (2nd) or two phosphor bands (others). Perf 14 × 14½

2152	**1464**	(2nd) brownish black, grey-black and silver	75	70	☐	☐
2153	**1465**	(1st) multicoloured	1·25	1·00	☐	☐
2154	**1466**	45p multicoloured	1·50	1·75	☐	☐
2155	**1467**	65p multicoloured	2·50	2·50	☐	☐
Set of 4			5·50	5·75	☐	☐
First Day Cover				8·00		☐
Presentation Pack			7·50		☐	
PHQ Cards (*set of* 4)			8·50	13·00	☐	☐
Set of 4 Gutter Pairs			13·00		☐	

1468 Tree Roots ('Yews for the Millennium' Project)

1469 Sunflower ('Eden' Project, St. Austell)

1470 Sycamore Seeds (Millennium Seed Bank, Wakehurst Place, Surrey)

1471 Forest, Doire Dach ('Forest for Scotland')

Millennium Projects (8th series). 'Tree and Leaf'

2000 (1 Aug.) One centre phosphor band (2nd) or two phosphor bands (others). Perf 14 × 14½

2156	**1468**	(2nd) multicoloured	75	70	☐	☐
2157	**1469**	(1st) multicoloured	1·25	1·00	☐	☐
2158	**1470**	45p multicoloured	1·50	1·60	☐	☐
2159	**1471**	65p multicoloured	2·50	2·50	☐	☐
Set of 4			5·50	5·50	☐	☐
First Day Cover				8·00		☐
Presentation Pack			7·50		☐	
PHQ Cards (*set of* 4)			8·50	13·00	☐	☐
Set of 4 Gutter Pairs			13·00		☐	

1472 Queen Elizabeth the Queen Mother

1472a Royal Family on Queen Mother's 100th Birthday (from photo by J. Swannell)

Queen Elizabeth the Queen Mother's 100th Birthday

2000 (4 Aug.) Phosphorised paper plus two phosphor bands. Perf 14½

2160	**1472**	27p multicoloured	2·50	2·75	☐	☐
MS2161	121 × 89 mm. **1472a** 27p Queen Elizabeth II; 27p Prince William; 27p Queen Elizabeth the Queen Mother; 27p Prince Charles		11·00	11·00	☐	☐
First Day Cover (**MS**2161)				12·00		☐
Presentation Pack (**MS**2161)			38·00		☐	
PHQ Cards (*set of* 5)			11·00	24·00	☐	☐

No. 2160 was only issued in stamp booklets and in No. **MS**2161.

The complete miniature sheet is shown on one of the PHQ cards with the others depicting individual stamps.

1473 Head of Gigantiops destructor (Ant) (Wildscreen at Bristol)

1474 Gathering Water Lilies on Broads (Norfolk and Norwich Project)

1475 X-ray of Hand holding Computer Mouse (Millennium Point, Birmingham

1476 Tartan Wool Holder (Scottish Cultural Resources Access Network)

Millennium Projects (9th series). 'Mind and Matter'

2000 (5 Sept.) One centre phosphor band (2nd) or two phosphor bands (others). Perf 14 × 14½

2162	**1473**	(2nd) multicoloured	75	70	☐	☐
2163	**1474**	(1st) multicoloured	1·25	1·00	☐	☐
2164	**1475**	45p multicoloured	1·50	1·75	☐	☐
2165	**1476**	65p multicoloured	2·25	2·50	☐	☐
Set of 4			5·50	5·75	☐	☐
First Day Cover				8·00		☐
Presentation Pack			7·50		☐	
PHQ Cards (*set of* 4)			8·50	13·00	☐	☐
Set of 4 Gutter Pairs			13·00		☐	

1477 Acrobatic Performers (Millennium Dome)

1478 Football Players (Hampden Park, Glasgow)

1479 Bather (Bath Spa Project)

1480 Hen's Egg under Magnification (Centre for Life, Newcastle)

Millennium Projects (10th series). 'Body and Bone'

2000 (3 Oct.) One centre phosphor band (2nd) or two phosphor bands (others). Perf 14 × 14½ (2nd) or 13½ × 14 (others)

2166	**1477**	(2nd) black, slate-blue and silver	75	70	☐	☐

2167	**1478**	(1st) multicoloured	1·25	1·00	☐	☐
2168	**1479**	45p multicoloured	1·50	1·50	☐	☐
2169	**1480**	65p multicoloured	2·25	2·50	☐	☐
Set of 4			5·50	5·75	☐	☐
First Day Cover				8·00		☐
Presentation Pack			7·50		☐	
PHQ Cards (*set of* 4)			8·50	13·00	☐	☐
Set of 4 Gutter Pairs			13·00		☐	

1481 Virgin and Child Stained Glass Window, St. Edmundsbury Cathedral (Suffolk Cathedral Millennium Project)

1482 Floodlit Church of St. Peter and St. Paul, Overstowey (Church Floodlighting Trust)

1483 12th-cent. Latin Gradual (St. Patrick Centre, Downpatrick)

1484 Chapter House Ceiling, York Minster (York Millennium Mystery Plays)

Millennium Projects (11th series). 'Spirit and Faith'

2000 (7 Nov.) One centre phosphor band (2nd) or two phosphor bands (others). Perf 14 × 14½

2170	**1481**	(2nd) multicoloured	75	70	☐	☐
2171	**1482**	(1st) multicoloured	1·25	1·00	☐	☐
2172	**1483**	45p multicoloured	1·50	1·50	☐	☐
2173	**1484**	65p multicoloured	2·25	2·50	☐	☐
Set of 4			5·50	5·50	☐	☐
First Day Cover				8·00		☐
Presentation Pack			7·50		☐	
PHQ Cards (*set of* 4)			8·50	13·00	☐	☐
Set of 4 Gutter Pairs			13·00		☐	

Post Office Yearbook

2000 (7 Nov.) Comprises Nos. **MS**2125/6, 2127/32, 2134/45, 2148/59 and **MS**2161/77 in hardback book with slip case

YB2177a	Yearbook	£110	☐

The last two issues in the Millennium Projects Series were supplied for insertion into the above at a later date.

1485 Church Bells (Ringing in the Millennium)

1486 Eye (Year of the Artist)

1487 Top of Harp (Canolfan Mileniwn, Cardiff)

1488 Figure within Latticework (TS2K Creative Enterprise Centres, London)

Millennium Projects (12th series). 'Sound and Vision'

2000 (5 Dec.) One centre phosphor band (2nd) or two phosphor bands (others). Perf 14 × 14½

2174	**1485**	(2nd) multicoloured	75	70	☐	☐
2175	**1486**	(1st) multicoloured	1·25	1·00	☐	☐
2176	**1487**	45p multicoloured	1·50	1·50	☐	☐
2177	**1488**	65p multicoloured	2·25	2·50	☐	☐
Set of 4			5·50	5·50	☐	
First Day Cover				8·00	☐	
Presentation Pack			7·50		☐	
PHQ Cards (set of 4)			8·50	13·00	☐	☐
Set of 4 Gutter Pairs			13·00		☐	

Collectors Pack 2000

2000 (5 Dec.) Comprises Nos. **MS**2125/6, 2127/32, 2134/45, 2148/59 and **MS**2161/77

CP2181a	Collectors Pack	£120	☐

1489 'Flower' ('Nurture Children')

1490 'Tiger' ('Listen to Children')

1491 'Owl' ('Teach Children')

1492 'Butterfly' ('Ensure Children's Freedom')

New Millennium. Rights of the Child. Face Paintings

2001 (16 Jan.) One centre phosphor band (2nd) or two phosphor bands (others). Perf 14 × 14½

2178	**1489**	(2nd) multicoloured	75	75	☐	☐
2179	**1490**	(1st) multicoloured	1·00	1·10	☐	☐
2180	**1491**	45p multicoloured	1·60	1·75	☐	☐
2181	**1492**	65p multicoloured	2·40	2·50	☐	☐
Set of 4			5·75	5·75	☐	☐
First Day Cover				7·50	☐	
Presentation Pack			7·50		☐	
PHQ Cards (set of 4)			8·50	13·00	☐	☐
Set of 4 Gutter Pairs			14·00		☐	

1493 'Love'

1494 'THANKS'

1495 'abc' (New Baby)

1496 'WELCOME'

1497 'Cheers'

'Occasions' Greetings Stamps

2001 (6 Feb.) Two phosphor bands. Perf 14½ × 14

2182	**1493**	(1st) multicoloured	1·30	1·30	☐	☐
2183	**1494**	(1st) multicoloured	1·30	1·30	☐	☐
2184	**1495**	(1st) multicoloured	1·30	1·30	☐	☐
2185	**1496**	(1st) multicoloured	1·30	1·30	☐	☐
2186	**1497**	(1st) multicoloured	1·30	1·30	☐	☐
Set of 5			5·75	5·75	☐	☐
First Day Cover				7·50	☐	
Presentation Pack (13 Feb.)			8·00		☐	
PHQ Cards (set of 5)			8·50	13·00	☐	☐
Set of 5 Gutter Pairs			13·00		☐	

The silver-grey backgrounds are printed in Iriodin ink which gives a shiny effect.

Further packs of Nos. 2182/6 were sold from 3 July 2001. These comprised the listed stamps in blocks of ten (from sheets) with an insert describing the occasion (Price £10 per pack). Nos. 2182/6 were printed in photogravure. They were subsequently re-issued on 1 May, as sheets of 20, printed in lithography instead of photogravure with each stamp accompanied by a half stamp-size label showing either postal symbols or a personal photograph.

1498 Dog and Owner on Bench

1499 Dog in Bath

1500 Boxer at Dog Show

1501 Cat in Handbag

1502 Cat on Gate

1503 Dog in Car

1504 Cat at Window

1505 Dog behind Fence

1506 Cat watching Bird

1507 Cat in Washbasin

T **1498/1507** were printed together in sheetlets of 10 (5 × 2), with the surplus self-adhesive paper around each stamp retained. The booklet pane has vertical roulettes between rows 2/3 and 4/5.

Cats and Dogs

2001 (13 Feb.) Self-adhesive. Two phosphor bands. Die-cut perf 15 × 14

2187	**1498**	(1st) black, grey and silver	60	50	☐	☐
		a. Sheetlet.				
		Nos. 2187/96	15·00	15·00	☐	☐
		b. Booklet pane.				
		Nos.2187/96 plus				
		Nos. 2040 × 2	30·00		☐	
2188	**1499**	(1st) black, grey and silver	60	50	☐	☐
2189	**1500**	(1st) black, grey and silver	60	50	☐	☐
2190	**1501**	(1st) black, grey and silver	60	50	☐	☐
2191	**1502**	(1st) black, grey and silver	60	50	☐	☐
2192	**1503**	(1st) black, grey and silver	60	50	☐	☐
2193	**1504**	(1st) black, grey and silver	60	50	☐	☐
2194	**1505**	(1st) black, grey and silver	60	50	☐	☐
2195	**1506**	(1st) black, grey and silver	60	50	☐	☐
2196	**1507**	(1st) black, grey and silver	60	50	☐	☐
Set of 10			15·00	15·00	☐	☐
First Day Cover				15·00	☐	
Presentation Pack			20·00		☐	
PHQ Cards (*set of* 10)			14·00	30·00	☐	☐

1508 'RAIN'

1509 'FAIR'

1510 'STORMY'

1511 'VERY DRY'

Nos. 2197/200 show the four quadrants of a barometer dial which are combined on the miniature sheet.

The Weather

2001 (13 Mar.) One side phosphor band (19p) or two phosphor bands (others). Perf 14½

2197	**1508**	19p multicoloured	70	75	☐	☐
2198	**1509**	27p multicoloured	85	1·00	☐	☐
2199	**1510**	45p multicoloured	1·50	1·50	☐	☐
2200	**1511**	65p multicoloured	2·40	2·50	☐	☐
Set of 4			5·00	5·50	☐	☐
First Day Cover				7·50		☐
Presentation Pack			14·00		☐	
Set of 4 Gutter Pairs			14·00		☐	
MS2201	105 × 105 mm.					
		Nos. 2197/200	18·00	18·00	☐	☐
First Day Cover				19·00		☐
PHQ Cards (*set of* 5)			8·50	20·00	☐	☐

The reddish violet on both the 27p and the miniature sheet is printed in thermochromic ink which changes from reddish violet to light blue when exposed to heat.

The PHQ cards depict the four values and the miniature sheet.

1512 *Vanguard* Class Submarine, 1992

1513 *Swiftsure* Class Submarine, 1973

1514 *Unity* Class Submarine, 1939

1515 'Holland' Type Submarine, 1901

1516 White Ensign

1517 Union Jack

1518 Jolly Roger flown by H.M.S. *Proteus* (submarine)

1519 Flag of Chief of Defence Staff

Centenary of Royal Navy Submarine Service

2001 (10 Apr.–22 Oct.) One centre phosphor band (2nd) or two phosphor bands (others).

(a) Submarines. Ordinary gum. Perf 15 × 14

2202 **1512**	(2nd) multicoloured	70	75	☐ ☐
	a. Perf 15½ × 15			
	(22 Oct.)	3·75	3·00	☐ ☐
2203 **1513**	(1st) multicoloured	85	90	☐ ☐
	a. Perf 15½ × 15			
	(22 Oct.)	3·75	3·00	☐ ☐
2204 **1514**	45p multicoloured	1·75	1·60	☐ ☐
	a. Perf 15½ × 15			
	(22 Oct.)	3·75	3·00	☐ ☐
2205 **1515**	65p multicoloured	2·40	2·50	☐ ☐
	a. Perf 15½ × 15			
	(22 Oct.)	3·75	3·00	☐ ☐
Set of 4		5·25	5·25	☐ ☐
First Day Cover			7·50	☐
Presentation Pack		22·00		☐
PHQ Cards (*set of 4*)		8·50	14·00	☐ ☐
Set of 4 Gutter Pairs		13·50		☐

(b) Flags. Sheet 92 × 97 mm. Ordinary gum. Perf 14½

MS2206	**1516** (1st) multicoloured;			
	1517 (1st) multicoloured;			
	1518 (1st) multicoloured;			
	1519 (1st) multicoloured			
	(22 Oct.)	9·00	9·00	☐ ☐
First Day Cover			11·00	☐
Presentation Pack		20·00		☐
PHQ Cards (*set of 5*)		5·00	12·00	☐ ☐

(c) Self-adhesive. Die-cut perf 15½ × 14 (No. 2207) or 14½ (others)

2207 **1513**	(1st) multicoloured			
	(17 Apr.)	45·00	40·00	☐ ☐
2208 **1516**	(1st) multicoloured			
	(22 Oct.)	15·00	15·00	☐ ☐
2209 **1518**	(1st) multicoloured			
	(22 Oct.)	15·00	15·00	☐ ☐

Nos. 2202a/5a only come from stamp booklets.
The five PHQ cards depict the four designs and the complete miniature sheet.
Nos. 2207/9 only come from two different £1.62 booklets.
Type **1516** was re-issued on 21 June 2005 in sheets of 20, printed in lithography instead of photogravure, with half stamp-size *se-tenant* labels showing signal flags.
Designs as Type **1517** were issued on 27 July 2004 in sheets of 20 printed in lithography instead of photogravure with each vertical row of stamps alternated with half stamp-size labels.

1520 Leyland X2 Open-top, London General B Type, Leyland Titan TD1 and AEC Regent 1

1521 AEC Regent 1, Daimler COG5, Utility Guy Arab Mk II and AEC Regent III RT Type

1522 AEC Regent III RT Type, Bristol KSW5G Open-Top, AEC Routemaster and Bristol Lodekka FSF6G

1523 Bristol Lodekka FSF6G, Leyland Titan PD3/4, Leyland Atlantean PDR1/1 and Daimler Fleetline CRG6LX-33

1524 Daimler Fleetline CRG6LX-33, MCW Metrobus DR102/43, Leyland Olympian ONLXB/1R and Dennis Trident

T **1520/4** were printed together, *se-tenant*, in horizontal strips of 5 throughout the sheet. The illustrations of the first bus on No. 2210 and the last bus on No. 2214 continue onto the sheet margins.

150th Anniversary of First Double-decker Bus

2001 (15 May) 'All-over' phosphor. Perf 14½ × 14

2210 **1520**	(1st) multicoloured	60	50	☐ ☐
	a. Horiz strip of 5.			
	Nos. 2210/14	6·00	6·00	☐ ☐
2211 **1521**	(1st) multicoloured	60	50	☐ ☐
2212 **1522**	(1st) multicoloured	60	50	☐ ☐
2213 **1523**	(1st) multicoloured	60	50	☐ ☐
2214 **1524**	(1st) multicoloured	60	50	☐ ☐
Set of 5		6·00	6·00	☐ ☐
First Day Cover			6·50	☐
Presentation Pack		12·00		☐
PHQ Cards (*set of 5*)		8·50	15·00	☐ ☐
Gutter Strip of 10		12·00		☐
MS2215 120 × 105 mm. Nos. 2210/14		10·50	10·50	☐ ☐
First Day Cover			15·00	☐

In No. **MS**2215 the illustrations of the AEC Regent III RT Type and the Daimler Fleetline CRG6LX-33 appear twice.

1525 Toque Hat by Pip Hackett

1526 Butterfly Hat by Dai Rees

1527 Top Hat by Stephen Jones

1528 Spiral Hat by Philip Treacy

Fashion Hats

2001 (19 June) 'All-over' phosphor. Perf 14½

2216	**1525**	(1st) multicoloured	85	90	☐	☐
2217	**1526**	(E) multicoloured	1·10	1·25	☐	☐
2218	**1527**	45p multicoloured	1·60	1·60	☐	☐
2219	**1528**	65p multicoloured	2·50	2·50	☐	☐
Set of 4			5·50	5·50	☐	☐
First Day Cover				7·25		☐
Presentation Pack			7·50		☐	
PHQ Cards (*set of* 4)			8·50	14·00	☐	☐
Set of 4 Gutter Pairs			13·00			☐

1529 Common Frog

1530 Great Diving Beetle

1531 Three-spined Stickleback

1532 Southern Hawker Dragonfly

Europa. Pond Life

2001 (10 July) Two phosphor bands

2220	**1529**	(1st) multicoloured	1·00	1·00	☐	☐
2221	**1530**	(E) multicoloured	1·25	1·25	☐	☐
2222	**1531**	45p multicoloured	1·50	1·50	☐	☐
2223	**1532**	65p multicoloured	2·00	2·25	☐	☐
Set of 4			5·50	5·75	☐	☐
First Day Cover				11·00		☐
Presentation Pack			7·50		☐	
PHQ Cards (*set of* 4)			8·50	14·00	☐	☐
Set of 4 Gutter Pairs			13·00			☐

The 1st and E values incorporate the 'EUROPA' emblem. The bluish silver on all four values is in Iriodin ink and was used as a background for those parts of the design below the water line.

1533 Policeman

1534 Clown

1535 Mr. Punch

1536 Judy

1537 Beadle

1538 Crocodile

Nos. 2224/9 were printed together, *se-tenant*, in horizontal strips of 6 throughout the sheet.

Punch and Judy Show Puppets

2001 (4 Sept.) Two phosphor bands

		(a) Ordinary gum. Perf 14 × 15				
2224	**1533**	(1st) multicoloured	60	50	☐	☐
		a. Horiz strip of 6.				
		Nos. 2224/9	5·50	5·50	☐	☐
2225	**1534**	(1st) multicoloured	60	50	☐	☐
2226	**1535**	(1st) multicoloured	60	50	☐	☐
2227	**1536**	(1st) multicoloured	60	50	☐	☐
2228	**1537**	(1st) multicoloured	60	50	☐	☐
2229	**1538**	(1st) multicoloured	60	50	☐	☐
Set of 6			5·50	5·50	☐	☐
First Day Cover				7·00		☐
Presentation Pack			7·00		☐	
PHQ Cards (*set of* 6)			8·50	18·00	☐	☐
Gutter Block of 12			13·00		☐	
		(b) Self-adhesive. Die-cut perf 14 × 15½				
2230	1535	(1st) multicoloured	17·00	17·00	☐	☐
2231	1536	(1st) multicoloured	17·00	17·00	☐	☐

Nos. 2230/1 were only issued in £1.62 stamp booklets.

1539 Carbon 60 Molecule (Chemistry)

1540 Globe (Economic Sciences)

1541 Embossed Dove (Peace)

1542 Crosses (Physiology or Medicine)

1543 Poem 'The Addressing of Cats' by T.S. Eliot in Open Book (Literature)

1544 Hologram of Boron Molecule (Physics)

Centenary of Nobel Prizes

2001 (2 Oct.) One side phosphor band (2nd) or phosphor frame (others). Perf 14½

2232	**1539**	(2nd) black, silver and grey-black	75	65	☐	☐
2233	**1540**	(1st) multicoloured	1·50	90	☐	☐
2234	**1541**	(E) black, silver and bright green	1·50	1·25	☐	☐
2235	**1542**	40p multicoloured	2·00	1·25	☐	☐
2236	**1543**	45p multicoloured	3·00	1·75	☐	☐
2237	**1544**	65p black and silver	4·00	2·50	☐	☐
Set of 6			10·00	7·50	☐	☐
First Day Cover				9·50	☐	
Presentation Pack			50·00		☐	
PHQ Cards (set of 6)			10·00	18·00	☐	☐
Set of 6 Gutter Pairs			20·00		☐	

The grey-black on No. 2232 is printed in thermochromic ink which temporarily changes to pale grey when exposed to heat.
The centre of No. 2235 is coated with a eucalyptus scent.

1545 Robins with Snowman

1546 Robins on Bird Table

1547 Robins skating on Bird Bath

1548 Robins with Christmas Pudding

1549 Robins in Paper Chain Nest

Christmas. Robins

2001 (6 Nov.) Self-adhesive. One centre phosphor band (2nd) or two phosphor bands (others). Die-cut perf 14½

2238	**1545**	(2nd) multicoloured	75	70	☐	☐
2239	**1546**	(1st) multicoloured	1·00	1·00	☐	☐
2240	**1547**	(E) multicoloured	1·50	1·50	☐	☐
2241	**1548**	45p multicoloured	2·00	2·00	☐	☐
2242	**1549**	65p multicoloured	3·00	3·00	☐	☐
Set of 5			7·50	7·50	☐	☐
First Day Cover				9·50	☐	
Presentation Pack			8·00		☐	
PHQ Cards (set of 5)			11·00	16·00	☐	☐

The 1st value was re-issued on 30 September 2003, in sheets of 20, in lithography instead of photogravure, each stamp se-tenant with a Christmas label or a personal photograph. The sheet contained die-cut perforated stamps and labels. The 2nd and 1st class stamps were issued again on 1 November 2005 in sheets of 20 containing ten 1st class and ten 2nd class stamps, each stamp accompanied by a se-tenant label showing a snowman.

Collectors Pack 2001

2001 (6 Nov.) Comprises Nos. 2178/2200, 2202/**MS**2206, 2210/14, 2216/29 and 2232/42

CP2242a	Collectors Pack	£120	☐

Post Office Yearbook

2001 (6 Nov.) Comprises Nos. 2178/96, **MS**2201/6, **MS**2215/29 and 2232/42 in hardback book with slip case

YB2242a	Yearbook	£110	☐

1550 'How the Whale got his Throat'

1551 'How the Camel got his Hump'

1552 'How the Rhinoceros got his Skin'

1553 'How the Leopard got his Spots'

1554 'The Elephant's Child'

1555 'The Sing-Song of Old Man Kangaroo'

1556 'The Beginning of the Armadillos'

1557 'The Crab that played with the Sea'

1558 'The Cat that walked by Himself'

1559 'The Butterfly that stamped'

T **1550/9** were printed together in sheetlets of 10 (5 × 2), with the surplus self-adhesive paper around each stamp retained.

Centenary of Publication of Rudyard Kipling's Just So Stories

2002 (15 Jan.) Self-adhesive. Two phosphor bands. Die-cut perf 15 × 14

2243	**1550**	(1st) multicoloured	50	45	☐	☐
		a. Sheetlet.				
		Nos. 2243/52	10·00	10·00	☐	☐
2244	**1551**	(1st) multicoloured	50	45	☐	☐
2245	**1552**	(1st) multicoloured	50	45	☐	☐
2246	**1553**	(1st) multicoloured	50	45	☐	☐
2247	**1554**	(1st) multicoloured	50	45	☐	☐
2248	**1555**	(1st) multicoloured	50	45	☐	☐
2249	**1556**	(1st) multicoloured	50	45	☐	☐
2250	**1557**	(1st) multicoloured	50	45	☐	☐
2251	**1558**	(1st) multicoloured	50	45	☐	☐
2252	**1559**	(1st) multicoloured	50	45	☐	☐
Set of 10			10·00	10·00	☐	☐
First Day Cover				11·00		☐
Presentation Pack			16·00		☐	
PHQ Cards (*set of* 10)			8·50	28·00	☐	☐

1560 Queen Elizabeth II, 1952 (Dorothy Wilding)

1561 Queen Elizabeth II, 1968 (Cecil Beaton)

1562 Queen Elizabeth II, 1978 (Lord Snowdon)

1563 Queen Elizabeth II, 1984 (Yousef Karsh)

1564 Queen Elizabeth II, 1996 (Tim Graham)

1565

Golden Jubilee. Studio portraits of Queen Elizabeth II by photographers named

2002 (6 Feb.) One centre phosphor band (2nd) or two phosphor bands (others). W **1565**. Perf 14½ × 14

2253	**1560**	(2nd) multicoloured	75	55	☐	☐
2254	**1561**	(1st) multicoloured	1·00	80	☐	☐
2255	**1562**	(E) multicoloured	1·50	1·50	☐	☐
2256	**1563**	45p multicoloured	1·75	2·00	☐	☐
2257	**1564**	65p multicoloured	2·75	3·00	☐	☐
Set of 5			7·00	7·00	☐	☐
First Day Cover				9·00		☐
Presentation Pack			9·00		☐	
PHQ Cards (*set of* 5)			4·50	14·00	☐	☐
Set of 5 Gutter Pairs			16·00		☐	

Stamps from sheets had the watermark sideways: those from stamp booklets had the watermark upright.

1566

Booklet Stamps

2002 (6 Feb.) Designs as 1952-54 issue, but with service indicator as T **1566**. One centre phosphor band (2nd) or two phosphor bands (1st). W **1565**. Uncoated paper. Perf 15 × 14 (with one elliptical hole in each vertical side)

2258	**1566**	(2nd) carmine-red	1·20	1·00	☐	☐
2259	**154**	(1st) green	1·25	1·25	☐	☐
Set of 2			2·40	2·25	☐	☐

Nos. 2258/9 were only issued in £7.29 stamp booklets. See also Nos. 2031/3, MS2326, MS2367 and 2378/80.

1567 Rabbits ('a new baby')

1568 'LOVE'

1569 Aircraft Sky-writing 'hello'

1570 Bear pulling Potted Topiary Tree (Moving Home)

1571 Flowers ('best wishes')

'Occasions' Greetings Stamps

2002 (5 Mar.)-**03** Two phosphor bands

(a) Litho. Ordinary gum. Perf 15 × 14

2260	**1567**	(1st) multicoloured	1·10	1·10
2261	**1568**	(1st) multicoloured	1·10	1·10
2262	**1569**	(1st) multicoloured	1·10	1·10
2263	**1570**	(1st) multicoloured	1·10	1·10
2264	**1571**	(1st) multicoloured	1·10	1·10
Set of 5			5·00	5·00
First Day Cover				6·75
Presentation Pack			6·50	
PHQ Cards (set of 5)			4·50	14·00
Set of 5 Gutter Pairs			11·00	

(b) Photo. Self-adhesive. Die-cut perf 15 × 14

2264a	**1569**	(1st) multicoloured		
		(4.3.03)	6·00	6·00

Nos. 2260/4 were re-issued on 23 April 2002 in sheets of 20 perforated 14, either of one design or *se-tenant*, with each stamp accompanied by a half stamp-size label showing either greetings or a personal photograph.

No. 2262 was also issued in sheets of 20 with *se-tenant* labels in connection with the Hong Kong Stamp Expo on 30 January 2004. It was issued in sheets of 20 perforated 14 with *se-tenant* labels on 21 April 2005 for Pacific Explorer 2005 World Stamp Expo, on 25 May 2006 for Washington 2006 International Stamp Exhibition, on 14 November 2006 for Belgica 2006 International Stamp Exhibition, on 5 August 2008 for Beijing 2008 Olympic Expo, on 3 August 2009 for Thaipex 09 Stamp Exhibition, on 21 October 2009 for Italia 2009 International Stamp Exhibition and on 4 December 2009 for MonacoPhil International Stamp Exhibition.

No. 2264a was only issued in £1·62 stamp booklets in which the surplus self-adhesive paper around each stamp was removed.

1572 Studland Bay, Dorset

1573 Luskentyre, South Harris

1574 Cliffs, Dover, Kent

1575 Padstow Harbour, Cornwall

1576 Broadstairs, Kent

1577 St. Abb's Head, Scottish Borders

1578 Dunster Beach, Somerset

1579 Newquay Beach, Cornwall

1580 Portrush, County Antrim

1581 Sand-spit, Conwy

T **1572/81** were printed together, *se-tenant*, in blocks of 10 (5 × 2) throughout the sheet.

British Coastlines

2002 (19 Mar.) Two phosphor bands. Perf 14½

2265	**1572**	27p multicoloured	60	50
		a. Block of 10.		
		Nos. 2265/74	8·75	8·75
2266	**1573**	27p multicoloured	60	50
2267	**1574**	27p multicoloured	60	50
2268	**1575**	27p multicoloured	60	50
2269	**1576**	27p multicoloured	60	50
2270	**1577**	27p multicoloured	60	50
2271	**1578**	27p multicoloured	60	50
2272	**1579**	27p multicoloured	60	50
2273	**1580**	27p multicoloured	60	50
2274	**1581**	27p multicoloured	60	50
Set of 10			8·75	8·75
First Day Cover				11·50
Presentation Pack			10·50	
PHQ Cards (set of 10)			9·25	28·00
Gutter Block of 20			18·00	

1582 Slack Wire Act

1583 Lion Tamer

1584 Trick Tri-cyclists

1585 Krazy Kar

1586 Equestrienne

Europa. Circus

2002 (10 Apr.) One centre phosphor band (2nd) or two phosphor bands (others). Perf 14½

2275	**1582**	(2nd) multicoloured	50	60	☐ ☐
2276	**1583**	(1st) multicoloured	75	85	☐ ☐
2277	**1584**	(E) multicoloured	1·00	1·25	☐ ☐
2278	**1585**	45p multicoloured	1·75	1·50	☐ ☐
2279	**1586**	65p multicoloured	2·75	2·25	☐ ☐
Set of 5			6·00	6·00	☐ ☐
First Day Cover				8·00	☐
Presentation Pack			7·50		☐
PHQ Cards (*set of 5*)			4·50	14·00	☐ ☐
Set of 5 Gutter Pairs			14·00		☐

The 1st and E values incorporate the "EUROPA" emblem. Due to the funeral of the Queen Mother, the actual issue of Nos. 2275/9 was delayed from 9 April which is the date that appears on first day covers.

1587 Queen Elizabeth the Queen Mother

Queen Elizabeth the Queen Mother Commemoration

2002 (25 Apr.) Vert designs as T **955/8** with changed face values and showing both the Queen's head and frame in black as in T **1587**. Two phosphor bands. Perf 14 × 15

2280	**1587**	(1st) multicoloured	1·00	85	☐ ☐
2281	**956**	(E) black and indigo	1·25	1·10	☐ ☐
2282	**957**	45p multicoloured	1·50	1·50	☐ ☐
2283	**958**	65p black, stone and sepia	2·00	2·25	☐ ☐
Set of 4			5·50	5·50	☐ ☐
First Day Cover				8·00	☐
Presentation Pack			7·00		☐
Set of 4 Gutter Pairs			14·00		☐

1588 Airbus A340-600 (2002)

1589 Concorde (1976)

1590 Trident (1964)

1591 VC 10 (1964)

1592 Comet (1952)

50th Anniversary of Passenger Jet Aviation. Airliners

2002 (2 May) One centre phosphor band (2nd) or two phosphor bands (others). Perf 14½

		(a) Photo De La Rue. Ordinary gum			
2284	**1588**	(2nd) multicoloured	75	55	☐ ☐
2285	**1589**	(1st) multicoloured	1·25	1·00	☐ ☐
2286	**1590**	(E) multicoloured	1·50	1·50	☐ ☐
2287	**1591**	45p multicoloured	2·00	2·00	☐ ☐
2288	**1592**	65p multicoloured	3·00	3·00	☐ ☐
Set of 5			8·00	7·50	☐ ☐
First Day Cover				8·00	☐
Presentation Pack			10·00		☐
Set of 5 Gutter Pairs			14·00		☐
MS2289		120 × 105 mm. Nos. 2284/8	12·00	11·00	☐ ☐
First Day Cover				12·00	☐
PHQ Cards (*set of 6*)			5·25	18·00	☐ ☐
		(b) Photo Questa· Self-adhesive			
2290	**1589**	(1st) multicoloured	7·00	7·00	☐ ☐

The complete miniature sheet is shown on one of the PHQ cards with the others depicting individual stamps. No. 2290 was only issued in £1.62 stamp booklets.

1593 Crowned Lion with Shield of St. George

1594 Top Left Quarter of English Flag, and Football

1595 Top Right Quarter of English Flag, and Football

1596 Bottom Left Quarter of English Flag, and Football

1597 Bottom Right Quarter of English Flag, and Football

World Cup Football Championship, Japan and Korea

2002 (21 May) Two phosphor bands. Perf 14½ × 14

(a) Ordinary gum

2291	**1593**	(1st) deep turquoise-blue, scarlet-vermilion and silver	2·50	2·50	☐	☐
MS2292		145 × 74 mm. No. 2291; **1594** (1st) multicoloured; **1595** (1st) multicoloured; **1596** (1st) multicoloured; **1597** (1st) multicoloured	7·50	6·50	☐	☐
First Day Cover (**MS**2292)				9·00		☐
Presentation Pack (**MS**2292)			8·50		☐	
PHQ Cards (set of 6)			5·25	15·00	☐	☐
Gutter Pair (No. 2291)			12·00		☐	

(b) Self-adhesive. Die-cut perf 15 × 14

2293	**1594**	(1st) multicoloured	6·00	6·00	☐	☐
2294	**1595**	(1st) multicoloured	6·00	6·00	☐	☐

The complete miniature sheet is shown on one of the PHQ cards with the others depicting individual stamps from **MS**2292 and No. 2291.

Nos. 2293/4 were only issued in £1.62 stamp booklets.

Stamps as Type **1597** were also issued in sheets of 20, se-tenant with half stamp-sized labels, printed in lithography instead of photogravure. The labels show either match scenes or personal photographs.

Stamps as Type **1593** but with 'WORLD CUP 2002' inscription omitted were issued on 17 May 2007 in sheets of 20 with se-tenant labels showing scenes from Wembley Stadium.

Self-adhesive Stamps

2002 (5 June–4 July) Self-adhesive. Photo Questa, Walsall or Enschedé (No. 2295) or Walsall (others). Two phosphor bands. Perf 15 × 14 die-cut (with one elliptical hole in each vertical side)

2295	**914**	(1st) gold	1·00	1·00	☐	☐
2296	**1093a**	(E) deep blue (4 July)	2·00	2·00	☐	☐
2297	**367a**	42p deep olive-grey (4 July)	3·00	3·00	☐	☐
2298		68p grey-brown (4 July)	4·00	4·00	☐	☐
Set of 4			9·00	9·00		
PHQ Card (No. 2295)			60	3·50	☐	☐

Further printings of No. 2295 in sheets of 100 appeared on 4 July 2002 produced by Enschedé and on 18 March 2003 printed by Walsall.

1598 Swimming

1599 Running

1600 Cycling

1601 Long Jumping

1602 Wheelchair Racing

17th Commonwealth Games, Manchester

2002 (16 July) One side phosphor band (2nd) or two phosphor bands (others). Perf 14½

2299	**1598**	(2nd) multicoloured	75	55	☐	☐
2300	**1599**	(1st) multicoloured	1·00	80	☐	☐
2301	**1600**	(E) multicoloured	1·25	1·25	☐	☐
2302	**1601**	47p multicoloured	1·50	1·50	☐	☐
2303	**1602**	68p multicoloured	2·00	2·25	☐	☐
Set of 5			6·00	6·00	☐	☐
First Day Cover				8·00		☐
Presentation Pack			7·50		☐	
PHQ Cards (set of 5)			4·75	16·00	☐	☐
Set of 5 Gutter Pairs			14·00			☐

1603 Tinkerbell

1604 Wendy, John and Michael Darling in front of Big Ben

1605 Crocodile and Alarm Clock

1606 Captain Hook

1607 Peter Pan

150th Anniversary of Great Ormond Street Children's Hospital. Peter Pan by Sir James Barrie

2002 (20 Aug.) One centre phosphor band (2nd) or two phosphor bands (others). Perf 15 × 14

2304	**1603**	(2nd) multicoloured	75	55	☐	☐
2305	**1604**	(1st) multicoloured	1·00	80	☐	☐
2306	**1605**	(E) multicoloured	1·25	1·25	☐	☐
2307	**1606**	47p multicoloured	1·50	1·50	☐	☐
2308	**1607**	68p multicoloured	2·00	2·25	☐	☐
Set of 5			6·00	6·00	☐	☐
First Day Cover				8·00		☐
Presentation Pack			7·50		☐	
PHQ Cards (set of 5)			4·75	15·00	☐	☐
Set of 5 Gutter Pairs			14·00		☐	

1608 Millennium Bridge, 2001

1609 Tower Bridge, 1894

1610 Westminster Bridge, 1864

1611 'Blackfriars Bridge, c1800' (William Marlow)

1612 'London Bridge, c1670' (Wenceslaus Hollar)

Bridges of London

2002 (10 Sept.) One centre phosphor band (2nd) or two phosphor bands (others)

(a) Litho. Ordinary gum. Perf 15 × 14

2309	**1608**	(2nd) multicoloured	75	55	☐	☐
2310	**1609**	(1st) multicoloured	1·00	80	☐	☐
2311	**1610**	(E) multicoloured	2·00	1·50	☐	☐
2312	**1611**	47p multicoloured	2·50	2·00	☐	☐
2313	**1612**	68p multicoloured	3·50	3·00	☐	☐
Set of 5			9·00	7·50	☐	☐
First Day Cover				9·00		☐
Presentation Pack			55·00		☐	
PHQ Cards (set of 5)			4·00	12·00	☐	☐
Set of 5 Gutter Pairs			20·00		☐	

(b) Photo. Self-adhesive. Die-cut perf 15 × 14

2314	**1609**	(1st) multicoloured	6·00	6·00	☐	☐

No. 2314 was only issued in £1.62 stamp booklets.

1613 Galaxies and Nebula

Astronomy

2002 (24 Sept.) Sheet 120 × 89 mm. Multicoloured. Two phosphor bands. Perf 14½ × 14

MS2315	1613	(1st) Planetary nebula in Aquila; (1st) Seyfert 2 galaxy in Pegasus; (1st) Planetary nebula in Norma; (1st) Seyfert 2 galaxy in Circinus	5·25	5·25	☐	☐
First Day Cover				6·00		☐
Presentation Pack			18·00		☐	
PHQ Cards (set of 5)			4·75	18·00	☐	☐

The five PHQ cards depict the four designs and the complete miniature sheet.

1614 Green Pillar Box, 1857

1615 Horizontal Aperture Box, 1874

1616 Air Mail Box, 1934

1617 Double Aperture Box, 1939

1618 Modern Style Box, 1980

150th Anniversary of the First Pillar Box

2002 (8 Oct.) One centre phosphor band (2nd) or two phosphor bands (others). Perf 14 × 14½

2316 **1614**	(2nd) multicoloured	75	55	☐	☐
2317 **1615**	(1st) multicoloured	1·00	80	☐	☐
2318 **1616**	(E) multicoloured	1·75	1·75	☐	☐
2319 **1617**	47p multicoloured	2·00	2·50	☐	☐
2320 **1618**	68p multicoloured	2·50	3·00	☐	☐
Set of 5		7·50	7·50	☐	☐
First Day Cover			8·50	☐	
Presentation Pack		8·00		☐	
PHQ Cards (set of 5)		4·75	16·00	☐	☐
Set of 5 Gutter Pairs		16·00		☐	

1619 Blue Spruce Star

1620 Holly

1621 Ivy

1622 Mistletoe

1623 Pine Cone

Christmas

2002 (5 Nov.) Self-adhesive. One centre phosphor band (2nd) or two phosphor bands (others). Die-cut perf 14½ × 14

2321 **1619**	(2nd) multicoloured	75	55	☐	☐
2322 **1620**	(1st) multicoloured	1·00	80	☐	☐
2323 **1621**	(E) multicoloured	1·50	1·50	☐	☐
2324 **1622**	47p multicoloured	2·00	1·75	☐	☐
2325 **1623**	68p multicoloured	3·00	2·75	☐	☐
Set of 5		8·00	7·50	☐	☐
First Day Cover			8·50	☐	
Presentation Pack		7·50		☐	
PHQ Cards (set of 5)		4·75	16·00	☐	☐

Collectors Pack 2002

2002 (5 Nov.) Comprises Nos. 2243/57, 2260/4, 2265/88, **MS**2292, 2299/313 and **MS**2315/25

CP2325a	Collectors Pack	£110	☐

Post Office Yearbook

2002 (5 Nov.) Comprises Nos. 2243/57, 2260/4, 2265/88, 2291/2, 2299/313 and **MS**2315/25 in hardback book with slip case

YB2325a	Yearbook	£100	☐

50th Anniversary of Wilding Definitives (1st issue)

2002 (5 Dec.) Sheet, 124 × 70 mm, containing designs as T **154/5** and **157/60** (1952–54 issue), but with values in decimal currency as T **1348** or with service indicator as T **1566**, printed on pale cream. One centre phosphor band (2nd) or two phosphor bands (others). W **1565**. Perf 15 × 14 (with one elliptical hole in each vertical side)

MS2326	1p orange-red; 2p ultramarine; 5p red-brown; (2nd) carmine-red; (1st) green; 33p brown; 37p magenta; 47p bistre-brown; 50p green and label showing national emblems	10·00	10·00	☐	☐
First Day Cover			10·00		☐
Presentation Pack		£100		☐	
PHQ Cards (set of 5)		3·00	12·00	☐	☐

The PHQ cards depict the (2nd), (1st), 33p, 37p and 47p stamps.
See also No. **MS**2367.

1624 Barn Owl landing

1625 Barn Owl with folded Wings and Legs down

1626 Barn Owl with extended Wings and Legs down

1627 Barn Owl in Flight with Wings lowered

1628 Barn Owl in Flight with Wings raised

1629 Kestrel with Wings folded

1630 Kestrel with Wings fully extended upwards

1631 Kestrel with Wings horizonta l

1632 Kestrel with Wings partly extended downwards

1633 Kestrel with Wings fully extended downwards

T **1624/33** were printed together, *se-tenant*, in blocks of 10 (5 × 2) throughout the sheet.

Birds of Prey

2003 (14 Jan.) Phosphor background. Perf 14½

2327	**1624**	(1st) multicoloured	70	80	☐	☐
		a. Block of 10.				
		Nos. 2327/36	10·00	10·00	☐	☐
2328	**1625**	(1st) multicoloured	70	80	☐	☐
2329	**1626**	(1st) multicoloured	70	80	☐	☐
2330	**1627**	(1st) multicoloured	70	80	☐	☐
2331	**1628**	(1st) multicoloured	70	80	☐	☐
2332	**1629**	(1st) multicoloured	70	80	☐	☐
2333	**1630**	(1st) multicoloured	70	80	☐	☐
2334	**1631**	(1st) multicoloured	70	80	☐	☐
2335	**1632**	(1st) multicoloured	70	80	☐	☐
2336	**1633**	(1st) multicoloured	70	80	☐	☐
Set of 10			10·00	10·00	☐	☐
First Day Cover				11·00		☐
Presentation Pack			12·00		☐	
PHQ Cards (*set of* 10)			9·25	28·00	☐	☐
Gutter Block of 20			24·00		☐	

1634 'Gold star, See me, Playtime'

1635 '1♥U, XXXX, S.W.A.L.K.'

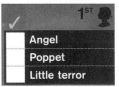

1636 'Angel, Poppet, Little terror'

1637 'Yes, No, Maybe'

1638 'Oops!, Sorry, Will try harder'

1639 'I did it!, You did it!, We did it!'

T **2337/42** were printed together, *se-tenant*, in blocks of 6 (3 × 2) throughout the sheet.

'Occasions' Greetings Stamps

2003 (4 Feb.) Two phosphor bands. Perf 14½ × 14

2337	**1634**	(1st) lemon and new blue	60	50	☐	☐
		a. Block of 6.				
		Nos. 2337/42	6·50	6·00	☐	☐
2338	**1635**	(1st) red and deep ultramarine	60	50	☐	☐
2339	**1636**	(1st) purple and bright yellow-green	60	50	☐	☐
2340	**1637**	(1st) bright yellow-green and red	60	50	☐	☐
2341	**1638**	(1st) deep ultramarine and lemon	60	50	☐	☐
2342	**1639**	(1st) new blue and purple	60	50	☐	☐
Set of 6			6·50	6·00	☐	☐
First Day Cover				9·00		☐
Presentation Pack			8·00		☐	
PHQ Cards (*set of 6*)			5·25	18·00	☐	☐
Gutter Block of 12			14·00		☐	

Nos. 2337/42 were also available in *se-tenant* sheets of 20 containing four examples of Nos. 2338 and 2340 and three of each of the others. The stamps are accompanied by half stamp-size printed labels or a personal photograph.

1640 Completing the Genome Jigsaw

1641 Ape with Moustache and Scientist

1642 DNA Snakes and Ladders

1643 'Animal Scientists'

1644 Genome Crystal Ball

50th Anniversary of Discovery of DNA

2003 (25 Feb.) One centre phosphor band (2nd) or two phosphor bands (others). Perf 14½

2343 **1640**	(2nd) multicoloured	1·00	55	☐ ☐
2344 **1641**	(1st) multicoloured	1·00	80	☐ ☐
2345 **1642**	(E) multicoloured	1·25	1·25	☐ ☐
2346 **1643**	47p multicoloured	1·50	1·50	☐ ☐
2347 **1644**	68p multicoloured	2·00	2·25	☐ ☐
Set of 5		6·50	6·00	☐ ☐
First Day Cover			10·00	☐
Presentation Pack		8·00		☐
PHQ Cards (set of 5)		4·75	18·00	☐ ☐
Set of 5 Gutter Pairs		15·00		☐

1645 Strawberry   **1646** Potato

1647 Apple   **1648** Red Pepper

1649 Pear   **1650** Orange

1651 Tomato   **1652** Lemon

1653 Brussels Sprout   **1654** Aubergine

T **1645/54** were printed together in sheets of 10 with the surplus self-adhesive paper around each stamp retained. The stamp pane is accompanied by a similar-sized pane of self-adhesive labels showing ears, eyes, mouths, hats etc which are intended for the adornment of fruit and vegetables depicted. This pane is separated from the stamps by a line of roulettes.

Fruit and Vegetables

2003 (25 Mar.) Self-adhesive. Two phosphor bands. Perf 14½ × 14 die-cut (without teeth around protruding tops or bottoms of the designs)

2348 **1645**	(1st) multicoloured		70	50	☐ ☐
	a. Sheetlet. Nos. 2348/57				
	and pane of				
	decorative labels	10·00		10·00	☐ ☐
2349 **1646**	(1st) multicoloured		70	50	☐ ☐
2350 **1647**	(1st) multicoloured		70	50	☐ ☐
2351 **1648**	(1st) multicoloured		70	50	☐ ☐
2352 **1649**	(1st) multicoloured		70	50	☐ ☐
2353 **1650**	(1st) multicoloured		70	50	☐ ☐
2354 **1651**	(1st) multicoloured		70	50	☐ ☐
2355 **1652**	(1st) multicoloured		70	50	☐ ☐
2356 **1653**	(1st) multicoloured		70	50	☐ ☐
2357 **1654**	(1st) multicoloured		70	50	☐ ☐
Set of 10			10·00	10·00	☐ ☐
First Day Cover				12·00	☐
Presentation Pack			60·00		☐
PHQ Cards (set of 10)			9·25	25·00	☐ ☐

Nos. 2348/57 were re-issued on 7th March 2006 in sheets of 20 containing two of each of the ten designs, each stamp accompanied by a *se-tenant* speech bubble label. These sheets were printed in lithography instead of photogravure, and have stickers showing eyes, hats, etc in the sheet margin.

1655

Overseas Booklet Stamps

2003 (27 Mar.)–**2010** Self-adhesive. Two phosphor bands. Perf 15 × 14 die-cut with one elliptical hole in each vertical side

2357a		(Worldwide postcard)			
		grey-black, rosine			
		and ultramarine	85	85	☐ ☐
2358	**1655**	(Europe) new blue			
		and rosine	1·10	1·10	☐ ☐
2358a		(Europe) deep blue-			
		green, new blue			
		and rosine	1·25	1·25	☐ ☐
2359		(Worldwide) rosine			
		and new blue	2·10	2·10	☐ ☐
2359a		(Worldwide) deep			
		mauve, new blue			
		and rosine	2·00	2·00	☐ ☐
First Day Cover (Nos. 2358/9)				5·25	☐
Presentation Pack (Nos. 2358/9)			6·00		☐
PHQ Card (No. 2358)			45	3·50	☐ ☐

Nos. 2358/9 were intended to pay postage on mail up to 40 grams to either Europe (52p) or to foreign destinations outside Europe (£1.12). No. 2357a was intended to pay postcard rate to foreign destinations (43p).

Operationally they were only available in separate booklets of

4, initially sold at £2.08, £4.48 and £1.72, with the surplus self-adhesive paper around each stamp removed. Single examples of the stamps were available from philatelic outlets as sets of two or in presentation packs.

Nos. 2358a and 2359a were intended to pay postage on mail up to 20 grams to either Europe (initially 56p, increasing to 60p from 6 April 2010) or to foreign destinations outside Europe (90p, 97p from 6 April).

They were only available in separate booklets of four (Nos. MI3 and MJ3) initially sold at £2.24 and £3.60, increasing to £2.40 and £3.88 from 6 April 2010, with the surplus self-adhesive paper around each stamp removed.

For first day covers and presentation packs for Nos. 2357a, 2358a and 2359a see below Nos. Y1667/1803.

1656 Amy Johnson (pilot) and Biplane

1657 Members of 1953 Everest Team

1658 Freya Stark (traveller and writer) and Desert

1659 Ernest Shackleton (Antarctic explorer) and Wreck of *Endurance*

1660 Francis Chichester (yachtsman) and *Gipsy Moth IV*

1661 Robert Falcon Scott (Antarctic explorer) and Norwegian Expedition at the Pole

Extreme Endeavours (British Explorers)

2003 (29 Apr.) One centre phosphor band (2nd) or two phosphor bands (others).

(a) Photo Questa. Ordinary gum. Perf 15 × 14½					
2360 **1656**	2nd) multicoloured	50	50	☐	☐
2361 **1657**	(1st) multicoloured	75	75	☐	☐
2362 **1658**	(E) multicoloured	1·50	1·50	☐	☐
2363 **1659**	42p multicoloured	1·75	1·75	☐	☐

2364 **1660**	47p multicoloured	2·00	2·00	☐	☐
2365 **1661**	68p multicoloured	2·50	2·50	☐	☐
Set of 6		8·00	8·50	☐	☐
First Day Cover			12·00		☐
Presentation Pack		9·00		☐	
PHQ Cards (*set of* 6)		3·25	14·00	☐	☐
Set of 6 Gutter Pairs		17·00		☐	

(b) Photo De La Rue. Self-adhesive. Die-cut perf 14½					
2366 **1657**	(1st) multicoloured	5·00	5·00	☐	☐

The phosphor bands on Nos. 2361/5 are at the centre and right of each stamp.

No. 2366 was only issued in £1.62 stamp booklets in which the surplus self-adhesive paper around each stamp was removed.

50th Anniversary of Wilding Definitives (2nd issue)

2003 (20 May) Sheet, 124 × 70 mm, containing designs as T **155/8** and **160** (1952–54 issue), but with values in decimal currency as T **1348** or with service indicator as T **1566**, printed on pale cream. One centre phosphor band (20p) or two phosphor bands (others). W **1565**. P 15 × 14 (with one elliptical hole in each vertical side).

MS2367	4p deep lilac; 8p ultramarine;				
	10p reddish purple; 20p bright green;				
	28p bronze-green; 34p brown-purple;				
	(E) chestnut; 42p Prussian blue;				
	68p grey-blue and label showing				
	national emblems	10·50	11·25	☐	☐
First Day Cover			13·00		☐
Presentation Pack		18·00		☐	

1662 Guardsmen in Coronation Procession

1663 East End Children reading Coronation Party Poster

1664 Queen Elizabeth II in Coronation Chair with Bishops of Durham and Bath & Wells

1665 Children in Plymouth working on Royal Montage

1666 Queen Elizabeth II in Coronation Robes (photograph by Cecil Beaton)

1667 Children's Race at East End Street Party

1668 Coronation Coach passing through Marble Arch

1669 Children in Fancy Dress

1670 Coronation Coach outside Buckingham Palace

1671 Children eating at London Street Party

T **1662/71** were printed together, *se-tenant*, as blocks of 10 (5 × 2) in sheets of 60 (2 panes of 30).

50th Anniversary of Coronation

2003 (2 June) W **1565**. Two phosphor bands. Perf 14½ × 14

2368	**1662**	(1st) multicoloured	45	50	☐	☐
		a. Block of 10. Nos. 2368/77	9·50	9·50	☐	☐
2369	**1663**	(1st) black and gold	45	50	☐	☐
2370	**1664**	(1st) multicoloured	45	50	☐	☐
2371	**1665**	(1st) black and gold	45	50	☐	☐
2372	**1666**	(1st) multicoloured	45	50	☐	☐
2373	**1667**	(1st) black and gold	45	50	☐	☐
2374	**1668**	(1st) multicoloured	45	50	☐	☐
2375	**1669**	(1st) black and gold	45	50	☐	☐
2376	**1670**	(1st) multicoloured	45	50	☐	☐
2377	**1671**	(1st) black and gold	45	50	☐	☐
Set of 10			9·50	9·50	☐	☐
First Day Cover				12·00	☐	
Presentation Pack			25·00		☐	
PHQ Cards (*set of* 10)			9·25	20·00	☐	☐
Gutter Block of 20			25·00		☐	

No. 2372 does not show the Queen's head in gold as do the other nine designs.

50th Anniversary of Coronation. Booklet Stamps

2003 (2 June) Designs as T **160** (Wilding definitive of 1952) and **163** (Coronation commemorative of 1953), but with values in decimal currency as T **1348**. W **1565**. Two phosphor bands. P 15 × 14 (with one elliptical hole in each vertical side for Nos. 2378/9)

2378	**160**	47p bistre-brown	5·00	2·50	☐	☐
2379		68p grey-blue	5·00	2·50	☐	☐
2380	**163**	£1 deep yellow-green	50·00	45·00	☐	☐
Set of 3			55·00	45·00	☐	☐

Nos. 2378/80 were only available in £7.46 stamp booklets. Stamps as Nos. 2378/9, but on pale cream, were also included in the Wilding miniature sheets, Nos. **MS**2326 or **MS**2367. A £1 design as No. 2380, but on phosphorised paper, was previously included in the "Stamp Show 2000" miniature sheet, No. **MS**2147.

1672 Prince William in September 2001 (Brendan Beirne)

1673 Prince William in September 2000 (Tim Graham)

1674 Prince William in September 2001 (Camera Press)

1675 Prince William in September 2001 (Tim Graham)

21st Birthday of Prince William of Wales

2003 (17 June) Phosphor backgrounds. Perf 14½

2381	**1672**	28p multicoloured	1·00	50	☐	☐
2382	**1673**	(E) dull mauve, grey-black and light green	2·25	1·50	☐	☐
2383	**1674**	47p multicoloured	2·75	2·00	☐	☐
2384	**1675**	68p sage-green, black and bright green	4·00	2·50	☐	☐
Set of 4			9·00	6·00	☐	☐
First Day Cover				10·00		☐
Presentation Pack			25·00		☐	
PHQ Cards (*set of* 4)			7·50	20·00		☐
Set of 4 Gutter Pairs			13·00		☐	

1676 Loch Assynt, Sutherland

1677 Ben More, Isle of Mull

1678 Rothiemurchus, Cairngorms

1679 Dalveen Pass, Lowther Hills

1680 Glenfinnan Viaduct, Lochaber

1681 Papa Little, Shetland Islands

A British Journey: Scotland

2003 (15 July) One centre phosphor band (2nd) or two phosphor bands (others). Perf 14½.

		(a) Ordinary gum				
2385	**1676**	(2nd) multicoloured	50	35	☐	☐
2386	**1677**	(1st) multicoloured	75	50	☐	☐
2387	**1678**	(E) multicoloured	1·25	1·25	☐	☐
2388	**1679**	42p multicoloured	1·25	1·50	☐	☐
2389	**1680**	47p multicoloured	1·50	2·00	☐	☐
2390	**1681**	68p multicoloured	2·00	2·50	☐	☐
Set of 6			7·00	7·75	☐	☐
First Day Cover				11·00		☐
Presentation Pack			9·50		☐	
PHQ Cards (*set of 6*)			3·00	14·00	☐	☐
Set of 6 Gutter Pairs			16·00		☐	

		(b) Self-adhesive. Die-cut perf 14½				
2391	**1677**	(1st) multicoloured	6·00	6·00	☐	☐

No. 2391 was only issued in £1.68 stamp booklets in which the surplus self-adhesive paper around each stamp was removed.

1682 'The Station' (Andrew Davidson)

1683 'Black Swan' (Stanley Chew)

1684 'The Cross Keys' (George Mackenney)

1685 'The Mayflower' (Ralph Ellis)

1686 'The Barley Sheaf' (Joy Cooper)

Europa. British Pub Signs

2003 (12 Aug.) Two phosphor bands. Perf 14 × 14½

2392	**1682**	(1st) multicoloured	75	50	☐	☐
2393	**1683**	(E) multicoloured	2·00	2·00	☐	☐
2394	**1684**	42p multicoloured	1·50	1·50	☐	☐
2395	**1685**	47p multicoloured	1·75	2·00	☐	☐
2396	**1686**	68p multicoloured	2·00	2·25	☐	☐
Set of 5			7·50	7·75	☐	☐
First Day Cover				11·00		☐
Presentation Pack			11·00		☐	
PHQ Cards (*set of 5*)			3·00	12·00	☐	☐
Set of 5 Gutter Pairs			17·00		☐	

The 1st and E values incorporate the "EUROPA" emblem.

1687 Meccano Constructor Biplane, c. 1931

1688 Wells-Brimtoy Clockwork Double-decker Omnibus, c. 1938

1689 Hornby M1 Clockwork Locomotive and Tender, c. 1948

1690 Dinky Toys Ford Zephyr, c. 1956

1691 Mettoy Friction Drive Space Ship Eagle, c. 1960

Classic Transport Toys

2003 (18 Sept.) Two phosphor bands.

		(a) Photo Enschedé. Ordinary gum. Perf 14½ × 14				
2397	**1687**	(1st) multicoloured	75	50	☐	☐
2398	**1688**	(E) multicoloured	1·25	1·25	☐	☐
2399	**1689**	42p multicoloured	1·50	1·50	☐	☐
2400	**1690**	47p multicoloured	1·75	1·75	☐	☐
2401	**1691**	68p multicoloured	2·50	2·50	☐	☐
Set of 5			7·50	7·50	☐	☐
First Day Cover				10·00		☐
Presentation Pack			9·00		☐	
PHQ Cards (*set of 6*)			3·00	14·00	☐	☐
Set of 5 Gutter Pairs			16·00		☐	
MS2402 115 × 105 mm. Nos. 2397/401			8·00	8·25	☐	☐
First Day Cover				14·00		☐

		(b) Photo DLR. Self-adhesive. Die-cut perf 14½ × 14				
2403	**1687**	(1st) multicoloured	6·00	6·00	☐	☐

The complete miniature sheet is shown on one of the PHQ cards with the others depicting individual stamps.

No. 2403 was only issued in £1.68 stamp booklets in which the surplus self-adhesive paper around each stamp was removed.

1692 Coffin of Denytenamun, Egyptian, c. 900BC

1693 Alexander the Great, Greek, c. 200BC

1694 Sutton Hoo Helmet, Anglo-Saxon, c. AD600

1695 Sculpture of Parvati, South Indian, c. AD1550

1696 Mask of Xiutechuhtli, Mixtec-Aztec, c. AD1500

1697 Hoa Hakananai'a, Easter Island, c. AD1000

250th Anniversary of the British Museum

2003 (7 Oct.) One side phosphor band (2nd), two phosphor bands ((1st), (E), 47p) or phosphor background at left and band at right (42p, 68p). Perf 14 × 14½

2404	**1692**	(2nd) multicoloured	50	35	☐	☐
2405	**1693**	(1st) multicoloured	75	50	☐	☐
2406	**1694**	(E) multicoloured	1·25	1·25	☐	☐
2407	**1695**	42p multicoloured	1·50	1·50	☐	☐
2408	**1696**	47p multicoloured	2·00	2·00	☐	☐
2409	**1697**	68p multicoloured	2·75	2·75	☐	☐
Set of 6			8·00	8·00	☐	☐
First Day Cover				11·00		☐
Presentation Pack			11·00		☐	
PHQ Cards (*set of* 6)			3·00	14·00	☐	☐
Set of 6 Gutter Pairs			16·00		☐	

1698 Ice Spiral

1699 Icicle Star

1700 Wall of Ice Blocks

1701 Ice Ball

1702 Ice Hole

1703 Snow Pyramids

Christmas. Ice Sculptures by Andy Goldsworthy

2003 (4 Nov.) Self-adhesive. One side phosphor band (2nd), 'all-over' phosphor (1st) or two bands (others). Die-cut perf 14½ × 14

2410	**1698**	(2nd) multicoloured	75	35	☐	☐
2411	**1699**	(1st) multicoloured	1·25	50	☐	☐
2412	**1700**	(E) multicoloured	1·50	1·50	☐	☐
2413	**1701**	53p multicoloured	2·00	2·00	☐	☐
2414	**1702**	68p multicoloured	2·50	2·50	☐	☐
2415	**1703**	£1.12 multicoloured	3·00	3·00	☐	☐
Set of 6			10·00	10·00	☐	☐
First Day Cover				12·50		☐
Presentation Pack			12·00		☐	
PHQ Cards (*set of* 6)			4·00	14·00	☐	☐

The 2nd and 1st class were also issued in separate sheets of 20, each stamp printed in lithography instead of photogravure and accompanied by a half stamp-size *se-tenant* label showing either animals, ice sculptures or a personal photograph.

Collectors Pack 2003

2003 (4 Nov.) Comprises Nos. 2327/57, 2360/5, 2368/77, 2381/90, 2392/401 and 2404/15

CP2415a	Collectors Pack	£110	☐

Post Office Yearbook

2003 (4 Nov.) Comprises Nos. 2327/57, 2360/5, 2368/77, 2381/90, 2392/401 and 2404/15

YB2415a	Yearbook	£100	☐

1704 Rugby Scenes

England's Victory in Rugby World Cup Championship, Australia

2003 (19 Dec.) Sheet 115 × 85 mm. Multicoloured. Two phosphor bands. Perf 14

MS2416 **1704** (1st) England flags and fans; (1st) England team standing in circle before match; 68p World Cup trophy; 68p Victorious England players after match	14·00	14·00	
First Day Cover		14·00	
Presentation Pack	35·00		

1705 Dolgoch, Rheilffordd Talyllyn Railway, Gwynedd

1706 CR Class 439, Bo'ness and Kinneil Railway, West Lothian

1707 GCR Class 8K, Leicestershire

1708 GWR Manor Class Bradley Manor, Severn Valley Railway, Worcestershire

1709 SR West Country class Blackmoor Vale, Bluebell Railway, East Sussex

1710 BR Standard class, Keighley & Worth Valley Railway, Yorkshire

Classic Locomotives

2004 (13 Jan.) One side phosphor band (20p) or two phosphor bands (others). Perf 14½

2417 **1705**	20p multicoloured	65	65		
2418 **1706**	28p multicoloured	90	90		
2419 **1707**	(E) multicoloured	1·20	1·20		
2420 **1708**	42p multicoloured	1·50	1·50		
2421 **1709**	47p multicoloured	2·00	2·00		
2422 **1710**	68p multicoloured	3·00	3·50		
Set of 6		8·00	8·50		
First Day Cover			12·00		
Presentation Pack		35·00			

PHQ Cards (set of 6)	8·50	15·00	
Set of 6 Gutter Pairs	15·00		
MS2423 190 × 67 mm. Nos. 2417/22	35·00	35·00	
First Day Cover		35·00	

1711 Postman   **1712** Face

1713 Duck   **1714** Baby

1715 Aircraft

T **1711/15** were printed together, *se-tenant*, as horizontal strips of 5 in sheets of 25 (5 × 5).

'Occasions' Greetings Stamps

2004 (3 Feb.) Two phosphor bands. Perf 14½ × 14

2424 **1711**	(1st) bright mauve and black	50	50	
	a. Horiz strip of 5. Nos. 2424/8	6·00	6·00	
2425 **1712**	(1st) magenta and black	50	50	
2426 **1713**	(1st) lemon and black	50	50	
2427 **1714**	(1st) pale turquoise-green and black	50	50	
2428 **1715**	(1st) bright new blue and black	50	50	
Set of 5		6·00	6·00	
First Day Cover			8·00	
Presentation Pack		8·00		
PHQ Cards (set of 5)		4·75	12·00	
Gutter Block of 10		13·00		

Nos. 2424/8 were also issued in sheets of 20 containing the five designs *se-tenant* with half stamp-size printed message labels. Similar sheets containing either Nos. 2424 and 2428 or Nos. 2425/7 came with personal photographs on the labels.

1716 Map showing Middle Earth   **1717** Forest of Lothlórien in Spring

1718 Dust-jacket for *The Fellowship of the Ring*

1719 Rivendell

1720 The Hall at Bag End

1721 Orthanc

1722 Doors of Durin

1723 Barad-dûr

1724 Minas Tirith

1725 Fangorn Forest

T **1716/25** were printed together, *se-tenant*, in blocks of 10 (5 × 2) throughout the sheet.

50th Anniversary of Publication of *The Fellowship of the Ring* and *The Two Towers* by J. R. R. Tolkien

2004 (26 Feb.) Two phosphor bands. Perf 14½

2429	**1716**	(1st) multicoloured	50	50	☐	☐
	a. Block of 10.					
		Nos. 2429/38	10·00	10·00	☐	☐
2430	**1717**	(1st) multicoloured	50	50	☐	☐
2431	**1718**	(1st) multicoloured	50	50	☐	☐
2432	**1719**	(1st) multicoloured	50	50	☐	☐
2433	**1720**	(1st) multicoloured	50	50	☐	☐
2434	**1721**	(1st) multicoloured	50	50	☐	☐
2435	**1722**	(1st) multicoloured	50	50	☐	☐
2436	**1723**	(1st) multicoloured	50	50	☐	☐
2437	**1724**	(1st) multicoloured	50	50	☐	☐
2438	**1725**	(1st) multicoloured	50	50	☐	☐
Set of 10			10·00	10·00	☐	☐
First Day Cover				10·00		☐
Presentation Pack			30·00		☐	
PHQ Cards (*set of* 10)			9·75	18·00	☐	☐
Gutter Block of 20			22·00		☐	

1726 Ely Island, Lower Lough Erne

1727 Giant's Causeway, Antrim Coast

1728 Slemish, Antrim Mountains

1729 Banns Road, Mourne Mountains

1730 Glenelly Valley, Sperrins

1731 Islandmore, Strangford Lough

A British Journey: Northern Ireland

2004 (16 Mar.) One side phosphor band (2nd) or two phosphor bands (others). Perf 14½

		(a) Ordinary gum				
2439	**1726**	(2nd) multicoloured	65	65	☐	☐
2440	**1727**	(1st) multicoloured	90	90	☐	☐
2441	**1728**	(E) multicoloured	1·20	1·20	☐	☐
2442	**1729**	42p multicoloured	1·30	1·30	☐	☐
2443	**1730**	47p multicoloured	1·50	1·50	☐	☐
2444	**1731**	68p multicoloured	2·20	2·20	☐	☐
Set of 6			7·75	7·75	☐	☐
First Day Cover				12·50		☐
Presentation Pack			14·00		☐	
PHQ Cards (*set of* 6)			5·75	14·00	☐	☐
Set of 6 Gutter Pairs			16·00		☐	

		(b) Self-adhesive. Die-cut perf 14½				
2445	**1727**	(1st) multicoloured	6·00	6·00	☐	☐

No. 2445 was only issued in £1.68 stamp booklets in which the surplus self-adhesive paper around each stamp was removed.

1732 'Lace 1 (trial proof) 1968' (Sir Terry Frost)

1733 'Coccinelle' (Sonia Delaunay)

Centenary of the Entente Cordiale. Contemporary Paintings

2004 (6 Apr.) Two phosphor bands. Perf 14 × 14½

2446	**1732**	28p grey, black and rosine	1·00	85	☐	☐
2447	**1733**	57p multicoloured	2·25	2·00	☐	☐
Set of 2			3·00	2·75	☐	☐
First Day Cover				4·50		☐
Presentation Pack			35·00		☐	
Presentation Pack (UK and						
		French stamps)	35·00		☐	
PHQ Cards (*set of* 2)			3·50	6·00	☐	☐
Set of 2 Gutter Pairs			7·00		☐	☐
Set of 2 Traffic Light Gutter						
		Blocks of 4	15·00		☐	

Stamps in similar designs were issued by France and these are included in the joint Presentation Pack.

1734 'RMS *Queen Mary 2*, 2004' (Edward D. Walker)

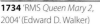

1735 'SS *Canberra* 1961' (David Cobb)

1736 'RMS *Queen Mary* 1936' (Charles Pears)

1737 'RMS *Mauretania*, 1907' (Thomas Henry)

1738 'SS *City of New York*, 1888' (Raphael Monleaon y Torres)

1739 'PS *Great Western*, 1838' (Joseph Walter)

Ocean Liners

2004 (13 Apr.) Two phosphor bands.

(a) Ordinary gum. Perf 14½ × 14

2448	**1734**	(1st) multicoloured	90	90	☐	☐
2449	**1735**	(E) multicoloured	1·30	1·30	☐	☐
2450	**1736**	42p multicoloured	1·30	1·30	☐	☐
2451	**1737**	47p multicoloured	1·50	1·50	☐	☐
2452	**1738**	57p multicoloured	1·80	1·80	☐	☐
2453	**1739**	68p multicoloured	2·20	2·20	☐	☐
Set of 6			9·00	9·00	☐	☐
First Day Cover				12·00		☐
Presentation Pack			11·00		☐	
PHQ Cards (*set of* 7)			6·75	20·00	☐	☐
Set of 6 Gutter Pairs			20·00		☐	
MS2454 114 × 104 mm. Nos. 2448/53			18·00	18·00	☐	☐
First Day Cover				18·00		☐

(b) Self-adhesive. Die-cut perf 14½ × 14

2455	**1734**	(1st) multicoloured	6·00	6·00	☐	☐

Nos. 2448/55 commemorate the introduction to service of the

Queen Mary 2.

No. 2455 was only issued in £1.68 stamp booklets in which the surplus self-adhesive paper around each stamp was removed. The complete miniature sheet is shown on one of the PHQ cards with the others depicting individual stamps.

1740 Dianthus Allwoodii Group

1741 Dahlia 'Garden Princess'

1742 Clematis 'Arabella'

1743 Miltonia 'French Lake'

1744 Lilium 'Lemon Pixie'

1745 Delphinium 'Clifford Sky'

Bicentenary of the Royal Horticultural Society (1st issue)

2004 (25 May) One side phosphor band (2nd) or 'all-over' phosphor (others). Perf 14½

2456	**1740**	(2nd) multicoloured	70	70	☐	☐
2457	**1741**	(1st) multicoloured	90	90	☐	☐
2458	**1742**	(E) multicoloured	1·30	1·30	☐	☐
2459	**1743**	42p multicoloured	2·00	2·00	☐	☐
2460	**1744**	47p multicoloured	2·50	2·50	☐	☐
2461	**1745**	68p multicoloured	3·50	3·50	☐	☐
Set of 6			10·00	10·00	☐	☐
First Day Cover				12·00		☐
Presentation Pack			11·00		☐	
PHQ Cards (*set of* 7)			6·75	20·00	☐	☐
Set of 6 Gutter Pairs			22·00		☐	
MS2462 115 × 105 mm. Nos. 2456/61			14·00	14·00	☐	☐
First Day Cover				16·00		☐

The complete miniature sheet is shown on one of the PHQ cards with the others depicting individual stamps.

The 1st class stamp was also issued in sheets of 20, printed in lithography instead of photogravure, each stamp accompanied by a *se-tenant* stamp-size label.

Bicentenary of the Royal Horticultural Society (2nd issue). Booklet stamps

2004 (25 May) Designs as Nos. 1955, 1958 and 1962 (1997 Greeting Stamps 19th-century Flower Paintings). Two phosphor bands. Perf 15 × 14 (with one elliptical hole in each vertical side)

2463	**1280**	(1st) multicoloured	8·00	8·00	☐	☐

2464	**1283**	(1st) multicoloured	4·00	4·00	☐	☐
2465	**1287**	(1st) multicoloured	8·00	8·00	☐	☐
Set of 3			18·00	18·00	☐	☐

On Nos. 2463/5 the phosphor bands appear at the left and the centre of each stamp.

Nos. 2463/5 were only available in £7.23 stamp booklets.

1746 Barmouth Bridge

1747 Hyddgen, Plynlimon

1748 Brecon Beacons

1749 Pen-pych, Rhondda Valley

1750 Rhewl, Dee Valley

1751 Marloes Sands

A British Journey: Wales

2004 (15 June) One centre phosphor band (2nd), 'all-over' phosphor (1st) or two phosphor bands (others).

(a) Ordinary gum. Perf 14½

2466	**1746**	(2nd) multicoloured	70	70	☐	☐
2467	**1747**	(1st) multicoloured	90	90	☐	☐
2468	**1748**	40p multicoloured	1·75	1·50	☐	☐
2469	**1749**	43p multicoloured	2·00	2·00	☐	☐
2470	**1750**	47p multicoloured	2·50	3·00	☐	☐
2471	**1751**	68p multicoloured	3·50	4·00	☐	☐
Set of 6			10·00	10·00	☐	☐
First Day Cover				11·00		☐
Presentation Pack			11·00		☐	
PHQ Cards (*set of 6*)			5·75	12·00	☐	☐
Set of 6 Gutter Pairs			22·00		☐	

(b) Self-adhesive. Die-cut perf 14½

2472	**1747**	(1st) multicoloured	8·00	8·00	☐	☐

The 1st and 40p values include the 'EUROPA' emblem.

No. 2472 was only issued in £1.68 stamp booklets in which the surplus self-adhesive paper around each stamp was removed.

1752 Sir Rowland Hill Award

1753 William Shipley (Founder of Royal Society of Arts)

1754 'RSA' as Typewriter Keys and Shorthand

1755 Chimney Sweep

1756 'Gill Typeface'

1757 'Zero Waste'

250th Anniversary of the Royal Society of Arts

2004 (10 Aug.) Two phosphor bands. Perf 14

2473	**1752**	(1st) multicoloured	95	95	☐	☐
2474	**1753**	40p multicoloured	1·30	1·30	☐	☐
2475	**1754**	43p multicoloured	1·40	1·40	☐	☐
2476	**1755**	47p multicoloured	1·50	1·50	☐	☐
2477	**1756**	57p silver, vermilion and black	2·20	2·20	☐	☐
2478	**1757**	68p silver, vermilion and black	3·00	3·00	☐	☐
Set of 6			10·00	10·00	☐	☐
First Day Cover				12·00		☐
Presentation Pack			11·00		☐	
PHQ Cards (*set of 6*)			5·75	14·00	☐	☐
Set of 6 Gutter Pairs			22·00		☐	

1758 Pine Marten

1759 Roe Deer

1760 Badger

1761 Yellow-necked Mouse

1762 Wild Cat

1763 Red Squirrel

1764 Stoat

1765 Natterer's Bat

1766 Mole

1767 Fox

T **1758/67** were printed together, *se-tenant*, in blocks of 10 (5 × 2) throughout the sheet.

Woodland Animals

2004 (16 Sept.) Two phosphor bands. Perf 14½

2479	**1758**	(1st) multicoloured	60	50	☐	☐
		a. Block of 10.				
		Nos. 2479/88	12·00	12·00	☐	☐
2480	**1759**	(1st) multicoloured	60	50	☐	☐
2481	**1760**	(1st) multicoloured	60	50	☐	☐
2482	**1761**	(1st) multicoloured	60	50	☐	☐
2483	**1762**	(1st) multicoloured	60	50	☐	☐
2484	**1763**	(1st) multicoloured	60	50	☐	☐
2485	**1764**	(1st) multicoloured	60	50	☐	☐
2486	**1765**	(1st) multicoloured	60	50	☐	☐
2487	**1766**	(1st) multicoloured	60	50	☐	☐
2488	**1767**	(1st) multicoloured	60	50	☐	☐
Set of 10			12·00	12·00	☐	☐
First Day Cover				13·00		☐
Presentation Pack			14·00		☐	
PHQ Cards (*set of* 10)			9·75	18·00	☐	☐
Gutter Block of 20			24·00		☐	

1768 Pte. McNamara, 5th Dragoon Guards, Heavy Brigade Charge, Battle of Balaklava

1769 Piper Muir, 42nd Regt of Foot, Amphibious Assault on Kerch

1770 Sgt. Maj. Edwards, Scots Fusilier Guards, Gallant Action, Battle of Inkerman

1771 Sgt. Powell, 1st Regt of Foot Guards, Battles of Alma and Inkerman

1772 Sgt. Maj. Poole, Royal Sappers and Miners, Defensive Line, Battle of Inkerman

1773 Sgt. Glasgow, Royal Artillery, Gun Battery besieged Sevastopol

150th Anniversary of the Crimean War

2004 (12 Oct.) One centre phosphor band (2nd) or two phosphor bands (others). Perf 14

2489	**1768**	(2nd) multicoloured	70	70	☐	☐
2490	**1769**	(1st) multicoloured	90	90	☐	☐
2491	**1770**	40p multicoloured	2·00	2·00	☐	☐
2492	**1771**	57p multicoloured	2·50	2·50	☐	☐
2493	**1772**	68p multicoloured	2·75	3·00	☐	☐
2494	**1773**	£1.12 multicoloured	4·50	5·00	☐	☐
Set of 6			12·00	12·00	☐	☐
First Day Cover				13·50		☐
Presentation Pack			14·00		☐	
PHQ Cards (*set of* 6)			5·75	16·00	☐	☐
Set of 6 Gutter Pairs			25·00		☐	
Set of 6 Traffic Light Pairs			30·00		☐	

Nos. 2489/94 show 'Crimean Heroes' photographs taken in 1856.

1774 Father Christmas on Snowy Roof

1775 Celebrating the Sunrise

1776 On Roof in Gale

1777 With Umbrella in Rain

1778 In Fog on Edge of Roof with Torch

1779 Sheltering from Hailstorm behind Chimney

Christmas

2004 (2 Nov.) One centre phosphor band (2nd) or two phosphor bands (others). Perf 14½ ×14.

(a) Self-adhesive.

2495	**1774**	(2nd) multicoloured	70	70
2496	**1775**	(1st) multicoloured	90	90
2497	**1776**	40p multicoloured	1·30	1·30
2498	**1777**	57p multicoloured	1·80	1·80
2499	**1778**	68p multicoloured	2·20	2·20
2500	**1779**	£1.12 multicoloured	3·75	3·75
Set of 6			11·00	12·00
First Day Cover				13·50
Presentation Pack			12·50	
PHQ Cards (set of 7)			6·75	18·00

(b) Ordinary gum

MS2501 115 × 105 mm.			
As Nos. 2495/500		12·00	13·00
First Day Cover			13·50

The seven PHQ cards depict the six individual stamps and the miniature sheet.

The 2nd and 1st class stamps were also issued in sheets of 20 printed in lithography instead of photogravure containing ten 1st class and ten 2nd class stamps, each stamp accompanied by a se-tenant stamp-size label showing Father Christmas. Separate sheets of either 20 1st or 20 2nd class were available with personal photographs.

Collectors Pack 2004

2004 (2 Nov.) Comprises Nos. 2417/22, 2424/44, 2446/53, 2456/61, 2466/71 and 2473/2500

CP2500a	Collectors Pack	£120

Post Office Yearbook

2004 (2 Nov.) Comprises Nos. 2417/22, 2424/44, 2446/53, 2456/61, 2466/71 and 2473/2500

YB2500a	Yearbook	£110

1780 British Saddleback Pigs

1781 Khaki Campbell Ducks

1782 Clydesdale Mare and Foal

1783 Dairy Shorthorn Cattle

1784 Border Collie Dog

1785 Light Sussex Chicks

1786 Suffolk Sheep

1787 Bagot Goat

1788 Norfolk Black Turkeys

1789 Embden Geese

T **1780/9** were printed together, se-tenant, in blocks of 10 (5 × 2) throughout the sheet.

Farm Animals

2005 (11 Jan.) Two phosphor bands. Perf 14½

2502	**1780**	(1st) multicoloured	50	60
		a. Block of 10.		
		Nos. 2502/11	12·00	12·00
2503	**1781**	(1st) multicoloured	50	60
2504	**1782**	(1st) multicoloured	50	60
2505	**1783**	(1st) multicoloured	50	60
2506	**1784**	(1st) multicoloured	50	60
2507	**1785**	(1st) multicoloured	50	60
2508	**1786**	(1st) multicoloured	50	60
2509	**1787**	(1st) multicoloured	50	60
2510	**1788**	(1st) multicoloured	50	60
2511	**1789**	(1st) multicoloured	50	60
Set of 10			12·00	12·00
First Day Cover				12·00
Presentation Pack			14·00	
PHQ Cards (set of 10)			9·75	15·00
Gutter Block of 20			24·00	
Traffic Light Gutter Block of 20			26·00	

Nos. 2502/11 were also issued in sheets of 20, printed in lithography instead of photogravure, containing two of each of the ten designs, arranged in vertical strips of five alternated with printed labels.

1790 Old Harry Rocks, Studland Bay

1791 Wheal Coates, St. Agnes

1792 Start Point, Start Bay

1793 Horton Down, Wiltshire

1794 Chiselcombe, Exmoor

1795 St. James's Stone, Lundy

A British Journey. South West England

2005 (8 Feb.) One centre phosphor band (2nd) or two phosphor bands (others). Perf 14½

2512	**1790**	(2nd) multicoloured	50	50
2513	**1791**	(1st) multicoloured	50	75
2514	**1792**	40p multicoloured	1·50	1·75
2515	**1793**	43p multicoloured	1·75	2·00
2516	**1794**	57p multicoloured	2·50	2·50
2517	**1795**	68p multicoloured	3·50	3·00
Set of 6			10·00	10·00
First Day Cover				12·00
Presentation Pack			11·00	
PHQ Cards (*set of* 6)			4·25	14·00
Set of 6 Gutter Pairs			21·00	

1796 'Mr Rochester'

1797 'Come to Me'

1798 'In the Comfort of her Bonnet

1799 'La Ligne des Rats'

1800 'Refectory'

1801 'Inspection'

150th Death Anniversary of Charlotte Brontë. Illustrations of Scenes from *Jane Eyre* by Paula Rego

2005 (24 Feb.) One centre phosphor band (2nd) or two phosphor bands (others). Perf 14 × 14½

2518	**1796**	(2nd) multicoloured	30	35
2519	**1797**	(1st) multicoloured	50	45
2520	**1798**	40p multicoloured	1·50	1·50
2521	**1799**	57p silver, brownish grey and black	3·00	2·50
2522	**1800**	68p multicoloured	3·75	3·00
2523	**1801**	£1.12 silver, brownish grey and black	4·50	3·50
Set of 6			12·00	11·00
First Day Cover				12·00
Presentation Pack			12·00	
PHQ Cards (*set of* 6)			11·00	18·00
Set of 6 Gutter Pairs			24·00	
Set of 6 Traffic Light gutter blocks of four			42·00	
MS2524 114 × 105 mm. Nos. 2518/23			10·00	10·00
First Day Cover				12·00

The complete miniature sheet is shown on one of the PHQ cards with the others depicting individual stamps.

1802 Spinning Coin

1803 Rabbit out of Hat Trick

1804 Knotted Scarf Trick

1805 Card Trick

1806 Pyramid under Fez Trick

Centenary of the Magic Circle

2005 (15 Mar.) Two phosphor bands. Perf 14½ × 14

2525	**1802**	(1st) multicoloured	65	45	☐	☐
2526	**1803**	40p multicoloured	1·00	65	☐	☐
2527	**1804**	47p multicoloured	2·50	2·75	☐	☐
2528	**1805**	68p multicoloured	3·00	3·00	☐	☐
2529	**1806**	£1.12 multicoloured	3·50	3·50	☐	☐
Set of 5			10·00	10·00	☐	☐
First Day Cover				11·75		☐
Presentation Pack			15·00		☐	
PHQ Cards (*set of 5*)			5·00	12·00	☐	☐
Set of 5 Gutter Pairs			21·00		☐	☐

Nos. 2525/9 are each printed with instructions for the illusion or trick on the stamp.

No. 2525 can be rubbed with a coin to reveal the 'head' or 'tail' of a coin. The two versions, which appear identical before rubbing, are printed in alternate rows of the sheet, indicated by the letters H and T in the side margins of the sheet.

No. 2525 was also issued in sheets of 20 with *se-tenant* labels showing magic tricks, printed in lithography instead of photogravure.

Nos. 2526 and 2528 each show optical illusions.

The spotted scarf on No. 2527 and the fezzes on No. 2529 are printed in thermochromic inks which fade temporarily when exposed to heat, making the pyramid under the centre fez visible.

50th Anniversary of First Castles Definitives

2005 (22 Mar.) Sheet 127 × 73 mm, containing horiz designs as T 166/9 (Castles definitive of 1955-58) but with values in decimal currency, printed on pale cream. 'All-over' phosphor. Perf 11 × 11½

MS2530	**166**	50p brownish-black;				
	169	50p black; **167** £1 dull				
		vermilion; **168** £1 royal blue	10·00	10·00	☐	☐
First Day Cover				12·00		☐
Presentation Pack			18·00		☐	
PHQ Cards (*set of 5*)			2·20	12·00	☐	☐

1807 Prince Charles and Mrs Camilla Parker Bowles

Royal Wedding

2005 (9 Apr.) Sheet 85 × 115 mm. Multicoloured. 'All-over' phosphor. Perf 13½ × 14

MS2531	**1807**	30p × 2 Prince Charles				
		and Mrs Camilla Parker Bowles				
		laughing; 68p × 2 Prince Charles				
		and Mrs Camilla Parker Bowles				
		smiling into camera	8·00	10·00	☐	☐
First Day Cover				10·00		☐
Presentation Pack			18·00		☐	

1808 Hadrian's Wall, England   **1809** Uluru-Kata Tjuta National Park, Australia

1810 Stonehenge, England   **1811** Wet Tropics of Queensland, Australia

1812 Blenheim Palace, England   **1813** Greater Blue Mountains Area, Australia

1814 Heart of Neolithic Orkney, Scotland   **1815** Purnululu National Park, Australia

Nos. 2532/3, 2534/5, 2536/7 and 2538/9 were each printed together, *se-tenant*, in horizontal pairs.

World Heritage Sites

2005 (21 Apr.) One side phosphor band (2nd) or two phosphor bands (others). Perf 14½

2532	**1808**	(2nd) multicoloured	30	35	☐	☐
		a. Horiz pair.				
		Nos. 2532/3	1·00	1·00	☐	☐
2533	**1809**	(2nd) multicoloured	30	35	☐	☐
2534	**1810**	(1st) multicoloured	45	45	☐	☐
		a. Horiz pair.				
		Nos. 2534/5	2·00	1·50	☐	☐
2535	**1811**	(1st) multicoloured	45	45	☐	☐

2536 **1812**	47p multicoloured		60	60	☐	☐
	a. Horiz pair.					
	Nos. 2536/7		3·00	3·50	☐	☐
2537 **1813**	47p multicoloured		60	60	☐	☐
2538 **1814**	68p multicoloured		90	90	☐	☐
	a. Horiz pair.					
	Nos. 2538/9		5·00	5·00	☐	☐
2539 **1815**	68p multicoloured		90	90	☐	☐
Set of 8			11·00	11·00	☐	☐
First Day Cover				13·00		☐
Presentation Pack			12·00		☐	
Presentation Pack						
(UK and Australian stamps)			16·00		☐	
PHQ Cards (*set of* 8)			5·00	16·00	☐	☐
Set of 4 Gutter Strips of 4			16·50		☐	
Set of 4 Traffic Light Gutter Blocks of 8			35·00		☐	

Stamps in these designs were also issued by Australia and these are included in the joint Presentation Pack.

1816 Ensign of the Scots Guards, 2002

1817 Queen taking the salute as Colonel-in-Chief of the Grenadier Guards, 1983

1818 Trumpeter of the Household Calvalry, 2004

1819 Welsh Guardsman, 1990s

1820 Queen riding side-saddle, 1972

1821 Queen and Duke of Edinburgh in Carriage, 2004

Trooping the Colour

2005 (7 June) One phosphor band (2nd), two phosphor bands (others). Perf 14½

2540 **1816**	(2nd) multicoloured	70	80	☐	☐
2541 **1817**	(1st) multicoloured	75	90	☐	☐
2542 **1818**	42p multicoloured	1·00	1·20	☐	☐
2543 **1819**	60p multicoloured	2·00	2·00	☐	☐
2544 **1820**	68p multicoloured	2·50	2·50	☐	☐
2545 **1821**	£1.12 multicoloured	3·50	3·50	☐	☐
Set of 6		10·00	10·00	☐	☐
First Day Cover			12·00		☐
Presentation Pack		12·00		☐	
PHQ Cards (*set of* 6)		5·00	20·00	☐	☐
Set of 6 Gutter Pairs		21·00		☐	
MS2546 115 × 105 mm. Nos. 2540/5		11·00	11·00	☐	☐

First Day Cover		12·00	☐

1822

60th Anniversary of End of the Second World War

2005 (5 July) Sheet 115 × 105 mm containing design as T **1200** (1995 Peace and Freedom) but with service indicator and No. 1664b × 5. Two phosphor bands. Perf 15 × 14 (with one elliptical hole in each vertical side) (1664b) or 14½ × 14 (other)

MS2547 **1822**	(1st) gold × 5; (1st)				
	silver, blue and grey-black	6·00	6·00	☐	☐
First Day Cover			8·00		☐

1823 Norton F.1, Road Version of Race Winner (1991)

1824 BSA Rocket 3, Early Three Cylinder 'Superbike' (1969)

1825 Vincent Black Shadow, Fastest Standard Motorcycle (1949)

1826 Triumph Speed Twin, Two Cylinder Innovation (1938)

1827 Brough Superior, Bespoke Luxury Motorcycle (1930)

1828 Royal Enfield, Small Engined Motor Bicycle (1914)

Motorcycles

2005 (19 July) Two phosphor bands. Perf 14 × 14½

2548	**1823**	(1st) multicoloured	75	80	☐	☐
2549	**1824**	40p multicoloured	90	1·00	☐	☐
2550	**1825**	42p multicoloured	1·25	1·00	☐	☐
2551	**1826**	47p multicoloured	1·75	2·00	☐	☐
2552	**1827**	60p multicoloured	2·50	2·50	☐	☐
2553	**1828**	68p multicoloured	3·00	3·00	☐	☐
Set of 6			9·00	9·00	☐	☐
First Day Cover				12·00		☐
Presentation Pack			15·00		☐	
PHQ Cards (set of 6)			5·00	14·00	☐	☐
Set of 6 Gutter Pairs			19·00		☐	

1829

London's Successful Bid for Olympic Games, 2012

2005 (5 Aug.) Sheet 115 × 105 mm containing designs as T **1255/9**, but with service indicator. Multicoloured. Two phosphor bands. Perf 14½

MS2554	**1829**	(1st) Athlete celebrating × 2; (1st) Throwing the javelin; (1st) Swimming; (1st) Athlete on starting blocks; (1st) Basketball	6·00	6·00	☐	☐
First Day Cover				8·00		☐
Presentation Pack			12·00		☐	

Stamps from **MS**2554 are all inscribed 'London 2012—Host City' and have imprint date '2005'. The design as Type 1259 omits the Olympic rings.

1830 African Woman eating Rice

1831 Indian Woman drinking Tea

1832 Boy eating Sushi

1833 Woman eating Pasta

1834 Woman eating Chips

1835 Teenage Boy eating Apple

Europa. Gastronomy. Changing Tastes in Britain

2005 (23 Aug.) One side phosphor band (2nd) or two phosphor bands (others). Perf 14½

2555	**1830**	(2nd) multicoloured	60	70	☐	☐
2556	**1831**	(1st) multicoloured	90	1·00	☐	☐
2557	**1832**	42p multicoloured	1·30	1·40	☐	☐
2558	**1833**	47p multicoloured	1·50	1·60	☐	☐
2559	**1834**	60p multicoloured	2·00	1·90	☐	☐
2560	**1835**	68p multicoloured	2·50	2·20	☐	☐
Set of 6			8·00	8·00	☐	☐
First Day Cover				10·00		☐
Presentation Pack			9·00		☐	
PHQ Cards (set of 6)			5·00	12·00	☐	☐
Set of 6 Gutter Pairs			17·00		☐	

The 1st and 42p values include the 'EUROPA' emblem.

1836 Inspector Morse

1837 Emmerdale

1838 Rising Damp

1839 The Avengers

1840 The South Bank Show

1841 Who Wants to be a Millionaire

50th Anniversary of Independent Television. Classic ITV Programmes

2005 (15 Sept.) One side phosphor band (2nd) or two phosphor bands (others). Perf 14½ × 14.

2561	**1836**	(2nd) multicoloured	60	70	☐	☐
2562	**1837**	(1st) multicoloured	90	1·00	☐	☐
2563	**1838**	42p multicoloured	1·30	1·40	☐	☐
2564	**1839**	47p multicoloured	1·40	1·50	☐	☐
2565	**1840**	60p multicoloured	2·00	1·90	☐	☐
2566	**1841**	68p multicoloured	2·20	2·20	☐	☐
Set of 6			8·00	8·00	☐	☐
First Day Cover				12·00		☐
Presentation Pack			9·00		☐	

PHQ Cards (*set of 6*)	5·00	12·00	☐	☐
Set of 6 Gutter Pairs	17·00		☐	

The 1st class stamps were also issued in sheets of 20 with each stamp accompanied by a half stamp-size *se-tenant* label.

1842 Gazania Splendens (Charlotte Sowerby)   **1842a** "LOVE"

Nos. 2567/72 were printed together, *se-tenant*, in booklet panes of 6 in which the surplus self-adhesive paper around each stamp was removed.

'Smilers' Booklet stamps (1st series)

2005 (4 Oct.) Designs as Types **992, 1221, 1286, 1517** and 1568/9 but smaller, 20 × 23 mm, and inscribed 1st as T **1842**. Self-adhesive. Two phosphor bands. Die-cut perf 15 × 14.

2567	**1842**	(1st) multicoloured	2·00	2·00	☐	☐
		a· Booklet pane·				
		Nos· 2567/72	12·00	12·00	☐	☐
2568	**1569**	(1st) multicoloured	2·00	2·00	☐	☐
2569	**1842a**	(1st) multicoloured	2·00	2·00	☐	☐
2570	**1517**	(1st) multicoloured	2·00	2·00	☐	☐
2571	**992**	(1st) multicoloured	2·00	2·00	☐	☐
2572	**1221**	(1st) multicoloured	2·00	2·00	☐	☐
Set of 6			12·00	12·00	☐	☐
First Day Cover				12·00		☐

Nos. 2567/72 were re-issued on 4 July 2006 in sheets of 20 with *se-tenant* labels, printed in lithography instead of photogravure.

Nos. 2568/70 were re-issued on 18 January 2008 in sheets of 20 with circular *se-tenant* labels, printed in lithography.

No. 2567 was re-issued on 28 October 2008 in sheets of 10 with circular *se-tenant* 'Flower Fairy' labels, printed in lithography.

Stamps as Nos. 2569 and 2572 but perforated with one elliptical hole on each vertical side were issued, together with Nos. 2674 and 2821/3 and four designs from **MS**3024, on 8 May 2010 in sheets of 20 stamps with *se-tenant* greetings labels.

THE ASHES ENGLAND WINNERS 2005

1843 Cricket Scenes

England's Ashes Victory

2005 (6 Oct.) Sheet 115 × 90 mm. Multicoloured. Two phosphor bands. Perf 14½ ×14.

MS2573   **1843**   (1st) England team with Ashes trophy; (1st) Kevin

Pieterson, Michael Vaughan and Andrew Flintoff on opening day of First Test, Lords; 68p Michael Vaughan, Third Test, Old Trafford; 68p Second Test Edgbaston   7·50   7·50   ☐   ☐

First Day Cover		10·00		☐
Presentation Pack		10·00	☐	

1844 *Entrepreante* with dismasted British *Belle Isle*

1845 Nelson wounded on Deck of HMS *Victory*

1846 British Cutter *Entrepreante* attempting to rescue Crew of burning French *Achille*

1847 Cutter and HMS *Pickle* (schooner)

1848 British Fleet attacking in Two Columns

1849 Franco/Spanish Fleet putting to Sea from Cadiz

Nos. 2574/5, 2576/7 and 2578/9 were each printed together, *se-tenant*, in horizontal pairs throughout the sheets, each pair forming a composite design.

Bicentenary of the Battle of Trafalgar (1st issue). Scenes from 'Panorama of the Battle of Trafalgar' by William Heath

2005 (18 Oct.) Two phosphor bands. Perf 15 × 14½

2574	**1844**	(1st) multicoloured	45	45	☐	☐
		a. Horiz pair.				
		Nos. 2574/5	1·75	2·00	☐	☐
2575	**1845**	(1st) multicoloured	45	45	☐	☐
2576	**1846**	42p multicoloured	65	65	☐	☐
		a. Horiz pair.				
		Nos. 2576/7	2·50	2·75	☐	☐
2577	**1847**	42p multicoloured	65	65	☐	☐
2578	**1848**	68p multicoloured	90	90	☐	☐
		a. Horiz pair.				

	Nos. 2578/9	1·00	4·40	☐	☐
2579 **1849**	68p multicoloured	90	90	☐	☐
Set of 6		9·00	10·00	☐	☐
First Day Cover			11·00		☐
Presentation Pack		12·00		☐	
PHQ Cards (*set of 7*)		5·00	20·00	☐	☐
Set of 3 Gutter Strips of 4		11·00		☐	
MS2580 190 × 68 mm. Nos. 2574/9		10·00	11·00	☐	☐
First Day Cover			11·00		☐

The phosphor bands are at just left of centre and at right of each stamp

The seven PHQ cards depict the six individual stamps and the miniature sheet.

Bicentenary of the Battle of Trafalgar (2nd issue). Booklet stamp.

2005 (18 Oct.) Design as Type 1516 (White Ensign from 2001 Submarine Centenary). Two phosphor bands. Perf 14½.

2581 **1516**	(1st) multicoloured	6·75	6·75	☐	☐

No. 2581 was only available from two stamp booklets, sold for £7.26 and £7.40.

1850 Black Madonna and Child from Haiti

1851 'Madonna and Child' (Marianne Stokes)

1852 'The Virgin Mary with the Infant Christ'

1853 Choctaw Virgin Mother and Child (Fr. John Giuliani)

1854 'Madonna and the Infant Jesus' (from India)

1855 'Come let us adore Him' (Dianne Tchumut)

Christmas. Madonna and Child Paintings

2005 (1 Nov.) One side phosphor band (2nd) or two phosphor bands (others). Perf 14½ × 14

(a) Self-adhesive					
2582 **1850**	(2nd) multicoloured	60	70	☐	☐
2583 **1851**	(1st) multicoloured	90	1·00	☐	☐
2584 **1852**	42p multicoloured	1·30	1·40	☐	☐
2585 **1853**	60p multicoloured	1·80	1·90	☐	☐
2586 **1854**	68p multicoloured	2·00	2·20	☐	☐
2587 **1855**	£1.12 multicoloured	3·40	3·60	☐	☐
Set of 6		10·00	11·00	☐	☐
First Day Cover			12·00		☐
Presentation Pack		11·00		☐	

PHQ Cards (*set of 7*)		4·00	16·00	☐	☐

(b) Ordinary gum					
MS2588 115 × 102 mm.					
As Nos. 2582/7		10·50	11·00	☐	☐
First Day Cover			12·00		☐

The seven PHQ cards depict the six individual stamps and the miniature sheet.

Collectors Pack

2005 (1 Nov.) Comprises Nos. 2502/23, 2525/9, **MS**2531/45, 2548/53, 2555/66, 2574/9 and 2582/7

CP2587a	Collectors Pack	95·00	☐

Post Office Yearbook

2005 (1 Nov.) Comprises Nos. 2502/23, 2525/9, **MS**2531/45, 2548/53, 2555/66, 2574/9 and 2582/7

YB2587a	Yearbook	95·00	☐

Miniature Sheet Collection

2005 (21 Nov.) Comprises Nos. MS2524, MS2530/1, MS2546/7, MS2554, MS2573, MS2580 and MS2588 MS2588a Miniature Sheet Collection 75·00 ☐

1856 *The Tale of Mr. Jeremy Fisher* (Beatrix Potter)

1857 *Kipper* (Mick Inkpen)

1858 *The Enormous Crocodile* (Roald Dahl)

1859 *More About Paddington* (Michael Bond)

1860 *Comic Adventures of Boots* (Satoshi Kitamura)

1861 *Alice's Adventures in Wonderland* (Lewis Carroll)

1862 *The Very Hungry Caterpillar* (Eric Carle)

1863 *Maisy's ABC* (Lucy Cousins)

Nos. 2589/90, 2591/2, 2593/4 and 2595/6 were printed together, *se-tenant*, as horizontal pairs in sheets of 60 (2 panes 6 × 5).

Animal Tales

2006 (10 Jan.) One side phosphor band (2nd) or two phosphor bands (others). Perf 14½

2589	**1856**	(2nd) multicoloured	40	35	☐	☐	
		a. Horiz pair.					
		Nos. 2589/90	70	70	☐	☐	
2590	**1857**	(2nd) multicoloured	40	35	☐	☐	
2591	**1858**	(1st) multicoloured	50	50	☐	☐	
		a. Horiz pair.					
		Nos. 2591/2	1·50	1·50	☐	☐	
2592	**1859**	(1st) multicoloured	50	50	☐	☐	
2593	**1860**	42p multicoloured	65	70	☐	☐	
		a. Horiz pair.					
		Nos. 2593/4	4·00	4·00	☐	☐	
2594	**1861**	42p multicoloured	65	70	☐	☐	
2595	**1862**	68p multicoloured	1·00	1·10	☐	☐	
		a. Horiz pair.					
		Nos. 2595/6	5·00	5·00	☐	☐	
2596	**1863**	68p multicoloured	1·00	1·10	☐	☐	
Set of 8			10·00	10·00	☐		
First Day Cover				11·00		☐	
Presentation Pack			12·00		☐		
PHQ Cards (*set of* 8)			4·50	16·00	☐	☐	
Set of 4 Gutter Blocks of 4			13·00		☐		
Set of 4 Traffic Light Gutter Blocks of 8			28·00		☐		

No. 2595 contains two die-cut holes.

A design as No. 2592 but self-adhesive was also issued in sheets of 20 with each stamp accompanied by a *se-tenant* label.

1864 Carding Mill Valley, Shropshire

1865 Beachy Head, Sussex

1866 St. Paul's Cathedral, London

1867 Brancaster, Norfolk

1868 Derwent Edge, Peak District

1869 Robin Hood's Bay, Yorkshire

1870 Buttermere, Lake District

1871 Chipping Campden, Cotswolds

1872 St. Boniface Down, Isle of Wight

1873 Chamberlain Square, Birmingham

Nos. 2597/606 were printed together, *se-tenant*, as blocks of ten (5 × 2) in sheets of 60 (2 panes of 30).

A British Journey: England

2006 (7 Feb.) Two phosphor bands. Perf 14½

2597	**1864**	(1st) multicoloured	50	50	☐	☐	
		a. Block of 10.					
		Nos. 2597/606	10·00	10·00	☐	☐	
2598	**1865**	(1st) multicoloured	50	50	☐	☐	
2599	**1866**	(1st) multicoloured	50	50	☐	☐	
2600	**1867**	(1st) multicoloured	50	50	☐	☐	
2601	**1868**	(1st) multicoloured	50	50	☐	☐	
2602	**1869**	(1st) multicoloured	50	50	☐	☐	
2603	**1870**	(1st) multicoloured	50	50	☐	☐	
2604	**1871**	(1st) multicoloured	50	50	☐	☐	
2605	**1872**	(1st) multicoloured	50	50	☐	☐	
2606	**1873**	(1st) multicoloured	50	50	☐	☐	
Set of 10			10·00	10·00	☐	☐	
First Day Cover				11·00		☐	
Presentation Pack			12·00		☐		
PHQ Cards (*set of* 10)			5·75	16·00	☐	☐	
Gutter Block of 20			20·00		☐		

1874 Royal Albert Bridge

1875 Box Tunnel

1876 Paddington Station

1877 PSS Great Eastern (paddle steamer)

1878 Clifton Suspension Bridge Design

1879 Maidenhead Bridge

Birth Bicentenary of Isambard Kingdom Brunel (engineer) (1st issue)

2006 (23 Feb.) Phosphor-coated paper (42p) or two phosphor bands (others). Perf 14 × 13½

2607	**1874**	(1st) multicoloured	50	50	☐	☐
2608	**1875**	40p multicoloured	75	75	☐	☐
2609	**1876**	42p multicoloured	1·00	1·00	☐	☐
2610	**1877**	47p multicoloured	1·50	1·00	☐	☐
2611	**1878**	60p multicoloured	2·00	1·75	☐	☐
2612	**1879**	68p multicoloured	2·50	2·25	☐	☐
Set of 6			8·00	8·00	☐	☐
First Day Cover				9·00		☐
Presentation Pack			10·00		☐	
PHQ Cards (*set of 7*)			4·00	14·00	☐	☐
Set of 6 Gutter Pairs			16·00		☐	
MS2613 190 × 65 mm. Nos. 2607/12			8·50	8·50	☐	☐
First Day Cover				9·00	☐	☐

The phosphor bands on Nos. 2607/8 and 2610/12 are at just left of centre and at right of each stamp.

The complete miniature sheet is shown on one of the PHQ cards with the others depicting individual stamps.

Birth Bicentenary of Isambard Kingdom Brunel (engineer) (2nd issue). Booklet stamp

2006 (23 Feb.) Design as Type **1739** (PS Great Western from 2004 Ocean Liners). Two phosphor bands. Perf 14½ × 14

2614	**1739**	68p multicoloured	10·00	10·50	☐	☐

No. 2614 was only available in £7·40 stamp booklets.

1880 Sabre-tooth Cat

1881 Giant Deer

1882 Woolly Rhino

1883 Woolly Mammoth

1884 Cave Bear

Ice Age Animals

2006 (21 Mar.) Two phosphor bands. Perf 14½

2615	**1880**	(1st) black and silver	50	50	☐	☐
2616	**1881**	42p black and silver	75	80	☐	☐
2617	**1882**	47p black and silver	2·00	2·00	☐	☐
2618	**1883**	68p black and silver	2·25	2·25	☐	☐
2619	**1884**	£1·12 black and silver	3·25	3·25	☐	☐
Set of 5			8·50	8·50	☐	☐
First Day Cover				9·00		☐
Presentation Pack			12·00		☐	
PHQ Cards (*set of 5*)			2·75	12·00	☐	☐
Set of 5 Gutter Pairs			16·00		☐	

1885 On *Britannia*, 1972

1886 At Royal Windsor Horse Show, 1985

1887 At Heathrow Airport, 2001

1888 As Young Princess Elizabeth with Duchess of York, 1931

1889 At State Banquet, Ottawa, 1951

1890 Queen Elizabeth II in 1960

1891 As Princess Elizabeth, 1940

1892 With Duke of Edinburgh, 1951

Nos. 2620/1, 2622/3, 2624/5 and 2626/7 were each printed together, *se-tenant*, as horizontal pairs in sheets of 60 (2 panes 6 × 5).

80th Birthday of Queen Elizabeth II

2006 (18 Apr.) One side phosphor band (No. 2620), one centre phosphor band (No. 2621) or two phosphor bands (others). Perf 14½

2620	**1885**	(2nd)	black, turquoise green and grey	40	40	☐ ☐
		a.	Horiz pair. Nos. 2620/1	95	95	☐ ☐
2621	**1886**	(2nd)	black, turquoise-green and grey	40	40	☐ ☐
2622	**1887**	(1st)	black, turquoise-green and grey	50	45	☐ ☐
		a.	Horiz pair. Nos. 2622/3	1·75	1·75	☐ ☐
2623	**1888**	(1st)	black, turquoise-green and grey	50	50	☐ ☐
2624	**1889**	44p	black, turquoise-green and grey	65	65	☐ ☐
		a.	Horiz pair. Nos. 2624/5	2·75	2·75	☐ ☐
2625	**1890**	44p	black, turquoise-green and grey	65	65	☐ ☐
2626	**1891**	72p	black, turquoise-green and grey	1·10	1·10	☐ ☐
		a.	Horiz pair. Nos. 2626/7	4·50	4·50	☐ ☐
2627	**1892**	72p	black, turquoise-green and grey	1·10	1·10	☐ ☐
Set of 8				9·50	9·50	☐ ☐
First Day Cover					10·00	☐
Presentation Pack				12·00		☐
PHQ Cards (set of 8)				4·50	16·00	☐ ☐
Set of 4 Gutter Strips of 4				19·00		☐

1893 England (1966)

1894 Italy (1934, 1938, 1982)

1895 Argentina (1978, 1986)

1896 Germany (1954, 1974, 1990)

64
1897 France (1998)

72
1898 Brazil (1958, 1962, 1970, 1994, 2002)

World Cup Football Championship, Germany. World Cup Winners

2006 (6 June) Two phosphor bands. Perf 14½

2628	**1893**	(1st) multicoloured	50	50	☐ ☐
2629	**1894**	42p multicoloured	65	70	☐ ☐
2630	**1895**	44p multicoloured	1·25	1·25	☐ ☐
2631	**1896**	50p multicoloured	2·00	2·00	☐ ☐
2632	**1897**	64p multicoloured	3·00	3·00	☐ ☐
2633	**1898**	72p multicoloured	3·50	3·50	☐ ☐
Set of 6			9·00	9·00	☐ ☐
First Day Cover				9·00	☐
Presentation Pack			12·00		☐
PHQ Cards (set of 6)			4·00	12·00	☐ ☐
Set of 6 Gutter Pairs			18·00		☐

The 1st class stamp was also issued in sheets of 20 with each stamp accompanied by a *se-tenant* label showing scenes from the 1966 World Cup final.

1899 30 St. Mary Axe, London

1900 Maggie's Centre, Dundee

1901 Selfridges, Birmingham

1902 Downland Gridshell, Chichester

1903 An Turas, Isle of Tiree

1904 The Deep, Hull

Modern Architecture

2006 (20 June). Two phosphor bands. Perf 14½

2634	**1899**	(1st) multicoloured	45	50	☐	☐
2635	**1900**	42p multicoloured	65	70	☐	☐
2636	**1901**	44p multicoloured	1·25	1·25	☐	☐
2637	**1902**	50p multicoloured	2·00	2·00	☐	☐
2638	**1903**	64p multicoloured	3·00	3·00	☐	☐
2639	**1904**	72p multicoloured	3·50	3·50	☐	☐
Set of 6			9·00	9·00	☐	☐
First Day Cover				9·00		☐
Presentation Pack			12·00		☐	
PHQ Cards (set of 6)			4·00	12·00	☐	☐
Set of 6 Gutter Pairs			18·00		☐	

1905 'Sir Winston Churchill' (Walter Sickert)

1906 'Sir Joshua Reynolds' (self-portrait)

1907 'T. S. Eliot' (Patrick Heron)

1908 'Emmeline Pankhurst' (Georgina Agnes Brackenbury)

1909 Virginia Woolf (photo by George Charles Beresford)

1910 Bust of Sir Walter Scott (Sir Francis Leggatt Chantry)

1911 'Mary Seacole' (Albert Charles Challen)

1912 'William Shakespeare' (attrib to John Taylor)

1913 'Dame Cicely Saunders' (Catherine Goodman)

1914 'Charles Darwin' (John Collier)

Nos. 2640/9 were printed together, *se-tenant*, as blocks of ten (5 × 2) in sheets of 60 (2 panes of 30).

150th Anniversary of National Portrait Gallery, London

2006 (18 July) Two phosphor bands. Perf 14½

2640	**1905**	(1st) multicoloured	50	50	☐	☐
		a. Block of 10.				
		Nos. 2640/9	9·00	9·00	☐	☐
2641	**1906**	(1st) multicoloured	50	50	☐	☐
2642	**1907**	(1st) multicoloured	50	50	☐	☐
2643	**1908**	(1st) multicoloured	50	50	☐	☐
2644	**1909**	(1st) multicoloured	50	50	☐	☐
2645	**1910**	(1st) multicoloured	50	50	☐	☐
2646	**1911**	(1st) multicoloured	50	50	☐	☐
2647	**1912**	(1st) multicoloured	50	50	☐	☐
2648	**1913**	(1st) multicoloured	50	50	☐	☐
2649	**1914**	(1st) multicoloured	50	50	☐	☐
Set of 10			9·00	9·00	☐	☐
First Day Cover				10·00		☐
Presentation Pack			12·00		☐	
PHQ Cards (set of 10)			6·75	16·00	☐	☐
Gutter Block of 20			19·00		☐	
Traffic Light Gutter Block of 20			25·00		☐	

1915

1916

'Pricing in Proportion'

2006 (1 Aug–12 Sept.) Perf 15 × 14 (with one elliptical hole in each vertical side).

(a) Ordinary gum. Photo De La Rue (No. 2651 also from Enschedé prestige booklet).

		(i) As T **1915**				
2650	(2nd)	bright blue (1 centre band)	65	40	☐	☐
2651	(1st)	gold (2 bands)	75	50	☐	☐

		(ii) As T **1916**.				
2652	(2nd Large)	bright blue (2 bands)	1·00	60	☐	☐
2653	(1st Large)	gold (2 bands)	1·50	70	☐	☐

(b) Self-adhesive. Photo Walsall.

		(i) As T **1915**				
2654	(2nd)	bright blue (1 centre band)				
		(12 Sept)	65	40	☐	☐
2655	(1st)	gold (2 bands) (12 Sept)	75	50	☐	☐

(ii) As T 1916.

2656 (2nd Large)	bright blue (2 bands)		
	(15 Aug)	1·00	60 ☐ ☐
2657 (1st Large)	gold (2 bands) (15 Aug)	1·40	70 ☐ ☐
First Day Cover (Nos. Y1676b/c, 2650/3)		5·00	☐
Presentation Pack			
(Nos. Y1676b/c, 2650/3)		4·75	☐

No. 2654 was issued in booklets of twelve sold at £2.76.

No. 2655 was available in booklets of six or twelve, sold at £1.92 or £3.84.

Nos. 2656/7 were issued in separate booklets of four, sold at £1.48 or £1.76.

All these booklets had the surplus self-adhesive paper around each stamp removed.

1917

70th Anniversary of the Year of Three Kings

2006 (31 Aug.) Sheet 127 × 72 mm containing No. Y1728. Multicoloured. Two phosphor bands. Perf 15 × 14 (with one elliptical hole in each vertical side).

MS2658	**1917**	£3 deep mauve	10·00	10·00 ☐ ☐
First Day Cover			11·00	☐

1918 Corporal Agansing Rai

1919 Boy Seaman Jack Cornwell

1920 Midshipman Charles Lucas

1921 Captain Noel Chavasse

1922 Captain Albert Ball

1923 Captain Charles Upham

Nos. 2659/60, 2661/2 and 2663/4 were each printed together, *se-tenant*, as horizontal pairs in sheets of 60 (2 panes 6 × 5).

150th Anniversary of the Victoria Cross (1st issue)

2006 (21 Sept.) One side phosphor band. Perf 14½ × 14

2659	**1918**	(1st) multicoloured	50	50 ☐ ☐
		a. Horiz pair.		
		Nos. 2659/60	1·00	1·00 ☐ ☐
2660	**1919**	(1st) multicoloured	50	50 ☐ ☐
2661	**1920**	64p multicoloured	1·25	1·25 ☐ ☐
		a. Horiz pair.		
		Nos. 2661/2	5·00	5·00 ☐ ☐
2662	**1921**	64p multicoloured	1·25	1·25 ☐ ☐
2663	**1922**	72p multicoloured	2·00	2·25 ☐ ☐
		a. Horiz pair.		
		Nos. 2663/4	7·00	7·00 ☐ ☐
2664	**1923**	72p multicoloured	2·00	2·25 ☐ ☐
Set of 6			12·00	12·00 ☐ ☐
First Day Cover				13·00 ☐
Presentation Pack			14·00	☐
Set of 3 Gutter Strips of 4			16·00	☐
MS2665 190 × 67 mm. No. 2666 and				
as Nos. 2659/64 but 'all-over'				
phosphor			13·00	13·00 ☐ ☐
First Day Cover				14·00 ☐
PHQ Cards (*set of* 7)			4·50	15·00 ☐ ☐

The seven PHQ cards depict the six individual stamps and the miniature sheet.

150th Anniversary of the Victoria Cross (2nd issue). Booklet stamp

2006 (21 Sept.) Design as No. 1517 (1990 Gallantry Awards). 'All-over' phosphor. Perf 14

2666	**959**	20p multicoloured	6·50	7·00 ☐ ☐

No. 2666 was only issued in No. **MS**2665 and in £7.44 stamp booklets.

1924 Sitar Player and Dancer **1925** Reggae Bass Guitarist and African Drummer

1926 Fiddler and Harpist **1927** Sax Player and Blues Guitarist

1928 Maraca Player and Salsa Dancers

Europa. Integration. Sounds of Britain

2006 (3 Oct.) 'All-over' phosphor. Perf 14½

2667	**1924**	(1st) multicoloured	45	50	☐	☐
2668	**1925**	42p multicoloured	1·00	1·00	☐	☐
2669	**1926**	50p multicoloured	1·25	1·25	☐	☐
2670	**1927**	72p multicoloured	1·75	1·75	☐	☐
2671	**1928**	£1.19 multicoloured	2·50	3·00	☐	☐
Set of 5			9·00	9·00	☐	☐
First Day Cover				11·00		☐
Presentation Pack			12·00		☐	
PHQ Cards (set of 5)			3·75	10·00	☐	☐
Set of 5 Gutter Pairs			19·00		☐	
Set of 5 Traffic Light Gutter Blocks of 4			38·00		☐	

The 1st class and 50p values include the 'EUROPA' emblem.

1929 'New Baby' (Alison Carmichael) **1930** 'Best Wishes' (Alan Kitching)

1931 'THANK YOU' (Alan Kitching) **1932** Balloons (Ivan Chermayeff)

1933 Firework (Kam Tang) **1934** Champagne, Flowers and Butterflies (Olaf Hajek)

Nos. 2672/7 were printed together, *se-tenant*, in booklet panes of 6 in which the surplus self-adhesive paper around each stamp was removed.

'Smilers' Booklet stamps (2nd series). Occasions

2006 (17 Oct.) Self-adhesive. Two phosphor bands. Die-cut perf 15 × 14.

2672	**1929**	(1st) chrome-yellow	1·40	1·20	☐	☐
		a. Booklet pane. Nos. 2672/7	8·00	7·00	☐	☐
2673	**1930**	(1st) turquoise-blue	1·40	1·20	☐	☐
2674	**1931**	(1st) scarlet-vermilion, rosine and yellow	1·40	1·20	☐	☐
2675	**1932**	(1st) multicoloured	1·40	1·20	☐	☐
2676	**1933**	(1st) multicoloured	1·40	1·20	☐	☐
2677	**1934**	(1st) multicoloured	1·40	1·20	☐	☐
Set of 6			8·00	7·00	☐	☐
First Day Cover				8·00		☐
Presentation Pack			18·00		☐	
PHQ Cards			2·75	8·00	☐	☐

Nos. 2672/7 were issued in £1.92 stamp booklets.
They were also issued in sheets of 20, containing four of Nos. 2672 and 2677 and three of the other designs, and *se-tenant* labels. Separate sheets of each design were available with personal photographs on the labels.
Stamps as No. 2672 but perforated with one eliptical hole on each vertical side were issued on 28 October 2008 in sheets of 10 or 20 with circular *se-tenant* Peter Rabbit labels.
Stamps as Nos. 2674 but perforated with one elliptical hole in each vertical side were issued, together with Nos. 2569, 2572, 2821/3 and four designs from **MS**3024, on 8 May 2010 in sheets of 20 stamps with *se-tenant* greetings labels.
These generic sheets were all printed in lithography instead of photogravure.

1935 Snowman **1936** Father Christmas

1937 Snowman **1938** Father Christmas

1939 Reindeer **1940** Christmas Tree

Christmas

2006 (7 Nov.) One centre phosphor band (2nd) or two phosphor bands (others). Perf 15 × 14.

(a) Self-adhesive

2678 **1935**	(2nd) multicoloured	35	40	☐	☐
2679 **1936**	(1st) multicoloured	50	50	☐	☐
2680 **1937**	(2nd Large) multicoloured	65	65	☐	☐
2681 **1938**	(1st Large) multicoloured	75	75	☐	☐
2682 **1939**	72p multicoloured	3·25	3·25	☐	☐
2683 **1940**	£1.19 multicoloured	4·50	4·50	☐	☐
Set of 6		9·00	9·00	☐	☐
First Day Cover			9·50	☐	
Presentation Pack		12·00		☐	
PHQ Cards (*set of* 7)		3·00	18·00	☐	☐

(b) Ordinary gum

MS2684 115 × 102 mm.				
As Nos. 2678/83	9·00	9·00	☐	☐
First Day Cover		10·00	☐	

The seven PHQ cards depict the six individual stamps and the miniature sheet.

The 2nd and 1st class stamps were also issued in sheets of 20 printed in lithography instead of photogravure containing ten 1st class and ten 2nd class stamps, each stamp accompanied by a *se-tenant* label. Separate sheets of 20 1st or 20 2nd class were available with personal photographs.

1941

'Lest We Forget' (1st issue). 90th Anniversary of the Battle of the Somme

2006 (9 Nov.) Sheet 124 × 71 mm containing new stamp and designs as Nos. EN15, W107, S118 and NI101. Two phosphor bands. Perf 14½ (1st) or 15 × 14 (72p).

MS2685 **1941** (1st) Poppies on barbed wire stems; 72p ×4 As Nos. EN13, W105, S116 and NI101	9·00	9·00	☐	☐
First Day Cover		9·50	☐	
Presentation Pack	12·00		☐	

No. **MS**2685 (including the Northern Ireland stamp) is printed in gravure.

The 1st class stamp was also issued in sheets of 20 with *se-tenant* labels showing war memorials, printed in lithography instead of photogravure.

Collectors Pack

2006 (9 Nov.) Comprises Nos. 2589/612, 2615/49, 2659/64, 2667/71, 2678/83 and **MS**2685

CP2685a Collectors Pack	£120	☐	

Post Office Yearbook

2006 (9 Nov.) Comprises Nos. 2589/612, 2615/49, 2659/64, 2667/71, 2678/83 and **MS**2685

YB2685a Yearbook	£100	☐	

Miniature Sheet Collection

2006 (30 Nov.) Comprises Nos. **MS**2613, **MS**2658, **MS**2665, **MS**2684/5 and **MS**S133

MS2685a Miniature Sheet Collection 50·00		☐

1942 'with the beatles'

1943 'Sgt Pepper's Lonely Hearts Club Band

1944 'Help!'

1945 'Abbey Road'

1946 'Revolver'

1947 'Let It Be'

1948 Beatles Memorabilia

The Beatles. Album Covers

2007 (9 Jan.) Two phosphor bands.

(a) Photo Walsall. Self-adhesive. Die-cut irregular perf 13½ × 14½

2686 **1942**	(1st) multicoloured	75	70	☐	☐
2687 **1943**	(1st) multicoloured	75	70	☐	☐
2688 **1944**	64p multicoloured	1·50	1·50	☐	☐
2689 **1945**	64p multicoloured	1·50	1·50	☐	☐
2690 **1946**	72p multicoloured	1·60	1·60	☐	☐
2691 **1947**	72p multicoloured	1·60	1·60	☐	☐
Set of 6		10·00	10·00	☐	☐
First Day Cover			11·00	☐	
Presentation Pack		15·00		☐	
PHQ Cards (*set of* 11)		5·00	18·00	☐	☐

(b) Litho Walsall. Ordinary gum. Two phosphor bands. Perf 14
MS2692 115 × 89 mm. **1948** (1st) Guitar;
(1st) Yellow Submarine lunch-box

and key-rings; (1st) Record 'Love
Me Do'; (1st) Beatles badges 5·00 5·00 ☐ ☐

First Day Cover	7·00	☐

Nos. 2686/91 are all die-cut in the shape of a pile of records.
Nos. 2686/7, 2688/9 and 2690/1 were each printed together in
sheets of 60 (2 panes of 30), with the two designs alternating
horizontally and the surplus backing paper around each
stamp removed.

Nos. 2686/92 commemorate the 50th anniversary of the first
meeting of Paul McCartney and John Lennon.

'Smilers' Booklet stamp (3rd series)

2007 (16 Jan.) – **2008** As No. 2569. Self-adhesive. Two
phosphor bands. Perf 15 × 14 (with one elliptical hole in each
vertical side)

2693	(1st)multicoloured		10·00	10·00	☐ ☐
	a. Booklet pane. No. 2655 × 5				
	and No. 2693		30·00		☐
	b. Booklet pane. No. 2693 × 2				
	with two attached labels				
	and No. 1668 × 4		20·00		☐

No. 2693 was only issued in stamp booklets in which the
surplus backing paper around each stamp was removed.
Nos. 2694/8 are left vacant.

1949 Moon Jellyfish

1950 Common Starfish

1951 Beadlet Anemone

1952 Bass

1953 Thornback Ray

1954 Lesser Octopus

1955 Common Mussels

1956 Grey Seal

1957 Shore Crab

1958 Common Sun Star

Nos. 2699/708 were printed together, *se-tenant*, as blocks of
ten (5 × 2) in sheets of 60 (2 panes of 30).

Sea Life

2007 (1 Feb.) Two phosphor bands. Perf 14½

2699	**1949**	(1st) multicoloured	75	80	☐ ☐
	a. Block of 10.				
	Nos. 2699/708	10·00	10·00	☐ ☐
2700	**1950**	(1st) multicoloured	75	80	☐ ☐
2701	**1951**	(1st) multicoloured	75	80	☐ ☐
2702	**1952**	(1st) multicoloured	75	80	☐ ☐
2703	**1953**	(1st) multicoloured	75	80	☐ ☐
2704	**1954**	(1st) multicoloured	75	80	☐ ☐
2705	**1955**	(1st) multicoloured	75	80	☐ ☐
2706	**1956**	(1st) multicoloured	75	80	☐ ☐
2707	**1957**	(1st) multicoloured	75	80	☐ ☐
2708	**1958**	(1st) multicoloured	75	80	☐ ☐
Set of 10			10·00	10·00	☐ ☐
First Day Cover				11·00	☐
Presentation Pack			14·00		☐
PHQ Cards (*set of* 10)			4·50	14·00	☐ ☐
Gutter Block of 20			20·00		☐

1959 Saturn Nebula
C55

1960 Eskimo Nebula
C39

1961 Cat's Eye Nebula
C6

1962 Helix Nebula
C63

1963 Flaming Star
Nebula C31

1964 The Spindle C53

50th Anniversary of 'The Sky at Night' (TV programme). Nebulae

2007 (13 Feb.) Self-adhesive. Two phosphor bands. Die-cut
perf 14½ × 14

2709	**1959**	(1st) multicoloured	75	75	☐ ☐
2710	**1960**	(1st) multicoloured	75	75	☐ ☐

2711	**1961**	50p multicoloured	1·20	1·20	☐	☐
2712	**1962**	50p multicoloured	1·20	1·20	☐	☐
2713	**1963**	72p multicoloured	1·70	1·70	☐	☐
2714	**1964**	72p multicoloured	1·70	1·70	☐	☐
Set of 6			10·00	10·00	☐	☐
First Day Cover				10·00		☐
Presentation Pack			14·00		☐	
PHQ Cards (*set of 6*)			4·50	14·00	☐	☐

Nos. 2709/10, 2711/12 and 2713/14 were each printed together in sheets of 60 (2 panes of 30), with the two designs alternating horizontally and the surplus backing paper around each stamp removed.

1965 Iron Bridge (Thomas Telford)

1966 Steam Locomotive and Railway Tracks

1967 Map of British Isles and Australia (telephone)

1968 Camera and Television (John Logie Baird)

1969 Globe as Web (email and internet)

1970 Couple with Suitcases on Moon (space travel)

World of Invention (1st series)

2007 (1 Mar.) Self-adhesive. Two phosphor bands. Die-cut perf 14½ × 14

2715	**1965**	(1st) multicoloured	75	50	☐	☐
2716	**1966**	(1st) multicoloured	75	50	☐	☐
2717	**1967**	64p multicoloured	1·25	1·25	☐	☐
2718	**1968**	64p multicoloured	1·25	1·25	☐	☐
2719	**1969**	72p multicoloured	2·00	2·25	☐	☐
2720	**1970**	72p multicoloured	2·00	2·25	☐	☐
Set of 6			10·00	10·00	☐	☐
First Day Cover				11·00		☐
Presentation Pack			14·00		☐	
PHQ Cards (*set of 7*)			4·50	22·00	☐	☐

The seven PHQ Cards depict the six individual stamps and **MS**2727.

Nos. 2715/16, 2717/18 and 2719/20 were each printed together in sheets of 60 (2 panes of 30), with the two designs alternating horizontally and the surplus backing paper around each stamp removed.

World of Invention (2nd series)

2007 (1 Mar.) Two phosphor bands. Perf 14½ × 14

2721	**1965**	(1st) multicoloured	75	50	☐	☐

2722	**1966**	(1st) multicoloured	75	50	☐	☐
2723	**1967**	64p multicoloured	2·50	2·50	☐	☐
2724	**1968**	64p multicoloured	2·50	2·50	☐	☐
2725	**1969**	72p multicoloured	4·50	4·50	☐	☐
2726	**1970**	72p multicoloured	4·50	4·50	☐	☐
Set of 6			14·00	14·00	☐	☐
MS2727 115 × 104 mm. Nos. 2721/6			10·00	10·50	☐	☐
First Day Cover				11·00		☐

Nos. 2721/6 were only issued in £7.49 stamp booklets, No. DX38 and in **MS**2727.

1971 William Wilberforce and Anti-Slavery Poster

1972 Olaudah Equiano and Map of Slave Trade Routes

1973 Granville Sharp and Slave Ship

1974 Thomas Clarkson and Diagram of Slave Ship

1975 Hannah More and Title Page of *The Sorrows of Yamba*

1976 Ignatius Sancho and Trade/Business Card

Nos. 2728/9, 2730/1 and 2732/3 were each printed together, *se-tenant*, in horizontal pairs throughout the sheets.

Bicentenary of the Abolition of the Slave Trade

2007 (22 Mar.) Two phosphor bands. Perf 14½

2728	**1971**	(1st) multicoloured	75	75	☐	☐
		a. Horiz pair.				
		Nos. 2728/9	2·50	2·50	☐	☐
2729	**1972**	(1st) multicoloured	75	75	☐	☐
2730	**1973**	50p multicoloured	1·20	1·20	☐	☐
		a. Horiz pair.				
		Nos. 2730/1	4·00	4·00	☐	☐
2731	**1974**	50p multicoloured	1·20	1·20	☐	☐
2732	**1975**	72p multicoloured	1·70	1·70	☐	☐
		a. Horiz pair.				
		Nos. 2732/3	5·00	5·00	☐	☐
2733	**1976**	72p multicoloured	1·70	1·70	☐	☐
Set of 6			9·00	9·00	☐	☐
First Day Cover				11·00		☐
Presentation Pack			12·00		☐	
PHQ Cards (*set of 6*)			4·50	14·00	☐	☐

| Set of 3 Gutter Strips of 4 | 14·00 | ☐ |
| Set of 3 Traffic Light Gutter Strips of 4 | 16·00 | ☐ |

1977 Ice Cream Cone

1978 Sandcastle

1979 Carousel Horse

1980 Beach Huts

1981 Deckchairs

1982 Beach Donkeys

'Beside the Seaside'

2007 (15 May) Two phosphor bands. Perf 14½

2734	**1977**	(1st) multicoloured	75	75	☐	☐
2735	**1978**	46p multicoloured	1·00	1·00	☐	☐
2736	**1979**	48p multicoloured	1·50	1·50	☐	☐
2737	**1980**	54p multicoloured	2·00	2·00	☐	☐
2738	**1981**	69p multicoloured	2·50	2·50	☐	☐
2739	**1982**	78p multicoloured	2·75	2·75	☐	☐
Set of 6			9·00	9·00	☐	☐
First Day Cover				10·00		☐
Presentation Pack			12·00		☐	
PHQ Cards (set of 6)			4·50	14·00		☐
Set of 6 Gutter Pairs			18·00		☐	

1983

New Wembley Stadium, London

2007 (17 May) Sheet 113 × 103 mm containing design as Type

1593 but with 'WORLD CUP 2002' inscription omitted, and Nos. EN6 and EN15, each × 2. One centre band (2nd) or two phosphor bands (others). Perf 14½ × 14 (1st) or 15 × 14 (with one elliptical hole in each vertical side) (2nd, 78p)

MS2740	**1983**	(1st) As Type 1593; (2nd)				
		No. EN6 × 2; 78p No. EN15 × 2 and one				
		central stamp-size label	7·00	7·00	☐	☐
First Day Cover				7·50		☐

The design as Type 1593 omits the 'WORLD CUP 2002' inscription at the left of the stamp.

1984 Arnold Machin   **1985** 1967 4d. Machin

1986

40th Anniversary of the First Machin Definitives

2007 (5 June) Sheet 127 × 73 mm containing new stamps and Nos. Y1725 and Y1725b. Two phosphor bands (£1). Perf 14½ (1st) or 15 × 14 (with one elliptical hole in each vertical side) (£1)

2741	**1984**	(1st) multicoloured	2·00	2·00	☐	☐
2742	**1985**	(1st) multicoloured	2·00	2·00	☐	☐
MS2743	**1986**	Nos. 2741/2, Y1725				
		and Y1725b	8·00	8·00	☐	☐
First Day Cover (**MS**2743)				9·00		☐
Presentation Pack (**MS**2743)			10·00		☐	
PHQ Cards (Set of 3) (Nos. 2741/						
MS2743)				2·00	14·00	☐	☐

Nos. 2741/2 were only issued in £7.66 stamp booklets (No. DX39) and in **MS**2743.

Stamps as Type **1984** but with phosphor frames were issued in sheets of 20 with se-tenant labels showing the 1967–9 Machin definitives.

1987 Stirling Moss in Vanwall 2.5L, 1957   **1988** Graham Hill in BRM P57, 1962

1989 Jim Clark in Lotus 25 Climax, 1963

1990 Jackie Stewart in Tyrrell 006/2, 1973

1991 James Hunt in McLaren M23, 1976

1992 Nigel Mansell in Williams FW11, 1986

50th Anniversary of the British Grand Prix, Silverstone. Racing Cars

2007 (3 July) Two phosphor bands. Perf 14½

2744	**1987**	(1st) multicoloured	75	75	☐	☐
2745	**1988**	(1st) multicoloured	75	75	☐	☐
2746	**1989**	54p multicoloured	2·00	2·00	☐	☐
2747	**1990**	54p multicoloured	2·00	2·00	☐	☐
2748	**1991**	78p multicoloured	2·50	2·50	☐	☐
2749	**1992**	78p multicoloured	2·50	2·50	☐	☐
Set of 6			9·50	9·50	☐	☐
First Day Cover				10·00		☐
Presentation Pack			12·00		☐	
PHQ Cards (*set of* 6)			4·50	14·00	☐	☐
Set of 6 Gutter Pairs			19·00		☐	

1993 *Harry Potter and the Philosopher's Stone*

1994 *Harry Potter and the Chamber of Secrets*

1995 *Harry Potter and the prisoner of Azkaban*

1996 *Harry Potter and the Goblet of Fire*

1997 *Harry Potter and the Order of the Phoenix*

1998 *Harry Potter andthe Half-Blood Prince*

1999 *Harry Potter and the Deathly Hallows*

Nos. 2750/6 were printed together, *se-tenant*, as horizontal strips of seven stamps in sheets of 56 (2 panes 7 × 4).

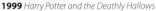

2000 Crests of Hogwarts School and its Four Houses

Publication of Final Book in the Harry Potter Series

2007 (17 July).

		(a) Book Covers. 'All-over' phosphor. Perf 14½				
2750	**1993**	(1st) multicoloured	75	75	☐	☐
		a. Horiz strip of 7.				
		Nos. 2750/6	8·00	8·00	☐	☐
2751	**1994**	(1st) multicoloured	75	75	☐	☐
2752	**1995**	(1st) multicoloured	75	75	☐	☐
2753	**1996**	(1st) multicoloured	75	75	☐	☐
2754	**1997**	(1st) multicoloured	75	75	☐	☐
2755	**1998**	(1st) multicoloured	75	75	☐	☐
2756	**1999**	(1st) multicoloured	75	75	☐	☐
Set of 7			8·00	8·00	☐	☐
First Day Cover				9·00		☐
Presentation Pack (Nos. 2750/**MS**2757) 16·00					☐	
PHQ Cards (*set of* 13)			7·50	27·00	☐	☐
Gutter Block of 14			16·00		☐	
Traffic Light Gutter Block of 14			20·00		☐	

(b) Crests of Hogwarts School and its Four Houses. Multicoloured. Two phosphor bands. Perf 15 × 14

MS2757 123 × 70 mm. 2000 (1st) Gryffindor; (1st) Hufflepuff; (1st) Hogwarts; (1st) Ravenclaw;

(1st) Slytherin	6·00	6·00	☐	☐
First Day Cover		7·50		☐

The complete miniature sheet is shown on one of the thirteen PHQ cards with the others depicting the individual stamps including those from **MS**2757.

Stamps as those within **MS**2757 but self-adhesive were issued in sheets of 20 containing the five designs *se-tenant* with labels depicting either magic spells or personal photographs. The magic spells labels are printed in thermochromic ink which fades temporarily when exposed to heat, revealing the meaning of the spells.

2001 Scout and Camp Fire

2002 Scouts Rock climbing

2003 Scout planting Tree

2004 Adult Volunteer teaching Scout Archery

2005 Scouts learning gliding

2006 Scouts from Many Nations

Centenary of Scouting and 21st World Scout Jamboree, Chelmsford, Essex

2007 (26 July) Two phosphor bands. Perf 14½ ×14

2758 **2001**	(1st) multicoloured	75	75	
2759 **2002**	46p multicoloured	1·00	1·00	
2760 **2003**	48p multicoloured	1·50	1·50	
2761 **2004**	54p multicoloured	2·00	2·00	
2762 **2005**	69p multicoloured	2·50	2·50	
2763 **2006**	78p multicoloured	2·75	2·75	
Set of 6		9·00	9·00	
First Day Cover			10·00	
Presentation Pack		12·00		
PHQ Cards (*set of* 6)		4·50	14·00	
Set of 6 Gutter Pairs		18·00		

2007 White-tailed Eagle

2008 Bearded Tit

2009 Red Kite

2010 Cirl Bunting

2011 Marsh Harrier

2012 Avocet

2013 Bittern

2014 Dartford Warbler

2015 Corncrake

2016 Peregrine Falcon

Nos. 2764/73 were printed together, *se-tenant*, in blocks of ten (5 × 2) in sheets of 60 (2 panes of 30).

'Action for Species' (1st series). Birds

2007 (4 Sept.) Two phosphor bands. Perf 14½

2764 **2007**	(1st) multicoloured	75	75		
	a. Block of 10.				
	Nos. 2764/73	10·00	10·00		
2765 **2008**	(1st) multicoloured	75	75		
2766 **2009**	(1st) multicoloured	75	75		
2767 **2010**	(1st) multicoloured	75	75		
2768 **2011**	(1st) multicoloured	75	75		
2769 **2012**	(1st) multicoloured	75	75		
2770 **2013**	(1st) multicoloured	75	75		
2771 **2014**	(1st) multicoloured	75	75		
2772 **2015**	(1st) multicoloured	75	75		
2773 **2016**	(1st) multicoloured	75	75		
Set of 10		10·00	10·00		
First Day Cover			10·00		
Presentation Pack		14·00			
PHQ Cards (*set of* 10)		6·00	16·00		
Gutter Block of 20		20·00			

2017 NCO, Royal Military Police, 1999

2018 Tank Commander, 5th Royal Tank Regiment, 1944

2019 Observer, Royal Field Artillery, 1917

2020 Rifleman, 95th Rifles, 1813

2021 Grenadier, Royal Regiment of Foot of Ireland, 1704

2022 Trooper, Earl of Oxford's Horse, 1661

Nos. 2774/6 and 2777/9 were each printed together, *se-tenant*, in horizontal strips of three stamps in sheets of 60 (2 panes 6 × 5).

Military Uniforms (1st series). British Army Uniforms

2007 (20 Sept.) Two phosphor bands. Perf 14½

2774	**2017**	(1st) multicoloured	80	80	☐	☐
		a. Horiz strip of 3.				
		Nos. 2774/6	4·00	4·00	☐	☐
2775	**2018**	(1st) multicoloured	80	80	☐	☐
2776	**2019**	(1st) multicoloured	80	80	☐	☐
2777	**2020**	78p multicoloured	1·70	1·70	☐	☐
		a. Horiz strip of 3.				
		Nos. 2777/9	7·00	7·00	☐	☐
2778	**2021**	78p multicoloured	1·70	1·70	☐	☐
2779	**2022**	78p multicoloured	1·70	1·70	☐	☐
Set of 6			10·00	10·00	☐	☐
First Day Cover				11·00		☐
Presentation Pack			14·00		☐	
PHQ Cards (*set of* 6)			4·50	14·00	☐	☐
Set of 2 Gutter Strips of 6			20·00		☐	
Set of 2 Traffic Light Gutter Strips of 6		24·00			☐	

2023 Leaving St. Paul's Cathedral after Thanksgiving Service, 2006

2024 Inspecting King's Troop Royal Horse Artillery, Regents Park, 1997

2025 At Garter Ceremony, Windsor, 1980

2026 At Royal Ascot, 1969

2027 At Premiere of The Guns of Navarone, 1961

2028 At Clydebank, 1947

Nos. 2780/1, 2782/3 and 2784/5 were each printed together, *se-tenant*, in horizontal pairs throughout the sheets.

2029 Photographs of the Royal Family

Diamond Wedding of Queen Elizabeth II and Duke of Edinburgh

2007 (16 Oct.)

(a) Ordinary gum. Litho Cartor. 'All-over' phosphor. Perf 14½ × 14

2780	**2023**	(1st) blackish-brown and black	75	75	☐	☐
		a. Horiz pair. Nos. 2780/1	1·60	1·60	☐	☐
2781	**2024**	(1st) blackish-brown and black	75	75	☐	☐
2782	**2025**	54p blackish-brown and black	1·20	1·20	☐	☐
		a. Horiz pair. Nos. 2782/3	3·75	3·75	☐	☐
2783	**2026**	54p blackish-brown and black	1·20	1·20	☐	☐
2784	**2027**	78p blackish-brown and black	1·90	1·90	☐	☐
		a. Horiz pair. Nos. 2784/5	5·50	5·50	☐	☐
2785	**2028**	78p blackish-brown and black	1·90	1·90	☐	☐
Set of 6			9·50	9·50	☐	☐
First Day Cover				10·00		☐
Presentation Pack (Nos. 2780/**MS**2786) 18·00					☐	
PHQ Cards (*set of* 11)			6·00	27·00	☐	☐
Set of 3 Gutter Strips of 4			20·00		☐	

(b) Self-adhesive. Photo Walsall. Two phosphor bands. Perf 14½

MS2786 115 × 89 mm. (1st) Royal family, Balmoral, 1972; (1st) Queen and Prince Philip, Buckingham Palace, 2007; 69p. Royal family, Windsor Castle, 1965; 78p. Princess Elizabeth, Prince Philip, Prince Charles and Princess Anne, Clarence House, 1951   6·00   6·00   ☐ ☐

First Day Cover 8·50 ☐

The complete miniature sheet is shown on one of the eleven PHQ cards with the others depicting individual stamps including those from **MS**2786.

2030 'Madonna and Child' (William Dyce), c 1827

2031 'The Madonna of Humility' (Lippo di Dalmasio), c 1390–1400

Christmas (1st issue). Paintings of the Madonna and Child

2007 (6 Nov.) One centre band (2nd) or two phosphor bands (1st). Self-adhesive. Die-cut perf 15 × 14 (with one elliptical hole in each vertical side)

2787	**2030**	(2nd) multicoloured	65	50	☐	☐
2788	**2031**	(1st) multicoloured	75	75	☐	☐
First Day Cover			4·00		☐	

2032 Angel playing Trumpet ('PEACE')

2033 Angel playing Lute ('GOODWILL')

2034 Angel playing Trumpet ('PEACE')

2035 Angel playing Lute ('GOODWILL')

2036 Angel playing Flute ('JOY')

2037 Angel playing Tambourine ('GLORY')

Christmas (2nd issue). Angels

2007 (6 Nov.) One centre band (2nd) or two phosphor bands (others). Perf 15 × 14.

		(a) Self-adhesive				
2789	**2032**	(2nd) multicoloured	65	55	☐	☐
2790	**2033**	(1st) multicoloured	75	75	☐	☐
2791	**2034**	(2nd Large) multicoloured	90	90	☐	☐
2792	**2035**	(1st Large) multicoloured	2·00	2·00	☐	☐
2793	**2036**	78p multicoloured	3·00	3·00	☐	☐
2794	**2037**	£1.24 multicoloured	4·50	4·50	☐	☐
Set of 6			9·50	9·50		
First Day Cover				10·00		☐
Presentation Pack (Nos. 2787/94)			14·00		☐	
PHQ Cards (*set of 9*)			6·00	18·00	☐	☐
		(b) Ordinary gum				
MS2795 115 × 102 mm.						
		As Nos. 2789/94	10·00	10·00	☐	☐

First Day Cover 11·00 ☐

The phosphor bands on Nos. 2791/2 are at the centre and right of each stamp.

The PHQ cards depict Nos. 2787/94 and **MS**2795.

The 2nd class, 1st class and 78p stamps were also issued in sheets of 20 printed in lithography instead of photogravure containing eight 1st class, eight 2nd class and four 78p stamps, each stamp accompanied by a *se-tenant* label. Separate sheets of 20 1st, 20 2nd or 10 78p were available with personal photographs.

2038

'Lest We Forget' (2nd issue). 90th Anniv of the Battle of Passchendaele

2007 (8 Nov.) Sheet 124 × 70 mm containing new stamp and designs as Nos. EN16, W108, S119 and NI106. Two phosphor bands. Perf 14½ (1st) or 15 × 14 (with one elliptical hole in each vertical side) (78p)

MS2796	**2038**	(1st) Soldiers in poppy flower; 78p. × 4 As Nos. EN15, NI103, S118 and W107	10·00	10·00	☐	☐
First Day Cover				11·00		☐
Presentation Pack			12·00		☐	

No. **MS**2796 (including the England, Scotland and Wales stamps) is printed in lithography.

The 1st class stamp was also issued in sheets of 20 with *se-tenant* labels showing soldiers and their letters home.

Collectors Pack

2007 (8 Nov.) Comprises Nos. 2686/92, 2699/720, 2728/39, **MS**2743/94 and **MS**2796

CP2796a	Collectors Pack	£180	☐

Post Office Yearbook

2007 (8 Nov.) Comprises Nos. 2686/92, 2699/720, 2728/39, **MS**2743/94 and **MS**2796

YB2796a	Yearbook	£130	☐

Miniature Sheet Collection

2007 (8 Nov.) Comprises Nos. **MS**2692, **MS**2727, **MS**2740, **MS**2743, **MS**2757, **MS**2786 and **MS**2795/6

MS2796a	Miniature Sheet Collection	70·00	☐

2039 *Casino Royale*

2040 *Dr. No*

2041 *Goldfinger*

2042 *Diamonds are Forever*

2043 *For Your Eyes Only*

2044 *From Russia with Love*

Birth Centenary of Ian Fleming (author of James Bond books) (1st issue). Book Covers

2008 (8 Jan.) Two phosphor bands. Perf 15 × 14½

2797	**2039**	(1st) multicoloured	75	75	□	□
2798	**2040**	(1st) multicoloured	75	75	□	□
2799	**2041**	54p multicoloured	2·00	1·20	□	□
2800	**2042**	54p multicoloured	2·00	1·20	□	□
2801	**2043**	78p multicoloured	3·00	3·00	□	□
2802	**2044**	78p multicoloured	3·00	3·00	□	□
Set of 6			10·00	10·00	□	□
First Day Cover				11·00		□
Presentation Pack			12·00		□	
PHQ Cards (*set of* 7)			4·75	20·00	□	□
Set of 6 Gutter Pairs			20·00		□	
MS2803 189 × 68 mm. Nos. 2797/802			10·00	10·00	□	□
First Day Cover				11·00		□

The seven PHQ cards depict the individual stamps and **MS**2803.

Birth Centenary of Ian Fleming (author of James Bond books) (2nd issue). Booklet stamps

2008 (8 Jan.) Design as Type **1517** but printed in lithography. Two phosphor bands. Perf 14½

2805	**1517**	(1st) multicoloured	85	85	□	□

No. 2805 was only issued in £7.40 stamp booklets.

2045 Assistance Dog carrying Letter (Labrador 'Rowan')

2046 Mountain Rescue Dog (Cross-bred 'Merrick')

2047 Police Dog (German Shepherd 'Max')

2048 Customs Dog (Springer Spaniel 'Max')

2049 Sheepdog (Border Collie 'Bob')

2050 Guide Dog (Labrador 'Warwick')

Working Dogs

2008 (5 Feb.) Two phosphor bands. Perf 14½

2806	**2045**	(1st) multicoloured	80	80	□	□
2807	**2046**	46p multicoloured	1·00	1·00	□	□
2808	**2047**	48p multicoloured	1·50	1·50	□	□
2809	**2048**	54p multicoloured	2·00	2·00	□	□
2810	**2049**	69p multicoloured	2·50	2·50	□	□
2811	**2050**	78p multicoloured	2·75	2·75	□	□
Set of 6			9·00	9·00	□	□
First Day Cover				10·00		□
Presentation Pack			12·00		□	
PHQ Cards (*set of* 6)			4·50	14·00	□	□
Set of 6 Gutter Pairs			18·00		□	

The 1st value includes the 'EUROPA' emblem.

2051 Henry IV (1399-1413)

2052 Henry V (1413–1422)

2053 Henry VI (1422-1461 & 1470-1471)

2054 Edward IV (1461–1470 & 1471–1473)

2055 Edward V (1483)

2056 Richard III (1483–1485)

2057 The Age of Lancaster and York

Kings and Queens (1st issue). Houses of Lancaster and York

2008 (28 Feb.) Two phosphor bands. Perf 14½

2812	**2051**	(1st) multicoloured	80	80	☐	☐
2813	**2052**	(1st) multicoloured	80	80	☐	☐
2814	**2053**	54p multicoloured	2·00	2·00	☐	☐
2815	**2054**	54p multicoloured	2·00	2·00	☐	☐
2816	**2055**	69p multicoloured	2·75	2·75	☐	☐
2817	**2056**	69p multicoloured	2·75	2·75	☐	☐
Set of 6			9·50	9·50	☐	☐
First Day Cover				10·00		☐
Presentation Pack			18·00		☐	
PHQ Cards (*set of 11*)			7·25	27·00	☐	☐
Set of 6 Gutter Pairs			20·00		☐	
Set of 6 Traffic Light Gutter Blocks of 4		26·00			☐	

MS2818 123 × 70 mm. **2057** (1st) Owain Glyn Dwr ('Parliament'), **1404**; (1st) Henry V's triumph at Battle of Agincourt, **1415**; 78p. Yorkish victory at Battle of Tewkesbury, **1471**; 78p. William Caxton, first English printer, **1477** 6·50 6·50 ☐ ☐

First Day Cover	8·00	☐

The complete miniature sheet is shown on one of the eleven PHQ cards with the others depicting individual stamps including those from **MS**2818.

'Smilers' Booklet stamps (4th series)

2008 (28 Feb.) Designs as Nos. 2567/8, 2570 and 2675/7. Self-adhesive. Two phosphor bands. Die-cut perf 15 × 14 (with one elliptical hole in each vertical side).

2819	**1569**	(1st) multicoloured	75	75	☐	☐
		a. Booklet pane. Nos. 2819/24	9·00	9·00	☐	☐
2820	**1842**	(1st) multicoloured	75	75	☐	☐
2821	**1517**	(1st) multicoloured	75	75	☐	☐
2822	**1932**	(1st) multicoloured	75	75	☐	☐
2823	**1933**	(1st) multicoloured	75	75	☐	☐
2824	**1934**	(1st) multicoloured	75	75	☐	☐
Set of 6			9·00	9·00	☐	☐

Nos. 2819/24 were issued in £2·04 booklets in which the surplus backing paper around each stamp was removed.

Nos. 2820 and 2822 were reissued on 28 October 2008 in separate sheets of 10 or 20 with circular *se-tenant* labels showing the Almond Blossom fairy (2820), Mr. Men or Noddy (2822).

Nos. 2819, 2820 and 2822 were issued again on 30 April 2009 in separate sheets of 10 or 20 with circular *se-tenant* labels showing Jeremy Fisher (2820), Wild Cherry fairy (2820), Little Miss Sunshine or Big Ears (2822).

No. 2819 was issued on 8 May 2010 in sheets of 20 with *se-tenant* labels showing London scenes for London 2010 Festival of Stamps.

Nos. 2821 (and Nos. 2822/3) were issued, together with Nos. 2569, 2572, 2674 and four designs from **MS**3024, on 8 May 2010 in sheets of 20 with *se-tenant* greetings labels.

All these sheets were printed in lithography instead of photogravure.

2058 Lifeboat, Barra

2059 Lifeboat approaching Dinghy, Appledore

2060 Helicopter Winchman, Portland

2061 Inshore lifeboat, St. Ives

2062 Rescue Helicopter, Lee-on-Solent

2063 Launch of Lifeboat, Dinbych-y-Pysgod, Tenby

Rescue at Sea

2008 (13 Mar.) 'All over' phosphor. Perf 14½ × 14

2825	**2058**	(1st) multicoloured	75	75	☐	☐
2826	**2059**	46p multicoloured	1·00	1·00	☐	☐
2827	**2060**	48p multicoloured	1·50	1·50	☐	☐
2828	**2061**	54p multicoloured	2·00	2·00	☐	☐
2829	**2062**	69p multicoloured	2·50	2·50	☐	☐
2830	**2063**	78p multicoloured	2·75	2·75	☐	☐
Set of 6			9·00	9·00	☐	☐
First Day Cover				10·00		☐
Presentation Pack			12·00		☐	
PHQ Cards (*set of 6*)			4·50	14·00	☐	☐
Set of 6 Gutter Pairs			18·00		☐	

*Nos. 2825/30 have interrupted perforations along the top and bottom edges of the stamps, the gaps in the perforations forming the three dots and three dashes that spell out 'SOS' in morse code.

2064 *Lysandra bellargus* (Adonis Blue)

2065 *Coenagrion mercuriale* (southern damselfly)

2066 *Formica rufibarbis* (red-barbed ant)

2067 *Pareulype berberata* (barberry carpet moth)

2068 *Lucanus cervus* (stag beetle)

2069 *Cryptocephalus coryli* (hazel pot beetle)

2070 *Gryllus campestris* (field cricket)

2071 *Hesperia comma* (silver-spotted skipper)

2072 *Pseudepipona herrichii* (Purbeck mason wasp)

2073 *Gnorimus nobilis* (noble chafer)

Nos. 2831/40 were printed together, *se-tenant*, in blocks of ten (5 × 2) in sheets of 60 (2 panes of 30).

'Action for Species' (2nd series). Insects

2008 (15 Apr.) Phosphor background. Perf 14½

2831	**2064**	(1st) multicoloured	80	80	☐	☐
		a. Block of 10.				
		Nos. 2831/40	10·00	10·00	☐	☐
2832	**2065**	(1st) multicoloured	80	80	☐	☐
2833	**2066**	(1st) multicoloured	80	80	☐	☐
2834	**2067**	(1st) multicoloured	80	80	☐	☐
2835	**2068**	(1st) multicoloured	80	80	☐	☐
2836	**2069**	(1st) multicoloured	80	80	☐	☐
2837	**2070**	(1st) multicoloured	80	80	☐	☐
2838	**2071**	(1st) multicoloured	80	80	☐	☐
2839	**2072**	(1st) multicoloured	80	80	☐	☐
2840	**2073**	(1st) multicoloured	80	80	☐	☐
Set of 10			10·00	10·00	☐	☐
First Day Cover				10·00		☐
Presentation Pack			14·00		☐	
PHQ Cards (*set of* 10)			6·75	16·00	☐	☐
Gutter Block of 20			20·00		☐	

2074 Lichfield Cathedral

2075 Belfast Cathedral

2076 Gloucester Cathedral

2077 St. David's Cathedral

2078 Westminster Cathedral

2079 St. Magnus Cathedral, Kirkwall, Orkney

2080 St. Paul's Cathedral

Cathedrals

2008 (13 May). 'All-over' phosphor. Perf 14½

2841	**2074**	(1st) multicoloured	85	85	☐	☐
2842	**2075**	48p multicoloured	1·10	1·10	☐	☐
2843	**2076**	50p multicoloured	1·50	1·50	☐	☐

2844 **2077**	56p multicoloured	2·50	2·50	☐ ☐
2845 **2078**	72p multicoloured	3·00	3·00	☐ ☐
2846 **2079**	81p multicoloured	3·50	3·50	☐ ☐
Set of 6		10·00	10·00	☐ ☐
First Day Cover			12·00	☐
Presentation Pack		17·00		☐
PHQ Cards (*set of* 11)		7·25	27·00	☐ ☐
Set of 6 Gutter Pairs		20·00		☐
Set of 6 Traffic Light Gutter Pairs		22·00		☐

MS2847 115 × 89 mm. (1st) multicoloured;
(1st) multicoloured; 81p. multicoloured;
81p. multicoloured. Perf 14½ × 14   6·00   6·00   ☐ ☐

First Day Cover		7·50	☐

No. **MS**2847 commemorates the 300th anniversary of St. Paul's Cathedral.

The complete miniature sheet is shown on one of the eleven PHQ cards with the others depicting individual stamps including those from **MS**2847.

'Beside the Seaside' (2nd series)

2008 (13 May). As Type 1977 but self-adhesive. Two phosphor bands. Die-cut perf 14½

2848 **1977**	(1st) multicoloured	80	80	☐ ☐

No. 2848 was only issued in £2.16 booklets.

2081 *Carry on Sergeant*

2082 *Dracula*

2083 *Carry on Cleo*

2084 *The Curse of Frankenstein*

2085 *Carry on Screaming*

2086 *The Mummy*

Posters for Carry On and Hammer Horror Films

2008 (10 June). Two phosphor bands. Perf 14

2849 **2081**	(1st) multicoloured	85	85	☐ ☐
2850 **2082**	48p multicoloured	1·10	1·10	☐ ☐
2851 **2083**	50p multicoloured	1·50	1·50	☐ ☐
2852 **2084**	56p multicoloured	2·50	2·50	☐ ☐
2853 **2085**	72p multicoloured	3·00	3·00	☐ ☐
2854 **2086**	81p multicoloured	3·50	3·50	☐ ☐
Set of 6		10·00	10·00	☐ ☐
First Day Cover			11·00	☐
Presentation Pack		17·00		☐
PHQ Cards (*set of* 6)		4·50	14·00	☐ ☐
PHQ Cards ("brick wall" background) and Stamps Set			9·00	☐
Set of 6 Gutter Pairs		20·00		☐

Nos. 2849/54 commemorate the 50th anniversary of *Dracula* and the first Carry On film (*Carry on Sergeant*).

2087 Red Arrows, Dartmouth Regatta Airshow, 2006

2088 RAF Falcons Parachute Team, Biggin Hill, 2006

2089 Spectator watching Red Arrows, Farnborough

2090 Prototype Avro Vulcan Bombers and Avro 707s, Farnborough, 1953

2091 Parachutist Robert Wyndham on Wing of Avro 504, 1933

2092 Air Race rounding the Beacon, Hendon, c. 1912

Air Displays

2008 (17 July). Two phosphor bands. Perf 14½ × 14

2855 **2087**	(1st) multicoloured	85	85	☐ ☐
2856 **2088**	48p multicoloured	1·10	1·10	☐ ☐
2857 **2089**	50p multicoloured	1·50	1·50	☐ ☐
2858 **2090**	56p multicoloured	2·50	2·50	☐ ☐
2859 **2091**	72p multicoloured	3·00	3·00	☐ ☐
2860 **2092**	81p multicoloured	3·50	3·50	☐ ☐
Set of 6		10·00	10·00	☐ ☐
First Day Cover			11·00	☐
Presentation Pack		14·00		☐
PHQ Cards (*set of* 6)		4·50	14·00	☐ ☐
Set of 6 Gutter Pairs		20·00		☐

The 1st class stamp was also issued in sheets of 20 with *se-tenant* labels, printed in lithography instead of photogravure.

2093 Landmarks of Beijing and London

Handover of Olympic Flag from Beijing to London

2008 (22 Aug.) Sheet 115 × 76 mm. Phosphorised paper. Perf 14½

MS2861   **2093**   (1st) National Stadium, Beijing; (1st) London Eye; (1st) Tower

Miniature Sheet Collection

2008 (6 Nov.) Comprises Nos. **MS**2803, **MS**2818, **MS**2847, **MS**2882, **MS**2886 and **MS**NI110/11

MS2886a Miniature Sheet Collection 75·00 ☐

2116 Supermarine Spitfire (R. J. Mitchell)

2117 Mini Skirt (Mary Quant)

2118 Mini (Sir Alec Issigonis)

2119 Anglepoise Lamp (George Carwardine)

2120 Concorde (Aérospatiale-BAC)

2121 K2 Telephone Kiosk (Sir Giles Gilbert Scott)

2122 Polypropylene Chair (Robin Day)

2123 Penguin Books (Edward Young)

2124 London Underground Map

2125 Routemaster Bus (design team led by AAM Durrant)

T **2116/25** were printed together, *se-tenant*, in blocks of ten (2×5) throughout the sheet.

British Design Classics (1st series)

2009 (13 Jan.) Printed in lithography. Phosphor background. Perf 14½

2887	**2116**	(1st) multicoloured	90	90	☐	☐
		a. Block of 10. Nos. 2887/96	10·00	10·00	☐	☐
2888	**2117**	(1st) multicoloured	90	90	☐	☐
2889	**2118**	(1st) multicoloured	90	90	☐	☐
2890	**2119**	(1st) multicoloured	90	90	☐	☐
2891	**2120**	(1st) multicoloured	90	90	☐	☐
2892	**2121**	(1st) multicoloured	90	90	☐	☐
2893	**2122**	(1st) multicoloured	90	90	☐	☐
2894	**2123**	(1st) multicoloured	90	90	☐	☐
2895	**2124**	(1st) multicoloured	90	90	☐	☐
2896	**2125**	(1st) multicoloured	90	90	☐	☐
Set of 10			10·00	10·00	☐	☐
First Day Cover				11·00	☐	
Presentation Pack			12·00		☐	
PHQ Cards (set of 10)			4·50	18·00	☐	☐
Gutter Block of 20			20·00		☐	

No. 2889 was also issued in sheets of 20 with *se-tenant* labels, perforated 14×14½.

No. 2891 was also issued in sheets of 20 with *se-tenant* labels, perforated 14×14½, issued on 2 March 2009.

British Design Classics (2nd series). Booklet stamp

2009 (13 Jan.) Design as Type **1589** (Concorde from 2002 Passenger Jet Aviation) but printed in lithography. Two phosphor bands. Perf 14½

2897 **1589** (1st) multicoloured   3.00   3.00 ☐ ☐

No. 2897 was only available from £7.68 booklets.

2126 Charles Darwin

2127 Marine Iguana

2128 Finches

2129 Atoll

2130 Bee Orchid

2131 Orang-utan

2132 Fauna and Map of the Galapagos Islands

Birth Bicentenary of Charles Darwin (naturalist and evolutionary theorist) (1st issue)

2009 (12 Feb.)

(a) Self-adhesive. Printed in photogravure. 'All-over' phosphor. Perf 14

2898	**2126**	(1st) multicoloured	85	85	☐	☐
2899	**2127**	48p multicoloured	1·10	1·10	☐	☐
2900	**2128**	50p multicoloured	1·50	1·50	☐	☐
2901	**2129**	56p multicoloured	2·00	2·00	☐	☐
2902	**2130**	72p multicoloured	2·50	2·50	☐	☐
2903	**2131**	81p multicoloured	3·00	3·00	☐	☐
Set of 6			9·00	9·00	☐	☐
First Day Cover				12·00		☐
Presentation Pack			18·00		☐	
PHQ Cards (set of 11)			4·50	18·00		☐

(b) Ordinary gum. Printed in lithography. Two phosphor bands. Perf 14

MS2904 115×89 mm. (1st) Flightless cormorant; (1st) Giant tortoise and cactus finch; 81p Marine iguana; 81p Floreana mockingbird	6·50	6·50	☐ ☐
First Day Cover		8·00	☐

Nos. 2898/903 have 'jigsaw' perforations on the two vertical sides.

Birth Bicentenary of Charles Darwin (naturalist) (2nd issue). Booklet stamps

2009 (12 Feb.) Printed in photogravure. 'All-over' phosphor. Perf 14

2905	**2126**	(1st) multicoloured	85	85	☐	☐
2906	**2127**	48p multicoloured	1·10	1·10	☐	☐
2907	**2128**	50p multicoloured	2·00	2·00	☐	☐
2908	**2129**	56p multicoloured	2·50	2·50	☐	☐
2909	**2130**	72p multicoloured	3·00	3·00	☐	☐
2910	**2131**	81p multicoloured	3·50	3·50	☐	☐
Set of 6			10·00	10·00	☐	☐

Nos. 2905/10 were only issued in £7.75 booklets. They have 'jigsaw' perforations on both vertical sides.

2132a

2132b

2132c

2132d

2009 (17 Feb)–**10**. Self-adhesive. Designs as T **367**, T **913/14**, T **1916** or T **2132a/d**. One centre band (U2911, U2931) or two bands (others). U-shaped slits. Iridescent overprint. Die-cut perf 14 (U2941) or 14½×14 (others) (both with one elliptical hole in each vertical side).

(a) Sheet stamps. Photo De La Rue				
U2911	(2nd) bright blue	65	60	☐ ☐
U2912	(1st) gold	80	80	☐ ☐
U2913	(2nd Large) bright blue	90	90	☐ ☐
U2914	50p grey	1·10	1·10	☐ ☐
U2915	(1st Large) gold	1·10	1·10	☐ ☐
U2916	£1 magenta	2·25	2·25	☐ ☐
U2917	£1.50 brown-red	3·25	3·25	☐ ☐
U2918	£2 deep blue-green	4·25	4·25	☐ ☐
U2919	£3 deep mauve	6·25	6·25	☐ ☐
U2920	£5 azure	10·50	10·50	☐ ☐
Set of 10		28·00	28·00	☐ ☐
First Day Cover (Nos. U2911/16)			9·00	☐
First Day Cover (Nos. U2917/20)			30·00	☐
Presentation Pack (Nos. U2911/16)		8·00		☐
Presentation Pack (Nos. U2917/20)		30·00		☐

(b) Booklet stamps. Photo Walsall				
U2931	(2nd) bright blue (31.3.09)	60	60	☐ ☐
U2932	(1st) gold (31.3.09)	80	80	☐ ☐
U2933	(2nd Large) bright blue (31.3.09)	95	95	☐ ☐
U2934	50p grey (8.5.09)	1·10	1·10	☐ ☐
U2935	(1st Large) gold (31.3.09)	1·25	1·25	☐ ☐

(c) Special Purpose stamps. Photo De La Rue				
U2940	(Recorded Signed for 1st) bright orange-red and lemon (17.11.09)	2·25	2·25	☐ ☐
U2941	(Recorded Signed for 1st Large) bright orange-red and lemon (17.11.09)	2·75	2·75	☐ ☐
U2942	(Special Delivery up to 100g) deep ultramarine and silver (26.10.10)	10·00	10·00	☐ ☐
U2943	(Special Delivery up to 500g) deep ultramarine and silver (26.10.10)	11·00	11·00	☐ ☐
Set of 4		24·00	24·00	☐ ☐
First Day Cover (Nos. U2940/1)			6·75	☐
First Day Cover (Nos. U2942/3)			25·00	☐
Presentation Pack (Nos. U2942/3)		22·00		☐ ☐

Nos. U2911/20 and U2931/5 each have four U-shaped die-cut slits to discourage the removal of used stamps for re-use. The booklet stamps, Nos. U2931/3 and U2935 can be distinguished from sheet stamps by having the four U-shaped slits broken at top and foot.

Nos. U2911/43 and U2931/5 all have an iridescent overprint with the words 'ROYAL MAIL' repeated throughout.

Nos. U2913 and U2933 were inscr '2nd Large' and initially sold for 42p.

Nos. U2914 and U2934 were inscr '1st Large' and initially sold for 52p.

No. U2934 was only issued in £11.15 stamp booklets. It has the top U-shaped slits unbroken.

No. U2940 was inscr 'RECORDED SIGNED FOR 1st' and was initially sold for £1.14.
No. U2941 was inscr 'RECORDED SIGNED FOR 1st Large' and was initially sold for £1.36.
No. U2942 was inscr 'SPECIAL DELIVERY UP TO 100g' and originally sold for £5.05.
No. U2943 was inscr 'SPECIAL DELIVERY UP TO 500g' and originally sold for £5.50.
For presentation pack containing Nos. U2940/1 see after No. Y1803.

British Design Classics (3rd series). Booklet stamps

2009 (10 Mar.)–**2010** Designs as Nos. 2887/9, 2891/2 and 2896. Printed in photogravure. Self-adhesive. Phosphor background. Die-cut perf 14½

2911	**2121**	(1st) multicoloured	85	85	☐	☐
2912	**2125**	(1st) multicoloured	85	85	☐	☐
2913	**2118**	(1st) multicoloured (21.4.09)	85	85	☐	☐
2914	**2120**	(1st) multicoloured (18.8.09)	85	85	☐	☐
2915	**2117**	(1st) multicoloured (17.9.09)	85	85	☐	☐
2915b	**2116**	(1st) multicoloured (15.9.10)	95	95	☐	☐
Set of 5			4·25	4·25	☐	☐

Nos. 2911/15b were only issued in booklets.

2133 Matthew Boulton and Factory (manufacturing)

2134 James Watt and Boulton & Watt Condensing Engine (steam engineering)

2135 Richard Arkwright and Spinning Machine (textiles)

2136 Josiah Wedgwood and Black Basalt Teapot and Vase (ceramics)

2137 George Stephenson and Locomotion (railways)

2138 Henry Maudslay and Table Engine (machine making)

2139 James Brindley and Bridgewater Canal Aqueduct (canal engineering)

2140 John McAdam (road building)

Nos. 2916/17, 2918/19, 2920/1 and 2922/3 were each printed together, *se-tenant*, in horizontal pairs throughout the sheets.

Pioneers of the Industrial Revolution

2009 (10 Mar.) 'All-over' phosphor. Perf 14×14½

2916	**2133**	(1st) multicoloured	85	85	☐	☐
		a. Horiz pair. Nos. 2916/17	2.50	2.50	☐	☐
2917	**2134**	(1st) multicoloured	85	85	☐	☐
2918	**2135**	50p multicoloured	1·00	1·00	☐	☐
		a. Horiz pair. Nos. 2918/19	3·00	3·00	☐	☐
2919	**2136**	50p multicoloured	1·00	1·00	☐	☐
2920	**2137**	56p multicoloured	1·25	1·25	☐	☐
		a. Horiz pair. Nos. 2920/1	3·50	3·50	☐	☐
2921	**2138**	56p multicoloured	1·25	1·25	☐	☐
2922	**2139**	72p multicoloured	1·75	1·75	☐	☐
		a· Booklet pane· Nos· 2922/3	4·00	4·00	☐	☐
2923	**2140**	72p multicoloured	1·75	1·75	☐	☐
Set of 8			11·00	11·00	☐	☐
First Day Cover				12·00		☐
Presentation Pack			14·00		☐	
PHQ Cards (*set of* 8)			4·75	16·00	☐	☐
Set of 4 Gutter Strips of 4			22·00		☐	

2141 Henry VII (1485–1509)

2142 Henry VIII (1509–47)

2143 Edward VI (1547–53)

2144 Lady Jane Grey (1553)

2145 Mary I (1553–8)

2146 Elizabeth I (1558–1603)

2152 *Saxifraga hirculus* (marsh saxifrage)

2153 *Stachys germanica* (downy woundwort)

2147 The Age of the Tudors

Kings and Queens (2nd issue). The House of Tudor

2009 (21 Apr.) Two phosphor bands. Perf 14

2924	**2141**	(1st) multicoloured	85	85	☐	☐
2925	**2142**	(1st) multicoloured	85	85	☐	☐
2926	**2143**	62p multicoloured	1·50	1·50	☐	☐
2927	**2144**	62p multicoloured	1·50	1·50	☐	☐
2928	**2145**	81p multicoloured	3·00	3·00	☐	☐
2929	**2146**	81p multicoloured	3·00	3·00	☐	☐
Set of 6			9·50	9·50	☐	☐
First Day Cover				10·00		☐
Presentation Pack			15·00		☐	
PHQ Cards (*set of* 11)			6·50	13·00	☐	☐
Set of 6 Gutter Pairs			16·00		☐	
Set of 6 Traffic Light Gutter Blocks of 4			32·00		☐	

MS2930 123×70 mm. **2147** (1st) Mary
Rose (galleon), **1510**; (1st) Field of
Cloth of Gold Royal Conference,
1520; 90p Royal Exchange (centre
of commerce), **1565**; 90p Francis
Drake (circumnavigation), **1580** 5·75 5·75 ☐ ☐
First Day Cover 7·50 ☐

The complete miniature sheet is shown on one of the eleven
PHQ cards with the others depicting individual stamps
including those from **MS**2930.

2148 *Allium sphaerocephalon* (round-headed leek)

2149 *Luronium natans* (floating water-plantain)

2150 *Cypripedium calceolus* (lady's slipper orchid)

2151 *Polygala amarella* (dwarf milkwort)

2154 *Euphorbia serrulata* (upright spurge)

2155 *Pyrus cordata* (Plymouth pear)

2156 *Polygonum
maritimum* (Sea knotgrass)

2157 *Dianthus armeria* (Deptford pink)

T **2148/57** were printed together, *se-tenant*, in blocks of ten
(5×2) throughout the sheet.

2158 Royal Botanic Gardens, Kew

'Action for Species' (3rd series). Plants and 250th Anniversary of Royal Botanic Gardens, Kew (MS2941)

2009 (19 May)

		(a) Phosphor background. Perf 14½				
2931	**2148**	(1st) multicoloured	85	85	☐	☐
		a. Block of 10.				
		Nos. 2931/40	8·50	8·50	☐	☐
2932	**2149**	(1st) multicoloured	85	85	☐	☐
2933	**2150**	(1st) multicoloured	85	85	☐	☐
2934	**2151**	(1st) multicoloured	85	85	☐	☐
2935	**2152**	(1st) multicoloured	85	85	☐	☐
2936	**2153**	(1st) multicoloured	85	85	☐	☐
2937	**2154**	(1st) multicoloured	85	85	☐	☐
2938	**2155**	(1st) multicoloured	85	85	☐	☐
2939	**2156**	(1st) multicoloured	85	85	☐	☐

2940 **2157**	(1st) multicoloured	85	85	☐ ☐
Set of 10		8·50	8·50	☐ ☐
First Day Cover			11·00	☐
Presentation Pack		15·00		☐
PHQ Cards (*set of* 15)		8·75	15·00	☐ ☐
Gutter Block of 10		16·00		☐

(b) Two phosphor bands. Perf 14×14½

MS2941 115×89 mm. **2158** (1st) Palm House, Kew Gardens; (1st) Millennium Seed Bank, Wakehurst Place; 90p Pagoda, Kew Gardens; 90p Sackler Crossing,

Kew Gardens	5·75	5·75	☐ ☐
First Day Cover		7·50	☐

The complete miniature sheet is shown on one of the fifteen PHQ cards with the others depicting individual stamps including those from **MS**2941.

50th Anniversary of NAFAS (National Association of Flower Arrangement Societies). Booklet stamps

2009 (21 May) Designs as Nos. 1958 and 1962 (1997 Greeting Stamps 19th-century FlowerPaintings) but printed in photogravure. Self-adhesive. Two phosphor bands. Die-cut perf 14 (with one elliptical hole in each vert side)

2942 **1287**	(1st) multicoloured	85	85	☐ ☐
2943 **1283**	(1st) multicoloured	85	85	☐ ☐

Nos. 2942/3 were only issued in stamp booklets.

2159 Dragon

2161 Giant

2163 Mermaid

2160 Unicorn

2162 Pixie

2164 Fairy

Mythical Creatures

2009 (16 June) 'All-over' phosphor. Perf 14½

2944 **2159**	(1st) multicoloured	85	85	☐ ☐
2945 **2160**	(1st) multicoloured	85	85	☐ ☐
2946 **2161**	62p multicoloured	1·50	1·50	☐ ☐
2947 **2162**	62p multicoloured	1·50	1·50	☐ ☐
2948 **2163**	90p multicoloured	3·00	3·00	☐ ☐
2949 **2164**	90p multicoloured	3·00	3·00	☐ ☐
Set of 6		9·50	9·50	☐ ☐
First Day Cover			11·00	☐

Presentation Pack		11·00		☐
PHQ Cards (*set of* 6)		2·50	12·00	☐ ☐
Set of 6 Gutter Pairs		19·00		☐

2165 George V Type B Wall Letter Box, 1933–6

2166 Edward VII Ludlow Letter Box, 1901–10

2167 Victorian Lamp Letter Box, 1896

2168 Elizabeth II Type A Wall Letter Box, 1962–3

2169 Post Boxes

Post Boxes (1st series)

2009 (18 Aug.) 'All-over' phosphor. Perf 14

2950 **2165**	(1st) multicoloured	85	85	☐ ☐
2951 **2166**	56p multicoloured	1·25	1·25	☐ ☐
2952 **2167**	81p multicoloured	1·75	1·75	☐ ☐
2953 **2168**	90p multicoloured	2·00	2·00	☐ ☐
Set of 4		6·50	6·50	☐ ☐

MS2954 **2169** 145×74 mm. 2169

Nos. 2950/3		6·50	6·50	☐ ☐
First Day Cover			8·25	☐
Presentation Pack		7·00		☐
PHQ Cards (*set of* 5)		2·50	9·00	☐ ☐

Nos. 2950/3 were only issued in £8.18 stamp booklets and in **MS**2954.

Type **2165** was also issued in sheets of 20 with *se-tenant* labels showing post boxes.

'Treasures of the Archive' (1st series). Booklet stamps

2009 (18 Aug.) Designs as Type **929** (1990 150th anniv of the Penny Black) and **1446** (with with redrawn 1st face value). Printed in lithography. Two phosphor bands. Perf 14½ × 14 (with one elliptical hole in each vertical side)

2955 **929**	20p brownish-black and			
	grey-brown	45	45	☐ ☐
2956	(1st) brownish-black and			
	grey-brown	90	90	☐ ☐

Nos. 2955/6 were only available from £8.18 stamp booklets.

'Treasures of the Archive' (2nd series). Booklet stamps

2009 (18 Aug.) Design as Type **919** (1989 Lord Mayor's Show) but printed in lithography. 'All-over' phosphor. Perf 14

2957	**919**	20p multicoloured	45	45	☐	☐

No. 2957 was only available from £8.18 stamp booklets.

2170 Firefighting

2171 Chemical Fire

2172 Emergency Rescue

2173 Flood Rescue

2174 Search and Rescue

2175 Fire Safety

Fire and Rescue Service

2009 (1 Sept.) 'All-over' phosphor. Perf 14×14½

2958	**2170**	(1st) multicoloured	85	85	☐	☐
2959	**2171**	54p multicoloured	1·10	1·10	☐	☐
2960	**2172**	56p multicoloured	1·25	1·25	☐	☐
2961	**2173**	62p multicoloured	1·50	1·50	☐	☐
2962	**2174**	81p multicoloured	2·00	2·00	☐	☐
2963	**2175**	90p multicoloured	3·00	3·00	☐	☐
Set of 6			9·50	9·50	☐	☐
First Day Cover				11·00		☐
Presentation Pack			11·00		☐	
PHQ Cards (set of 6)			3·50	12·00	☐	☐
Set of 6 Gutter Pairs			19·00		☐	

2176 Flight Deck Officer, 2009

2177 Captain, 1941

2178 Second Officer WRNS, 1918

2179 Able Seaman, 1880

2180 Royal Marine, 1805

2181 Admiral, 1795

Nos. 2964/6 and 2967/9 were each printed together, *se-tenant*, in horizontal strips of three throughout the sheets.

Military Uniforms (3rd series). Royal Navy Uniforms

2009 (17 Sept.) Phosphor background. Perf 14

2964	**2176**	(1st) multicoloured	85	85	☐	☐
		a. Horiz strip of 3.				
		Nos. 2964/6	3·50	3·50	☐	☐
2965	**2177**	(1st) multicoloured	85	85	☐	☐
2966	**2178**	(1st) multicoloured	85	85	☐	☐
2967	**2179**	90p multicoloured	2·00	2·00	☐	☐
		a. Horiz strip of 3.				
		Nos. 2967/9	6·00	6·00	☐	☐
2968	**2180**	90p multicoloured	2·00	2·00	☐	☐
2969	**2181**	90p multicoloured	2·00	2·00	☐	☐
Set of 6			9·50	9·50	☐	☐
First Day Cover				11·00		☐
Presentation Pack			9·50		☐	
PHQ Cards (set of 6)			3·50	12·00	☐	☐
Set of 2 Gutter Strips of 6			16·00		☐	
Set of 2 Traffic Light Gutter Blocks of 12			32·00		☐	

Royal Navy Uniforms. Booklet stamp

2009 (17 Sept.) Design as Type **1518** (Jolly Roger flag from 2001 Submarine Centenary) but printed in lithography. Two phosphor bands. Perf 14½

2970	**1518**	(1st) multicoloured	90	90	☐	☐

No. 2970 was only issued in £7.93 stamp booklets.

2182 Fred Perry 1909–95 (lawn tennis champion)

2183 Henry Purcell 1659–95 (composer and musician)

2184 Sir Matt Busby 1909–94 (footballer and football manager)

2185 William Gladstone 1809–98 (statesman and Prime Minister)

2186 Mary Wollstonecraft 1759–97 (pioneering feminist)

2187 Sir Arthur Conan Doyle 1859–1930 (writer and creator of Sherlock Holmes)

2188 Donald Campbell 1921–67 (water speed record broken 1959)

2189 Judy Fryd 1909–2000 (campaigner and founder of MENCAP)

2190 Samuel Johnson 1709–84 (lexicographer, critic and poet)

2191 Sir Martin Ryle 1918–84 (radio survey of the Universe 1959)

Nos. 2971/5 and 2976/80 were each printed together, *se-tenant*, in horizontal strips of five stamps throughout the sheets.

Eminent Britons

2009 (8 Oct.) Phosphor background. Perf 14½

2971	**2182**	(1st) multicoloured	85	85	☐	☐
		a. Horiz strip of 5.				
		Nos. 2971/5	5·00	5·00	☐	☐
2972	**2183**	(1st) multicoloured	85	85	☐	☐
2973	**2184**	(1st) multicoloured	85	85	☐	☐
2974	**2185**	(1st) multicoloured	85	85	☐	☐
2975	**2186**	(1st) multicoloured	85	85	☐	☐
2976	**2187**	(1st) multicoloured	85	85	☐	☐
		a. Horiz strip of 5.				
		Nos. 2976/80	5·00	5·00	☐	☐
2977	**2188**	(1st) multicoloured	85	85	☐	☐
2978	**2189**	(1st) multicoloured	85	85	☐	☐
2979	**2190**	(1st) multicoloured	85	85	☐	☐
2980	**2191**	(1st) multicoloured	85	85	☐	☐
Set of 10			9·50	9·50	☐	☐

First Day Cover		11·00	☐
Presentation Pack		11·00	☐
PHQ Cards (*set of* 10)	5·75	13·00	☐ ☐
Set of 2 Gutter Strips of 10		19·00	☐

2192 Canoe Slalom

2193 Paralympic Games Archery

2194 Athletics: Track

2195 Diving

2196 Paralympic Games Boccia

2197 Judo

2198 Paralympic Games Dressage

2199 Badminton

2200 Weightlifting

2201 Basketball

Nos. 2981/5 and 2986/90 were each printed together, *se-tenant*, in horizontal strips of five stamps throughout the sheets.

Olympic and Paralympic Games, London (2012) (1st issue)

2009 (22 Oct.) 'All-over' phosphor. Perf 14½

2981	**2192**	(1st) multicoloured	85	85	☐	☐
		a. Horiz strip of 5.				
		Nos. 2981/5	5·00	5·00	☐	☐
2982	**2193**	(1st) multicoloured	85	85	☐	☐
2983	**2194**	(1st) multicoloured	85	85	☐	☐
2984	**2195**	(1st) multicoloured	85	85	☐	☐

2985	**2196**	(1st) multicoloured	85	85	☐	☐
2986	**2197**	(1st) multicoloured	85	85	☐	☐
		a. Horiz strip of 5.				
		Nos. 2986/90	5·00	5·00	☐	☐
2987	**2198**	(1st) multicoloured	85	85	☐	☐
2988	**2199**	(1st) multicoloured	85	85	☐	☐
2989	**2200**	(1st) multicoloured	85	85	☐	☐
2990	**2201**	(1st) multicoloured	85	85	☐	☐
Set of 10			9·50	9·50	☐	☐
First Day Cover				11·00		☐
Presentation Pack			11·00		☐	
PHQ Cards (*set of* 10)			5·75	12·00	☐	☐
Set of 2 Gutter Strips of 10			19·00		☐	

2202 Angel playing Lute (William Morris), Church of St. James, Staveley, Kendal, Cumbria

2203 Madonna and Child (Henry Holiday), Church of Ormesby St. Michael, Great Yarmouth, Norfolk

2204 Angel playing Lute (William Morris), Church of St. James, Staveley, Kendal, Cumbria

2205 Madonna and Child (Henry Holiday), Church of Ormesby St. Michael, Ormesby, Great Yarmouth, Norfolk

2206 Joseph (Henry Holiday), Parish Church of St. Michael, Minehead, Somerset

2207 Wise Man (Sir Edward Burne-Jones), Church of St. Mary the Virgin, Rye, East Sussex

2208 Shepherd (Henry Holiday), St. Mary's Church, Upavon, Wiltshire

Christmas

2009 (3 Nov.) One centre band (2nd) or two phosphor bands (others). Perf 14½×14 (with one elliptical hole in- each vert side)

(a) Self-adhesive						
2991	**2202**	(2nd) multicoloured	60	60	☐	☐
2992	**2203**	(1st) multicoloured	85	85	☐	☐
2993	**2204**	(2nd Large) multicoloured	95	95	☐	☐
2994	**2205**	56p multicoloured	1·25	1·25	☐	☐
2995	**2206**	(1st Large) multicoloured	1·25	1·25	☐	☐
2996	**2207**	90p multicoloured	2·50	2·50	☐	☐

2997	**2208**	£1.35 multicoloured	3·00	3·00	☐	☐
Set of 7			10·00	10·00	☐	☐
First Day Cover				11·50		☐
Presentation Pack			11·00		☐	
PHQ Cards (*set of* 7)			4·75	13·00	☐	☐

(b) Ordinary gum						
MS2998 115×102 mm. As Nos. 2991/7		10·00	10·00	☐	☐	
First Day Cover				11·50		☐

The 2nd class, 1st class, 56p and 90p stamps were also issued in sheets of 20 containing eight 2nd class, eight 1st class, two 50p and two 81p stamps, each stamp accompanied by a *se-tenant* label. Separate sheets of 20 2nd, 20 1st, ten 1st, ten 56p and ten 90p were available with personal photographs.

Collectors Pack

2009 (3 Nov.) Comprises Nos. 2887/96, 2898/**MS**2904, 2916/**MS**2941, 2944/9, **MS**2954, 2958/69, 2971/97, **MS**S137 and **MS**W125.

CP2998a	Collectors Pack	£120	☐

Post Office Yearbook

2009 (3 Nov.) Comprises Nos. 2887/96, 2898/**MS**2904, 2916/**MS**2941, 2944/9, **MS**2954, 2958/69, 2971/97, **MS**S137 and **MS**W125.

YB2998a	Yearbook	£130	☐

Miniature Sheet Collection

2009 (3 Nov.) Comprises Nos. **MS**2904, **MS**2930, **MS**2941, **MS**2954, **MS**2998, **MS**S137 and **MS**W125.

MS2998a	Miniature Sheet Collection	42·00	☐

2209 *The Division Bell* (Pink Floyd)

2210 *A Rush of Blood to the Head* (Coldplay)

2211 *Parklife* (Blur)

2212 *Power Corruption and Lies* (New Order)

2213 *Let It Bleed* (Rolling Stones)

2214 *London Calling* (The Clash)

2215 *Tubular Bells* (Mike Oldfield)

2216 *IV* (Led Zeppelin)

2217 *Screamadelica* (Primal Scream)

2218 *The Rise and Fall of Ziggy Stardust and the Spiders from Mars* (David Bowie)

Classic Album Covers (1st issue)

2010 (7 Jan). "All-over" phosphor. Self-adhesive. Photo De La Rue. Die-cut perf 14½ (interrupted).

2999	**2209**	(1st) multicoloured	90	90	☐	☐
		a. Horiz strip of 5.				
		Nos. 2999/3003	4·50	4·50	☐	☐
3000	**2210**	(1st) multicoloured	90	90	☐	☐
3001	**2211**	(1st) multicoloured	90	90	☐	☐
3002	**2212**	(1st) multicoloured	90	90	☐	☐
3003	**2213**	(1st) multicoloured	90	90	☐	☐
3004	**2214**	(1st) multicoloured	90	90	☐	☐
		a. Horiz strip of 5.				
		Nos. 3004/8	4·50	4·50	☐	☐
3005	**2215**	(1st) multicoloured	90	90	☐	☐
3006	**2216**	(1st) multicoloured	90	90	☐	☐
3007	**2217**	(1st) multicoloured	90	90	☐	☐
3008	**2218**	(1st) multicoloured	90	90	☐	☐
Set of 10			8·50	8·50	☐	☐
First Day Cover				11·00		☐
Presentation Pack			9·75		☐	
PHQ Cards (set of 10)			6·00	15·00	☐	☐

Nos. 2999/3003 and 3004/8 were each printed together, *se-tenant*, as horizontal strips of five stamps in sheets of 50 (2 panes of 25).
The right-hand edges of Nos. 2999/3008 are all cut around to show the vinyl disc protruding from the open edge of the album cover.

Classic Album Covers (2nd issue)

2010 (7 Jan). "All-over" phosphor. Litho Cartor. Perf 14½ (interrupted).

3009	**2213**	(1st) multicoloured	90	90	☐	☐
3010	**2216**	(1st) multicoloured	90	90	☐	☐
3011	**2218**	(1st) multicoloured	90	90	☐	☐
3012	**2212**	(1st) multicoloured	90	90	☐	☐
3013	**2217**	(1st) multicoloured	90	90	☐	☐
3014	**2209**	(1st) multicoloured	90	90	☐	☐
3015	**2215**	(1st) multicoloured	90	90	☐	☐
3016	**2214**	(1st) multicoloured	90	90	☐	☐
3017	**2211**	(1st) multicoloured	90	90	☐	☐
3018	**2210**	(1st) multicoloured	90	90	☐	☐
3009/18 Set of 10			8·75	8·75	☐	☐
MS3019 223×189 mm. Nos. 3009/18			8·50	8·50	☐	☐
First Day Cover				11·00		☐

Nos. 3009/18 were only issued in £8.06 stamp booklets and miniature sheet **MS**3019.
The right-hand edges of Nos. 3009/18 and the miniature sheet **MS**3019 are all cut around in an imperforate section to show the vinyl disc protruding from the open edge of the album cover.
A miniature sheet containing No. 3014×10 *The Division Bell* (Pink Floyd) was issued on 6 March 2010 and sold for £4.75 per sheet.

Olympic and Paralympic Games, London (2012) (2nd issue). Booklet stamps

2010 (7 Jan–25 Feb). Designs as Nos. 2982 and 2986 but printed in photogravure. Self-adhesive. "All-over" phosphor. Die-cut perf 14½.

3020	**2197**	(1st) multicoloured	90	90	☐	☐
3021	**2193**	(1st) multicoloured	90	90	☐	☐
3022	**2194**	(1st) multicoloured (25 Feb)	90	90	☐	☐
3023	**2201**	(1st) multicoloured (25 Feb)	90	90	☐	☐
Set of 4			3·50	3·50	☐	☐

Nos. 3020/1 and 3022/3 were only issued in separate booklets, each originally sold for £2.34.

2219

Business and Consumer Smilers

2010 (26 Jan). Sheet 124×71 mm. Multicoloured. Two phosphor bands. Perf 14½×14 (with one elliptical hole in each vertical side).

MS3024	**2219**	(1st) Propeller driven airplane (Andrew Davidson); (1st) Vintage sports roadster (Andrew Davidson); (1st) Recreation of crown seal (Neil Oliver); (1st) Birthday cake (Annabel Wright); (1st) Steam locomotive (Andrew Davidson); (1st) Ocean liner (Andrew Davidson); (1st) As Type **2112**; (1st) Birthday present (Annabel Wright); (Europe up to 20 grams) Bird carrying envelope (Lucy Davey); (Worldwide up to 20 grams) "Hello" in plane vapour trail (Lucy Davey)		10·00	10·00	☐	☐
First Day Cover				13·00		☐
Presentation Pack			11·00		☐	
PHQ Cards (set of 11)			6·50	17·00	☐	☐

MS3024 was sold for £4.58.
The eleven PHQ cards show the ten individual stamps and the complete miniature sheet.
Stamps in designs as within **MS**3024 but self-adhesive were available printed together, *se-tenant*, in sheets of 20 containing two of each design with greetings labels.
The (1st) birthday cake, (1st) birthday present, Europe and Worldwide designs were also available in separate sheets with personal photographs.

The other 1st class designs were for the business customised service.

Stamps as the 1st Birthday cake (×4), 1st Birthday present (×4), Europe Bird carrying envelope (×2) and Worldwide "Hello" in plane vapour trail (×2) designs but self-adhesive were issued, together with Nos. 2569, 2572, 2674 and 2821/3 on 8 May 2010 in sheets of 20 stamps with *se-tenant* greetings labels.

2220 Girlguiding UK

2010 (2 Feb). Centenary of Girlguiding. Sheet 190×67 mm. Multicoloured. Phosphor background. Perf 14×14½.

MS3025 **2220** (1st) Rainbows; 56p Brownies; 81p Guides; 90p Senior

Section members	6·00	6·00	☐ ☐
First Day Cover		8·00	☐
Presentation Pack	7·00		☐
PHQ Cards (set of 5)	3·00	9·00	☐ ☐

The five PHQ cards show the four individual stamps and the complete miniature sheet.

2221 Sir Robert Boyle (chemistry)

2222 Sir Isaac Newton (optics)

2223 Benjamin Franklin (electricity)

2224 Edward Jenner (pioneer of smallpox vaccination)

2225 Charles Babbage (computing)

2226 Alfred Russel Wallace (theory of evolution)

2227 Joseph Lister (antiseptic surgery)

2228 Ernest Rutherford (atomic structure)

2229 Dorothy Hodgkin (crystallography)

2230 Sir Nicholas Shackleton (earth sciences)

350th Anniversary of the Royal Society

2010 (25 Feb). "All-over" phosphor. Perf 14½.

3026	**2221**	(1st) multicoloured	90	90	☐	☐
		a. Block of 10.				
		Nos. 3026/35	9·00	9·00	☐	☐
3027	**2222**	(1st) multicoloured	90	90	☐	☐
3028	**2223**	(1st) multicoloured	90	90	☐	☐
3029	**2224**	(1st) multicoloured	90	90	☐	☐
3030	**2225**	(1st) multicoloured	90	90	☐	☐
3031	**2226**	(1st) multicoloured	90	90	☐	☐
3032	**2227**	(1st) multicoloured	90	90	☐	☐
3033	**2228**	(1st) multicoloured	90	90	☐	☐
3034	**2229**	(1st) multicoloured	90	90	☐	☐
3035	**2230**	(1st) multicoloured	90	90	☐	☐
Set of 10			9·00	9·00	☐	
First Day Cover				11·00		☐
Presentation Pack			10·00		☐	
PHQ Cards (set of 10)			6·00	15·00	☐	☐
Gutter Block of 20			18·00		☐	

Nos. 3026/35 were printed together, *se-tenant*, as blocks of ten (5×2) in sheets of 60 (2 panes of 30).

2231 "Pixie" (mastiff cross)

2232 "Button"

2233 "Herbie" (mongrel)

2234 "Mr. Tumnus"

2235 "Tafka" (border collie)

2236 "Boris" (bulldog cross)

2237 "Casey" (lurcher)

2238 "Tigger"

2239 "Leonard" (Jack Russell cross)

2240 "Tia" (terrier cross)

150th Anniversary of Battersea Dogs and Cats Home.

2010 (11 Mar). Phosphor background. Perf 14½.

3036	**2231**	(1st) multicoloured	90	90		
		a. Block of 10.				
		Nos. 3036/45	9·00	9·00		
3037	**2232**	(1st) multicoloured	90	90		
3038	**2233**	(1st) multicoloured	90	90		
3039	**2234**	(1st) multicoloured	90	90		
3040	**2235**	(1st) multicoloured	90	90		
3041	**2236**	(1st) multicoloured	90	90		
3042	**2237**	(1st) multicoloured	90	90		
3043	**2238**	(1st) multicoloured	90	90		
3044	**2239**	(1st) multicoloured	90	90		
3045	2240	(1st) multicoloured	90	90		
Set of 10			9·00	9·00		
First Day Cover				11·00		
Presentation Pack			10·00			
PHQ Cards (set of 10)			6·00	15·00		
Gutter Block of 20			18·00			

Nos. 3036/45 were printed together, *se-tenant*, as blocks of ten (5×2) in sheets of 60 (2 panes of 30).

2241 James I (1406–37)

2243 James III (1460–88)

2242 James II (1437–60)

2244 James IV (1488–1513)

2245 James V (1513–42)

2246 Mary (1542–67)

2247 James VI (1567–1625)

2248 The Age of the Stewarts

Kings and Queens (3rd issue). House of Stewart

2010 (23 Mar). Two phosphor bands. Perf 14.

3046	**2241**	(1st) multicoloured	90	90		
3047	**2242**	(1st) multicoloured	90	90		
3048	**2243**	(1st) multicoloured	90	90		
3049	**2244**	62p multicoloured	1·40	1·40		
3050	**2245**	62p multicoloured	1·40	1·40		
3051	**2246**	81p multicoloured	1·75	1·75		
3052	**2247**	81p multicoloured	1·75	1·75		
Set of 7			9·00	9·00		
First Day Cover				11·75		
Presentation Pack			15·50			
PHQ Cards (set of 12)			7·25	15·00		
Set of 7 Gutter Pairs			18·00			
Set of 7 Traffic Light Gutter Blocks of 4			35·00			

MS3053 123×70 mm. **2248** (1st) Foundation of the University of St. Andrews, 1413; (1st) Foundation of the College of Surgeons, Edinburgh, 1505; 81p Foundation of Court of Session, 1532; 81p John Knox (Reformation, 1559)

	5·25	5·25	
First Day Cover	7·50	

The complete miniature sheet is shown on one of the twelve PHQ cards with the others depicting individual stamps including those from **MS**3053.

2249 Humpback Whale (*Megaptera novaeangliae*)

2251 Brown Long-eared Bat (*Plecotus auritus*)

2253 Sperm Whale (*Physeter macrocephalus*)

2255 Greater Horseshoe Bat (*Rhinolophus ferrumequinum*)

2257 Dormouse (*Muscardinus avellanarius*)

2250 Wildcat (*Felis silvestris*)

2252 Polecat (*Mustela putorius*)

2254 Water Vole (*Arvicola terrestris*)

2256 Otter (*Lutra lutra*)

2258 Hedgehog (*Erinaceus europaeus*)

'Action for Species' (4th series). Mammals.

2010 (13 Apr). 'All-over' phosphor. Perf 14½.

3054	**2249**	(1st) multicoloured	1·00	1·00	☐	☐
		a. Block of 10.				
		Nos. 3054/63	9·25	9·25	☐	☐
3055	**2250**	(1st) multicoloured	1·00	1·00	☐	☐
3056	**2251**	(1st) multicoloured	1·00	1·00	☐	☐
3057	**2252**	(1st) multicoloured	1·00	1·00	☐	☐
3058	**2253**	(1st) multicoloured	1·00	1·00	☐	☐
3059	**2254**	(1st) multicoloured	1·00	1·00	☐	☐
3060	**2255**	(1st) multicoloured	1·00	1·00	☐	☐
3061	**2256**	(1st) multicoloured	1·00	1·00	☐	☐
3062	**2257**	(1st) multicoloured	1·00	1·00	☐	☐
3063	**2258**	(1st) multicoloured	1·00	1·00	☐	☐
Set of 10			9·25	9·25	☐	☐

First Day Cover		12·00	☐
Presentation Pack		10·50	☐
PHQ Cards (*set of* 10)	6·00	16·00	☐ ☐
Gutter Block of 20		19·00	☐

Nos. 3054/63 were printed together, *se-tenant*, as blocks of ten (5×2) in sheets of 60 (2 panes of 30).
No. 3064, T **2259** are vacant.

2260 King George V and Queen Elizabeth II (1st); Two portraits of King George V (£1)

2010 (6 May). London 2010 Festival of Stamps and Centenary of Accession of King George V (1st issue). Sheet 141×74 mm. 'All-over' phosphor. Perf 14½×14.

MS3065 **2260** (1st) rosine;			
£1 blackish brown, grey-brown and			
silver	3·25	3·25	☐ ☐
First Day Cover		4·75	☐
Presentation Pack (**MS**3065			
and **MS**3072)	10·50		☐
PHQ Cards (*set of* 8)	4·75	16·00	☐ ☐

A miniature sheet as No. **MS**3065 but inscr 'BUSINESS DESIGN CENTRE, LONDON 8–15 MAY 2010' along the top right margin was only available at London 2010 Festival of Stamps.
The eight PHQ cards depict the individual stamps from **MS**3065 and **MS**3072 and the complete miniature sheets.

2261 King George V and Queen Elizabeth II

2262 1924 British Empire Exhibition 1½d. Brown Stamp

2263 1924 British Empire Exhibition 1d. Scarlet Stamp

2264 Two Portraits of King George V

2265 1913 £1 Green 'Sea Horses' Design Stamp

2266 1913 10s. Blue 'Sea Horses' Design Stamp

2267

2010 (6 May)–**2010** (8 May). London 2010 Festival of Stamps and Centenary of Accession of King George V (2nd issue). Litho (Nos. 3066 and 3069) or recess and litho. 'All-over' phosphor. Perf 14½×14.

3066	**2261**	(1st) rosine (6 May)	1·00	1·00	□	□
3067	**2262**	(1st) multicoloured (8 May)	1·00	1·00	□	□
3068	**2263**	(1st) multicoloured (8 May)	1·00	1·00	□	□
3069	**2264**	£1 blackish brown, grey-brown and silver (8 May)	2·25	2·25	□	□
3070	**2265**	£1 multicoloured (8 May)	2·25	2·25	□	□
3071	**2266**	£1 multicoloured (8 May)	2·25	2·25	□	□
3066/71	*Set of* 6		9·00	9·00	□	□
Gutter Pair (No. 3066)			2·25		□	
MS3072 115×90 mm. **2267**						
	Nos. 3067/8 and 3070/1 (8 May)		6·50	6·50	□	□
First Day Cover (**MS**3072)			8·50		□	

No. 3066 was issued as a sheet stamp on 6 May 2010.
Nos. 3066/71 all come from an £11.15 stamp booklet issued on 8 May 2010.
Nos. 3066 and 3069 also come from miniature sheet **MS**3065, issued on 8 May 2010.
Nos. 3067/8 and 3070/1 also come from **MS**3072, issued on 8 May 2010.
For presentation pack and PHQ cards for No. **MS**3072 see under **MS**3065.

2268

London 2010 Festival of Stamps.
Jeffery Matthews Colour Palette

2010 (8 May). Sheet, 104×95 mm, containing stamps as T **367** with a label. Two phosphor bands. Perf 15×14 (with one elliptical hole in each vertical side).

MS3073	**2268**	1p reddish purple; 2p deep grey-green; 5p reddish-brown; 9p bright orange; 10p orange; 20p light green; 60p emerald; 67p bright mauve; 88p bright magenta; 97p bluish violet; £1.46 turquoise-blue	11·50	11·50 □ □

2269 Winston Churchill   **2270** Land Girl

2271 Home Guard   **2272** Evacuees

2273 Air Raid Wardens   **2274** Woman working in Factory

2275 Royal Broadcast by Princess Elizabeth and Princess Margaret

2276 Fire Service

'Britain Alone' (1st issue)

2010 (13 May). 'All-over' phosphor. Perf 14½.

3074	**2269**	(1st) pale stone, pale bistre and black	1·00	1·00	☐	☐
3075	**2270**	(1st) pale stone, pale bistre and black	1·00	1·00	☐	☐
3076	**2271**	60p pale stone, pale bistre and black	1·50	1·50	☐	☐
3077	**2272**	60p pale stone, pale bistre and black	1·50	1·50	☐	☐
3078	**2273**	67p pale stone, pale bistre and black	1·60	1·60	☐	☐
3079	**2274**	67p pale stone, pale bistre and black	1·60	1·60	☐	☐
3080	**2275**	97p pale stone, pale bistre and black	2·40	2·40	☐	☐
3081	**2276**	97p pale stone, pale bistre and black	2·40	2·40	☐	☐
Set of 8			12·00	12·00	☐	☐
First Day Cover				15·00		☐
Presentation Pack			20·00			☐
PHQ Cards (set of 13)			7·75	29·00	☐	☐
Set of 8 Gutter Pairs			24·00			☐

The thirteen PHQ cards depict Nos. 3074/85 and the complete miniature sheet **MS**3086.

2277 Evacuation of British Soldiers from Dunkirk

2278 Vessels from Upper Thames Patrol in 'Operation Little Ships'

2279 Rescued Soldiers on Board Royal Navy Destroyer, Dover

2280 Steamship and Other Boat loaded with Troops

2281 Evacuation of British Troops from Dunkirk, 1940

'Britain Alone' (2nd issue)

2010 (13 May). 'All-over' phosphor. Perf 14½.

3082	**2277**	(1st) pale stone, pale bistre and black	1·00	1·00	☐	☐
3083	**2278**	60p pale stone, pale bistre and black	1·40	1·40	☐	☐
3084	**2279**	88p pale stone, pale bistre and black	2·00	2·00	☐	☐
3085	**2280**	97p pale stone, pale bistre and black	2·25	2·25	☐	☐
3082/85 Set of 4			6·00	6·00	☐	☐
MS3086 115×89 mm. **2281**						
	Nos. 3082/5		6·50	6·50	☐	☐
First Day Cover (**MS**3086)				8·50		☐

Nos. 3082/5 were only issued in £9.76 booklets and in **MS**3086.

2282 James I (1603–25)

2283 Charles I (1625–49)

2284 Charles II (1660–85)

2285 James II (1685–8)

2286 William III (1689–1702)

2287 Mary II (1689–94)

2288 Anne (1702–14)

2289 The Age of the Stuarts

Kings and Queens (4th series). House of Stuart

2010 (15 June). Two phosphor bands. Perf 14.

3087	**2282**	(1st) multicoloured	1·00	1·00	☐	☐
3088	**2283**	(1st) multicoloured	1·00	1·00	☐	☐
3089	**2284**	60p multicoloured	1·50	1·50	☐	☐
3090	**2285**	60p multicoloured	1·50	1·50	☐	☐
3091	**2286**	67p multicoloured	1·60	1·60	☐	☐
3092	**2287**	67p multicoloured	1·60	1·60	☐	☐
3093	**2288**	88p multicoloured	2·10	2·10	☐	☐
Set of 7			9·50	9·50	☐	☐
First Day Cover				11·50		☐
Presentation Pack			17·00		☐	
PHQ Cards (*set of* 12)			7·25	24·00	☐	☐
Set of 7 Gutter Pairs			19·00		☐	
Set of 7 Traffic Light Gutter Blocks of 4			38·00		☐	
First Day Cover				8·00		☐

MS3094 123×70 mm. **2289** (1st) William Harvey (discovery of blood circulation, 1628); 60p Civil War Battle of Naseby, 1645; 88p John Milton (*Paradise Lost*, 1667); 97p Castle Howard (John Vanbrugh, 1712)   6·50   6·50   ☐   ☐

The complete miniature sheet is shown on one of the twelve PHQ cards with the others depicting individual stamps including those from **MS**3094.

Mammals. Booklet stamps.

2010 (15 June). Designs as Nos. 3061 and 3063 but printed in photogravure. Self-adhesive. Die-cut perf 14½.

3095	**2256**	(1st) multicoloured	1·00	1·00	☐	☐
3096	**2258**	(1st) multicoloured	1·00	1·00	☐	☐

Nos. 3095/6 were only issued in stamp booklets, originally sold for £2.46.

2290 Paralympic Games: Rowing

2291 Shooting

2292 Modern Pentathlon

2293 Taekwondo

2294 Cycling

2295 Paralympic Games: Table Tennis

2296 Hockey

2297 Football

2298 Paralympic Games: Goalball

2299 Boxing

Olympic and Paralympic Games, London (2012) (3rd issue)

2010 (27 July). 'All-over' phosphor. Perf 14½.

3097	**2290**	(1st) multicoloured	1·00	1·00	☐	☐
		a. Horiz strip of 5.				
		Nos. 3097/101	5·50	5·50	☐	☐
3098	**2291**	(1st) multicoloured	1·00	1·00	☐	☐
3099	**2292**	(1st) multicoloured	1·00	1·00	☐	☐
3100	**2293**	(1st) multicoloured	1·00	1·00	☐	☐
3101	**2294**	(1st) multicoloured	1·00	1·00	☐	☐
3102	**2295**	(1st) multicoloured	1·00	1·00	☐	☐
		a. Horiz strip of 5.				
		Nos. 3102/6	5·50	5·50	☐	☐
3103	**2296**	(1st) multicoloured	1·00	1·00	☐	☐
3104	**2297**	(1st) multicoloured	1·00	1·00	☐	☐
3105	**2298**	(1st) multicoloured	1·00	1·00	☐	☐

3106 **2299**	(1st) multicoloured	1·00	1·00	☐ ☐
Set of 10		9·25	9·25	☐ ☐
First Day Cover			12·00	☐
Presentation Pack		10·50		☐
PHQ Cards (*set of* 10)		6·00	16·00	☐
Set of 2 Gutter Strips of 10			19·00	☐

Nos. 3097/101 and 3102/6 were each printed together, *se-tenant*, in horizontal strips of five stamps in sheets of 50 (2 panes 5×5).

Olympic and Paralympic Games, London (2012) (4th issue). Booklet stamps

2010 (27 July–12 Oct). Designs as Nos. 3097, 3101/2 and 3104 but printed in photogravure. Self-adhesive. 'All-over' phosphor. Die-cut perf 14½

3107	**2290**	(1st) multicoloured	1·00	1·00	☐ ☐
3108	**2295**	(1st) multicoloured	1·00	1·00	☐ ☐
3108a	**2297**	(1st) multicoloured (12 Oct)	1·00	1·00	☐ ☐
3108b	**2298**	(1st) multicoloured (12 Oct)	1·00	1·00	☐ ☐

Nos. 3107/8 and 3108a/b were only issued in two separate stamp booklets each originally sold for £2·46.

2300 LMS Coronation Class Locomotive, Euston Station, 1938

2301 BR Class 9F Locomotive *Evening Star*, Midsomer Norton, 1962

2302 GWR King Class Locomotive *King William IV*, near Teignmouth, 1935

2303 LNER Class A1 Locomotive *Royal Lancer*, 1929

2304 SR King Arthur Class Locomotive *Sir Mador de la Porte*, Bournemouth Central Station, 1935–9

2305 LMS NCC Class WT No. 2, Larne Harbour, c. 1947

Great British Railways

2010 (19 Aug). 'All-over' phosphor. Perf 14.

3109	**2300**	(1st) gold, bluish grey and black	1·00	1·00	☐ ☐
3110	**2301**	(1st) gold, bluish grey and black	1·00	1·00	☐ ☐
3111	**2302**	67p gold, bluish grey and black	1·60	1·60	☐ ☐
3112	**2303**	67p gold, bluish grey and black	1·60	1·60	☐ ☐
3113	**2304**	97p gold, bluish grey			

		and black	2·25	2·25	☐ ☐
3114	**2305**	97p gold, bluish grey and black	2·25	2·25	☐ ☐
Set of 6			9·00	9·00	☐ ☐
First Day Cover				11·50	☐
Presentation Pack			10·00		☐
PHQ Cards (*set of* 6)			3·50	14·00	☐ ☐
Set of 6 Gutter Pairs			19·00		☐

2306 Heart-regulating Beta Blockers (Sir James Black, 1962)

2307 Antibiotic Properties of Penicillin (Sir Alexander Fleming, 1928)

2308 Total Hip Replacement Operation (Sir John Charnley, 1962)

2309 Artificial Lens Implant Surgery (Sir Harold Ridley, 1949)

2310 Malaria Parasite transmitted by Mosquitoes (proved by Sir Ronald Ross, 1897)

2311 Computed Tomography Scanner (Sir Godfrey Hounsfield, 1971)

Medical Breakthroughs

2010 (16 Sept). 'All-over' phosphor. Perf 14×14½.

3115	**2306**	(1st) multicoloured	1·00	1·00	☐ ☐
3116	**2307**	58p multicoloured	1·40	1·40	☐ ☐
3117	**2308**	60p multicoloured	1·50	1·50	☐ ☐
3118	**2309**	67p multicoloured	1·60	1·60	☐ ☐
3119	**2310**	88p multicoloured	2·10	2·10	☐ ☐
3120	**2311**	97p multicoloured	2·40	2·40	☐ ☐
Set of 6			9·25	9·25	☐ ☐
First Day Cover				9·75	☐
Presentation Pack			10·50		☐
PHQ Cards (*set of* 6)			3·50	12·50	☐ ☐
Set of 6 Gutter Pairs			18·00		☐

2312 Winnie the Pooh and Christopher Robin (*Now we are Six*)

Winnie-the-Pooh and Christopher Robin

2313 Winnie the Pooh and Piglet (*The House at Pooh Corner*)

Winnie-the-Pooh and Piglet

Winnie-the-Pooh and Rabbit

2314 Winnie the Pooh and Rabbit (*Winnie the Pooh*)

Winnie-the-Pooh and Eeyore

2315 Winnie the Pooh and Eeyore (*Winnie the Pooh*)

Winnie-the-Pooh and Friends

2316 Winnie the Pooh and Friends (*Winnie the Pooh*)

Winnie-the-Pooh and Tigger

2317 Winnie the Pooh and Tigger (*The House at Pooh Corner*)

2318 Winnie the Pooh (Illustration reduced. Actual size 115×89 mm)

Europa. Children's Books. Winnie the Pooh by A. A. Milne. Book Illustrations by E. H. Shepard

2010 (12 Oct). 'All-over' phosphor. Perf 14×14½

3121	**2312**	(1st) yellow-brown, pale stone and black	1·00	1·00	☐	☐
3122	**2313**	58p yellow-brown, pale stone and black	1·40	1·40	☐	☐
3123	**2314**	60p yellow-brown, pale stone and black	1·50	1·50	☐	☐
3124	**2315**	67p yellow-brown, pale stone and black	1·60	1·60	☐	☐
3125	**2316**	88p yellow-brown, pale stone and black	2·10	2·10	☐	☐
3126	**2317**	97p yellow-brown, pale stone and black	2·40	2·40	☐	☐

Set of 6		9·25	9·25 ☐ ☐
First Day Cover			9·75 ☐
Presentation Pack		10·50	☐
PHQ Cards (*set of 11*)		6·50	15·00 ☐ ☐
Set of 6 *Gutter Pairs*		18·00	☐

MS3127 115×89 mm. **2318** (1st) Winnie the Pooh and Christopher Robin (from *Now we are Six*); 60p Christopher Robin reads to Winnie the Pooh (from *Winnie the Pooh*); 88p Winnie the Pooh and Christopher Robin sailing in umbrella (from *Winnie the Pooh*); 97p Christopher Robin (putting on wellingtons) and Pooh (from *Winnie the Pooh*). Perf 14½ 6·50 6·50 ☐ ☐

First Day Cover		8·00 ☐

Stamps from **MS**3127 show lines from poem 'We Too' by A. A. Milne: 'Wherever I am, there's always Pooh' (1st); 'There's always Pooh and Me. Whatever I do, he wants to do' (60p.); "Where are you going to-day?" says Pooh: "Well that's very odd 'cos I was too" (88p.); "Let's go together," says Pooh, says he. "Let's go together," says Pooh (97p.).

The eleven PHQ cards show the six stamps, the four individual stamps within **MS**3127 and the complete miniature sheet.

2319 Wallace and Gromit carol singing

2320 Gromit posting Christmas Cards

2321 Wallace and Gromit carol singing

2322 Wallace and Gromit decorating Christmas Tree

2323 Gromit posting Christmas Cards

2324 Gromit carrying Christmas Pudding

2325 Gromit putting on Bone-themed Pullover

Christmas with Wallace and Gromit

2010 (2 Nov). One centre band (3128) or two phosphor bands (others). Perf 14½×14 (with one elliptical hole in each vert side).

		(a) Self-adhesive				
3128	**2319**	(2nd) multicoloured	75	75	☐	☐
3129	**2320**	(1st) multicoloured	1·00	1·00	☐	☐
3130	**2321**	(2nd Large) multicoloured	1·25	1·25	☐	☐
3131	**2322**	60p multicoloured	1·50	1·50	☐	☐

3132	**2323**	(1st Large) multicoloured	1·60	1·60	☐	☐
3133	**2324**	97p multicoloured	2·40	2·40	☐	☐
3134	**2325**	£1.46 multicoloured	3·25	3·25	☐	☐
Set of 7			10·50	10·50	☐	
First Day Cover				13·50	☐	
Presentation Pack			12·00		☐	
PHQ Cards (*set of* 8)			4·75	17·00	☐	☐

(b) Ordinary gum.

MS3135 115×102 mm.

As Nos. 3128/34	10·50	10·50	☐	☐
First Day Cover		13·50	☐	

The eight PHQ cards show the seven individual stamps and the miniature sheet.

Collectors Pack

2010 (2 Nov). Comprises Nos. 2999/3008, **MS**3025/63, **MS**3065, **MS**3072, 3074/94, 3097/106 and 3109/34
CP3135*a* Collectors Pack £120 ☐

Post Office Yearbook

2010 (2 Nov). Comprises Nos. 2999/3008, **MS**3025/63, **MS**3065, **MS**3072, 3074/94, 3097/106 and 3109/34
YB3135*a* Yearbook £130 ☐

Miniature Sheet Collection

2010 (2 Nov). Comprises Nos. **MS**3024, **MS**3025, **MS**3053, **MS**3065, **MS**3072, **MS**3086, **MS**3094, **MS**3197 and **MS**3135
MS3135*a* Miniature Sheet Collection 48·00 ☐

Are you looking to sell all or part of your collection?

You could include it in one of our all world public auctions or specialised sales.

- Reach over 200,000 potential buyers

- The largest philatelic audience in the UK

- Unrivalled expertise in the field of philately

- 100% exceptional clearance rate

- Download each catalogue for FREE

- We can offer featured write-ups about any auction in GSM

- Confidence and trust make Stanley Gibbons Auctions the first port of call for people selling their collections

- Auctions hosted on www.stanleygibbons.com, offering massive worldwide exposure

Consignments now being accepted for our next public auction

Est 1856

STANLEY GIBBONS

Stanley Gibbons Auction Department
399 Strand, London, WC2R 0LX
Contact Steve Matthews or Ryan Epps on Tel: +44 (0)20 7836 8444
Fax: +44 (0)20 7836 7342 | Email: auctions@stanleygibbons.co.uk
www.stanleygibbons.com/auctions

DAUWALDERS *of Salisbury*

From Britain's Largest Provincial Stamp Shop
Our air-conditioned store is open 6 full days each week

PARAGON STOCKBOOKS

Super quality
Every page
interleaved
and to house
thousands of stamps.

WHITE PAGES:
9 Strips per page size 12"x9".
Available: Green, Red or Blue binding.

16 sides Single book each	£4.60
3 or more each	£4.10
32 sides Single book each	£6.80
3 or more each	£6.20
64 sides Single book each	£13.20
3 or more each	£11.95

BLACK PAGES:
9 Glass clear strips per page.
12"x9" Green, Red or Blue

16 sides Single book each	£5.90
3 or more each	£5.25
32 sides Single book each	£8.90
3 or more each	£8.20
64 sides Single book each	£16.35
3 or more each	£14.80

SALISBURY 2-up FIRST DAY COVER ALBUM

A4 size to accept 2 new size
Post Office envelopes. 20
Polypropylene leaves, holds 80
covers. Red, Blue or Green
leatherette finish.
Each pocket size is 230x130mm

2-up Album - each	**£9.95**
2 Albums	**£19.00**
4 Albums	**£35.25**
Binder only - each	**£5.95**
3 Binders	**£16.50**
6 Binders	**£31.50**
10 extra double pocket leaves	**£3.95**
Complete Album with leaves & matching slipcase - each	**£14.95**

STAMP COLLECTIONS FOR SALE

500 DIFFERENT
GREAT BRITAIN QV to Date
includes Q.Victoria 2d blue
and many scarcer items.
500 stamps A fine lot of
used £15.50

1000 DIFFERENT
Over 30% of all GB
stamps issued
many higher values
includes 2/6d KGV
Seahorse 1000 different used at only 2½p
per stamp! £25

1841-1935 Collection
A wonderful, all
different, lot.
*50 different types
used.*
A fascinating
collection. £47.50

High Value Commemoratives only

Absolutely no 1st or
2nd class values. 100
different, all good
used, high values
1948-1997 £12.50

STAMP STORAGE CARDS
3 strip black with flip over foil.
7"x5"
Qty: 100 - £10.50

SERVICE AND ADVICE

Since 1958 we have
provided an excellent
mail order service
for stamp collectors.

Visit our Website
www.worldstamps.co.uk

AND THIS IS OUR BOOK OF BRITISH STAMPS 2010 EDITION.

Free upon request
Lists GB
stamps at low
prices.

Watermark Detector
**The Morley Bright
Instatector.** *IT WORKS!!*
Price: **£15.95** + p&p £1.50

TROUBLE WITH PHOSPHOR LINES?

Lamp shows all
phosphor
lines. Battery
operated
with unique
test card.
£25.50 +
p&p £2.50

**Choosing a
Stamp Album
for GB
stamps?** Our
experts can
advise the
best type for
your needs.
Phone today
for help!

POSTAGE: Please add £2.50
inland p&p unless
otherwise stated

42 Fisherton Street, Salisbury,
Wiltshire, SP2 7RB
Tel: (01722) 412100
Fax: (01722) 410074
E-mail:
sales@worldstamps.co.uk

Did you miss the boat or did you take our advice?

In 1973 we recommended and sold the British definitive 1/2p (SGX842) with one phosphor band on side. We told our customers to buy them at 25p each. WE WERE RIGHT!! Today this stamp is catalogued at £55.00 each. If you had taken our advice, for an outlay of only £50 in1973, the current catalogue value of your investment would be a staggering total of £11,000.00.

In 1999 we recommended our customers to buy the Princess Diana Welsh Language Presentation Packs. The catalogue value was only £2.50 each, but we were telling our customers to buy them for up to double catalogue value £5 each. Within only 6 years they had increased by 5,900%.

As everyone knows, investments can go down as well as up and the past in not necessarily a guide to the future. However, being selective and taking sound advice is the best way to make your hobby pay for itself.

In 2003 we recommended our customers to buy the Coronation £1 Green (SG 2380) which was catalogued by Stanley Gibbons at £1.50 per stamp. Within 1 year the catalogue value had increased to £50 per stamp, an increase of over 3,200%. In 2004 we told our customers to buy the Fruit & Veg Presentation Pack – it was catalogued at £4.50. We said ignore the catalogue value, it's cheap at even treble the catalogue value – this pack increased in Stanley Gibbons Catalogue to £60 within two years; an increase of well over 1,200%.

We hope that you took our advice in 2004. We recommended you to buy the Locomotives Miniature Sheet (SG.MS.2423). The Stanley Gibbons Catalogue value was £3.75 each. Within 1 year the Stanley Gibbons Catalogue had increased to £25 each - An increase of over 550% in only one year.

In 2005 we recommended the 2003 Rugby Presentation Pack. The 2005 Stanley Gibbons concise catalogue listed this at £6 and, within 3 years, the catalogue value had soared. The 2008 Concise Catalogue value for the Rugby Presentation Pack was £35 each, a truly massive increase. We hope you took our advice.

In 2008 we recommended the 2002 Bridges of London Presentation pack (number 338). At the time the catalogue value was £8 each. Within 1 year of our recommendation the catalogue value of the Presentation Pack increased to £25 each. This year the catalogue value increased once again from £25 per pack to £55 per pack.

Earlier this year we recommended our customers to buy the Nobel Prizes Presentation Pack, the SG catalogue value was £10 each. In the latest SG catalogue the price zoomed to a staggering £50 each. Our customers have complimented us and said once again "You were right!"

PLEASE LISTEN TO US NOW!

We now strongly recommend you to buy the Great Britain 2001 Flags Presentation packs No. MO6, at the best possible price.

**For our most recent up to the minute recommendations
Please telephone 01273 326994**

12 Prince Albert Street, Brighton,
Sussex BN1 1HE
Tel: 01273 326994

REGIONAL ISSUES

PERFORATION AND WATERMARK. All the following Regional stamps are perforated 15 × 14, unless otherwise stated. For listing of First Day Covers at the end of this section.

1 England

EN **1** Three Lions

EN **2** Crowned Lion with Shield of St. George

EN **3** Oak Tree

EN **4** Tudor Rose

2001 (23 Apr.)–**02** Printed in photogravure by De La Rue or Questa (Nos. EN1/2), De La Rue (others). One centre phosphor band (2nd) or two phosphor bands (others). Perf 15 × 14 (with one elliptical hole in each vertical side)

EN1	EN **1**	(2nd)	slate-green and silver	1·00	1·00	☐	☐
EN2	EN **2**	(1st)	lake-brown and silver	1·00	1·00	☐	☐
EN3	EN **3**	(E)	olive-green and silver	1·75	1·75	☐	☐
EN4	EN **4**	65p	deep reddish lilac and silver	3·00	3·00	☐	☐
EN5		68p	deep reddish lilac and silver	3·00	3·00	☐	☐

Presentation Pack (P.O. Pack No. 54) (Nos. EN1/4)		7·50	☐
PHQ Cards (set of 4) (Nos. EN1/4)	8·00	14·00	☐ ☐

Nos. EN1/3 were initially sold at 19p, 27p and 36p, the latter representing the basic European airmail rate.

Combined Presentation Packs for England, Northern Ireland, Scotland and Wales

Presentation Pack (P.O. Pack No. 59) (contains 68p from England, Northern Ireland, Scotland and Wales (Nos. EN5, NI93, S99, W88)) 9·00 ☐

Presentation Pack (P.O. Pack No. 68) (contains 40p from England, Northern Ireland, Scotland and Wales (Nos. EN9, NI97, S112, W101)) 8·00 ☐

Presentation Pack (P.O. Pack No. 70) (contains 42p from England, Northern Ireland, Scotland and Wales (Nos. EN10, NI98, S113, W102)) 8·00 ☐

Presentation Pack (P.O. Pack No. 73) (contains 44p and 72p from England, Northern Ireland, Scotland and Wales (Nos. EN11, EN15, NI99, NI101, S114, S118, W103 and W107) 10·00 ☐

Presentation Pack (P.O. Pack No. 76) (contains 48p and 78p from England, Northern Ireland, Scotland and Wales (Nos. EN12, EN16, NI104, NI106, S115, S119, W104 and W108)) 12·50 ☐

Presentation Pack (P.O. Pack No. 79) (contains 50p and 81p from England, Northern Ireland, Scotland and Wales (Nos. EN13, EN17, NI105, NI107, S116, S120, W105 and W109)), 11·50 ☐

Presentation Pack (P.O. Pack No. 81) (contains 2nd, 1st, 50p and 81p from England, Northern Ireland, Scotland and Wales (Nos. EN6/7, EN13, EN17, NI102/3, NI105, NI107, S109/10, S116, S120, W98/9, W105 and W109)) 16·00 ☐

Presentation Pack (P.O. Pack No. 85) (contains 56p and 90p from England, Northern Ireland, Scotland and Wales (Nos. EN13a, EN17a, NI105a, NI 107a, S116a, S120a, W105a and W109a) 13·50 ☐

Presentation Pack (P.O. Pack No. 87) (contains 60p and 97p from England, Northern Ireland, Scotland and Wales (Nos. EN13b, EN17b, NI 105b, NI107b, S116b, S120b, W105b and W109b)) 15·00 ☐

2003 (14 Oct.)–**10**. As Nos. EN1/3 and EN5 but with white borders. One centre phosphor band (2nd) or two phosphor bands (others). Perf 15 × 14 (with one elliptical hole in each vertical side)

(a) Printed in photogravure by Walsall or De La Rue (2nd), 40p, 42p) or De La Rue (others)

EN6	EN **1**	(2nd)	slate-green and silver	75	60	☐	☐
EN7	EN **2**	(1st)	lake-brown and silver	80	75	☐	☐
EN8	EN **3**	(E)	olive-green and silver	2·00	2·00	☐	☐
EN9		40p	olive-green and silver	1·50	1·50	☐	☐
EN10		42p	olive-green and silver	1·25	1·25	☐	☐
EN11		44p	olive-green and silver	1·50	1·50	☐	☐
EN12		48p	olive-green and silver	1·25	1·25	☐	☐
EN13		50p	olive-green and silver	90	85	☐	☐
EN 13a		56p	olive-green and silver	1·25	1·25	☐	☐
EN 13b		60p	olive-green and silver	1·40	1·40	☐	☐
EN14	EN**4**	68p	deep reddish lilac and silver	2·50	2·50	☐	☐
EN15		72p	deep reddish lilac and silver	2·50	2·50	☐	☐
EN16		78p	deep reddish lilac and silver	2·50	2·50	☐	☐
EN17		81p	deep reddish lilac and silver	2·00	2·00	☐	☐
EN 17a		90p	deep reddish lilac and silver	2·00	2·00	☐	☐
EN17b		97p	deep reddish lilac and silver	2·25	2·25	☐	☐

(b) Printed in lithography by Enschedé

EN18	EN **2**	(1st)	lake-brown and silver	7·00	7·00	☐ ☐

Presentation Pack (P.O. Pack No. 63) (Nos. EN6/8, EN14)		6·00	☐
PHQ Cards (set of 4) (Nos. EN6/8, EN14)	2·00	12·00	☐ ☐

Nos. EN6/8 were initially sold at 20p, 28p and 38p, the latter representing the basic European airmail rate.

Stamps as No. EN18 but self-adhesive were issued on 23 April 2007 in sheets of 20 with *se-tenant* labels. These sheets were printed in lithography by Cartor and perforated 15 × 14 without the elliptical holes. The labels show either English scenes or personal photographs.

No. EN18 was only issued in £7.66 stamp booklets.

Stamps as Nos. EN18, NI95, S131 and W120 but self-adhesive were issued on 29 September 2008 in sheets of 20 containing five of each design with *se-tenant* labels. These sheets were printed in lithogrphy by Cartor and perforated 15 × 14 with one elliptical hole in each vertical side.

EN **5**

Celebrating England

2007 (23 Apr.) Sheet 123 × 70 mm. Printed in photogravure by De La Rue. Two phosphor bands. Perf 15 × 14 (with one elliptical hole in each vertical side) (1st) or 15 × 14½ (78p)

MSEN19 (1st) No. EN7; (1st) St. George's flag; 78p St. George; 78p Houses of Parliament, London	9·00	9·00	☐ ☐
First Day Cover		9·00	☐
Presentation Pack	10·00		☐
PHQ Cards (set of 5)	4·00	15·00	☐ ☐

The five PHQ cards show the four individual stamps and the complete miniature sheet.

Stamps as the 1st class St. George's flag stamp within **MS**EN19 but self-adhesive were issued on 23 April 2009 in sheets of 20 with *se-tenant* labels showing English castles. These sheets were printed in lithography by Cartor.

2 Northern Ireland

N **1**   N **2**   N **3**   N **4**

1958–67 Wmk 179

NI1	N **1**	3d	lilac	15	10	☐ ☐
		p.	One centre phosphor band	15	15	☐ ☐
NI2		4d	blue	15	15	☐ ☐
		p.	Two phosphor bands	15	15	☐ ☐
NI3	N **2**	6d	purple	30	30	☐ ☐
NI4		9d	bronze-green (2 phosphor bands)	30	70	☐ ☐
NI5	N **3**	1s 3d	green	30	70	☐ ☐
NI6		1s 6d	blue (2 phosphor bands)	30	70	☐ ☐

1968–69 One centre phosphor band (Nos. NI8/9) or two phosphor bands (others). No wmk

NI7	N **1**	4d	blue	15	15	☐ ☐
NI8		4d	sepia	15	15	☐ ☐
NI9		4d	vermilion	20	20	☐ ☐
NI10		5d	blue	20	20	☐ ☐
NI11	N **3**	1s 6d	blue	2·25	2·50	☐ ☐
Presentation Pack (comprises Nos. NI1p, NI4/6, NI8/10)				3·50		☐

Decimal Currency

1971–91 Type N **4**. No wmk

(a) Printed in photogravure with phosphor bands

NI12	2½p	magenta (1 centre band)	70	60	☐ ☐
NI13	3p	ultramarine (2 bands)	30	30	☐ ☐
NI14	3p	ultramarine (1 centre band)	20	15	☐ ☐
NI15	3½p	olive-grey (2 bands)	20	25	☐ ☐
NI16	3½p	olive-grey (1 centre band)	20	25	☐ ☐
NI17	4½p	grey-blue (2 bands)	30	25	☐ ☐
NI18	5p	violet (2 bands)	1·00	1·00	☐ ☐
NI19	5½p	violet (2 bands)	20	20	☐ ☐
NI20	5½p	violet (1 centre band)	20	25	☐ ☐
NI21	6½p	blue (1 centre band)	20	20	☐ ☐
NI22	7p	brown (1 centre band)	35	25	☐ ☐
NI23	7½p	chestnut (2 bands)	1·75	1·75	☐ ☐
NI24	8p	rosine (2 bands)	35	35	☐ ☐
NI25	8½p	yellow-green (2 bands)	35	40	☐ ☐
NI26	9p	violet (2 bands)	40	40	☐ ☐
NI27	10p	orange-brown (2 bands)	40	50	☐ ☐
NI28	10p	orange-brown (1 centre band)	50	50	☐ ☐
NI29	10½p	blue (2 bands)	40	50	☐ ☐
NI30	11p	scarlet (2 bands)	50	50	☐ ☐

(b) Printed in photogravure on phosphorised paper

NI31	12p	yellowish green	50	50	☐ ☐
NI32	13½p	purple-brown	60	70	☐ ☐
NI33	15p	ultramarine	60	70	☐ ☐

(c) Printed in lithography. Perf 14 (11½p, 12½p, 14p (No. NI38), 15½p, 16p, 18p, (No. NI45), 19½p, 20½p, 22p (No. NI53), 26p (No. NI60), 28p (No. NI62)) or 15 × 14 (others)

NI34	11½p	drab (1 side band)	85	85	☐ ☐
NI35	12p	bright emerald (1 side band)	90	90	☐ ☐
NI36	12½p	light emerald (1 side band)	60	60	☐ ☐
		a. Perf 15 × 14	5·25	5·25	☐ ☐
NI37	13p	pale chestnut (1 side band)	80	50	☐ ☐
NI38	14p	grey-blue (phosphorised paper)	75	75	☐ ☐
NI39	14p	deep blue (1 centre band)	75	60	☐ ☐
NI40	15p	bright blue (1 centre band)	90	60	☐ ☐
NI41	15½p	pale violet (phosphorised paper)	80	80	☐ ☐
NI42	16p	drab (phosphorised paper)	1·00	1·00	☐ ☐
		a. Perf 15 × 14	8·25	8·50	☐ ☐
NI43	17p	grey-blue (phosphorised paper)	90	95	☐ ☐
NI44	17p	deep blue (1 centre band)	1·00	80	☐ ☐
NI45	18p	deep violet (phosphorised paper)	1·00	1·00	☐ ☐
NI46	18p	olive-grey (phosphorised paper)	1·00	90	☐ ☐
NI47	18p	bright green (1 centre band)	1·00	95	☐ ☐
		a. Perf 14	5·00	5·00	☐ ☐
NI48	18p	bright green (1 side band)	2·25	2·25	☐ ☐
NI49	19p	bright orange-red (phosphorised paper)	1·00	1·00	☐ ☐
NI50	19½p	olive-grey (phosphorised paper)	1·50	1·75	☐ ☐
NI51	20p	brownish black			

		(phosphorised paper)	1·00	80	☐	☐
NI52	20½p	ultramarine				
		(phosphorised paper)	4·50	4·25	☐	☐
NI53	22p	blue				
		(phosphorised paper)	1·10	1·10	☐	☐
NI54	22p	yellow-green				
		(phosphorised paper)	1·10	1·10	☐	☐
NI55	22p	bright orange-red				
		(phosphorised paper)	1·25	90	☐	☐
NI56	23p	bright green				
		(phosphorised paper)	1·25	1·10	☐	☐
NI57	24p	Indian red				
		(phosphorised paper)	1·25	1·25	☐	☐
NI58	24p	chestnut				
		(phosphorised paper)	1·10	90	☐	☐
NI59	24p	chestnut (2 bands)	2·25	2·50	☐	☐
NI60	26p	rosine (phosphorised				
		paper)	1·25	1·25	☐	☐
	a.	Perf 15 × 14	3·00	3·25	☐	☐
NI61	26p	drab				
		(phosphorised paper)	1·75	1·75	☐	☐
NI62	28p	deep violet-blue				
		(phosphorised paper)	1·50	1·50	☐	☐
	a.	Perf 15 × 14	1·25	1·25	☐	☐
NI63	28p	deep bluish grey				
		(phosphorised paper)	1·50	1·50	☐	☐
NI64	31p	bright purple				
		(phosphorised paper)	1·75	2·00	☐	☐
NI65	32p	greenish blue				
		(phosphorised paper)	1·75	1·75	☐	☐
NI66	34p	deep bluish grey				
		(phosphorised paper)	1·75	1·75	☐	☐
NI67	37p	rosine (phosphorised				
		paper)	2·00	2·50	☐	☐
NI68	39p	bright mauve				
		(phosphorised paper)	2·00	2·25	☐	☐

Nos. NI48 and NI59 were only issued in stamp booklets.

Presentation Pack (P.O. Pack No. 29) (contains
2½p (NI12), 3p (NI13), 5p (NI18), 7½p (NI23))   3·50   ☐

Presentation Pack (P.O. Pack No. 61) (contains 3p
(NI14), 3½p (NI15), 5½p (NI19), 8p (NI24) later
with 4½p (NI17) added)   2·25   ☐

Presentation Pack (P.O. Pack No. 84) (contains
6½p (NI21), 8½p (NI25), 10p (NI27),
11p (NI30))   2·00   ☐

Presentation Pack (P.O. Pack No. 129d) (contains
7p (NI22), 9p (NI26), 10½p (NI29), 11½p (NI34),
12p (NI31), 13½p (NI32), 14p (NI38), 15p (NI33),
18p (NI45), 22p (NI53))   9·00   ☐

Presentation Pack (P.O. Pack No. 4) (contains 10p
(NI28), 12½p (NI36), 16p (NI42), 20½p (NI52),
26p (NI60), 28p (NI62))   18·00   ☐

Presentation Pack (P.O. Pack No. 8) (contains 10p
(NI28), 13p (NI37), 16p (NI42a), 17p (NI43), 22p
(NI54), 26p (NI60), 28p (NI62), 31p (NI64))   18·00   ☐

Presentation Pack (P.O. Pack No. 12) (contains
12p (NI35), 13p (NI37), 17p (NI43), 18p (NI46),
22p (NI54), 26p (NI60a), 28p (NI62a),
31p (NI64))   20·00   ☐

**Combined Presentation Packs for Northern Ireland,
Scotland and Wales**

Presentation Pack (P.O. Pack No. 17) (contains
14p, 19p, 23p, 32p from Northern Ireland,
Scotland and Wales (Nos. NI39, NI49, NI56, NI65,
S54, S62, S67, S77, W40, W50, W57, W66))   17·00   ☐

Presentation Pack (P.O. Pack No. 20) (contains
15p, 20p, 24p, 34p from Northern Ireland,
Scotland and Wales (Nos. NI40, NI51, NI57, NI66,
S56, S64, S69, S78, W41, W52, W58, W67))   16·00   ☐

Presentation Pack (P.O. Pack No. 23) (contains
17p, 22p, 26p, 37p from Northern Ireland,
Scotland and Wales (Nos. NI44, NI55, NI61, NI67,
S58, S66, S73, S79, W45, W56, W62, W68))   16·00   ☐

Presentation Pack (P.O. Pack No. 26) (contains
18p, 24p, 28p, 39p from Northern Ireland,
Scotland and Wales (Nos. NI47, NI58, NI63, NI68,
S60, S70, S75, S80, W48, W59, W64, W69))   16·00   ☐

1993 (7 Dec.)–**2000**

(a) Printed in lithography by Questa. Perf 15 × 14 (with one
elliptical hole on each vertical side)

NI69	N **4**	19p bistre (1 centre band)	90	80	☐	☐
NI70		19p bistre (1 side band)	1·25	1·75	☐	☐
NI71		20p bright green				
		(1 centre band)	1·50	1·50	☐	☐
NI72		25p red (2 bands)	75	75	☐	☐
NI73		26p red-brown (2 bands)	1·75	1·75	☐	☐
NI74		30p deep olive-grey				
		(2 bands)	1·25	1·25	☐	☐
NI75		37p bright mauve				
		(2 bands)	2·75	3·00	☐	☐
NI76		41p grey-brown				
		(2 bands)	1·50	1·75	☐	☐
NI77		63p light emerald				
		(2 bands)	5·00	5·00	☐	☐

(b) Printed in photogravure by Walsall (19p, 20p, 26p (No.
NI81b), 38p, 40p, 63p, 64p, 65p), Harrison or Walsall (26p (No.
NI81), 37p). Perf 14 (No. NI80) or 15 × 14 (others) (both with
one elliptical hole in each vertical side)

NI78	N **4**	19p bistre (1 centre band)	3·00	3·00	☐	☐
NI79		20p bright green				
		(1 centre band)	90	80	☐	☐
NI80		20p bright green				
		(1 side band)	3·00	3·00	☐	☐
NI81		26p chestnut (2 bands)	1·25	1·00	☐	☐
	b.	Perf 14	3·00	3·00	☐	☐
NI82		37p bright mauve (2 bands)	2·25	2·25	☐	☐
NI83		38p ultramarine (2 bands)	8·00	8·00	☐	☐
NI84		40p deep azure (2 bands)	2·50	2·50	☐	☐
NI85		63p light emerald (2 bands)	5·00	5·00	☐	☐
NI86		64p turquoise-green				
		(2 bands)	9·00	9·00	☐	☐
NI87		65p greenish blue (2 bands)	2·75	3·00	☐	☐

Nos. NI70, NI80 and NI81b were only issued in stamp booklets.
No. NI70 exists with the phosphor band at the left or right of
the stamp.

Presentation Pack (P.O. Pack No. 47) (contains
19p, 26p, 38p, 64p (Nos. NI78, NI81,
NI83 NI86))   17·00   ☐

Presentation Pack (P.O. Pack No. 52) (contains 1st,
40p, 65p) (Nos. NI84, NI87, NI88b)   18·00   ☐

**Combined Presentation Packs for Northern Ireland,
Scotland and Wales**

Presentation Pack (P.O. Pack No. 31) (contains
19p, 25p, 30p, 41p from Northern Ireland,
Scotland and Wales (Nos. NI69, NI72, NI74, NI76,
S81, S84, S86, S88, W70, W73, W75, W77))   16·00   ☐

Presentation Pack (P.O. Pack No. 36) (contains
20p, 26p, 37p, 63p from Northern Ireland,
Scotland and Wales (Nos. NI71, NI73, NI75, NI77,

S83, S85, S87, S89, W72, W74 W76, W78))	26·00	☐		

Presentation Pack (P.O. Pack No. 42) (contains
20p (1 centre band), 26p, 37p, 63p from
Northern Ireland, Scotland and Wales (Nos.
NI79, NI81/2, NI85, S90/3, W79/82))   26·00   ☐

N 5

2000 (15 Feb.–25 Apr.) Type N **4** redrawn with '1st' face value as Type N **5**. Two phosphor bands. Perf 14 (with one elliptical hole in each vertical side)

NI88	N **5**	(1st)	bright orange-red	3·00	3·00	☐ ☐
		b.	Perf 15 × 14 (25 Apr.)	10·00	10·00	☐ ☐

No. NI88 was only issued in stamp booklets. No. NI88b was issued in sheets on 25 April.

N **6** Basalt Columns, Giant's Causeway   N **7** Aerial View of Patchwork Fields   N **8** Linen Pattern   N **9** Vase Pattern from Belleck

2001 (6 Mar.)–**02** Printed in lithography by De La Rue (68p), De La Rue or Walsall (E), Walsall or Enschedé (2nd) or Walsall (others). One centre phosphor band (2nd) or two phosphor bands (others). Perf 15 × 14 (with one elliptical hole in each vertical side)

NI89	N **6**	(2nd)	black, new blue, bright magenta and greenish yellow	75	75	☐ ☐
NI90	N **7**	(1st)	black, new blue and greenish yellow	1·20	1·20	☐ ☐
NI91	N **8**	(E)	black, new blue and pale orange	1·50	1·50	☐ ☐
NI92	N **9**	65p	black, bright magenta and greenish yellow	3·00	3·00	☐ ☐
NI93		68p	black, bright magenta and greenish yellow	3·25	3·25	☐ ☐

Presentation Pack (P.O. Pack No. 53)
(Nos. NI89/92)   7·00   ☐
PHQ Cards (set of 4) (Nos. NI89/92)   8·00   14·00   ☐ ☐

Nos. NI89, NI90 and NI91 were initially sold at 19p, 27p and 36p, the latter representing the basic European airmail rate. For combined presentation packs for all four Regions, see under England.

2003 (14 Oct.)–**10**. As Nos. NI89/91 and NI93 but with white borders. One centre phosphor band (2nd) or two phosphor bands (others). Perf 15 × 14 (with one elliptical hole on each vertical side)

(a) Printed in lithography by Walsall (NI98) or De La Rue (others)

NI94	N **6**	(2nd)	black, new blue, bright magenta and greenish yellow	1·00	1·00	☐ ☐
NI95	N **7**	(1st)	black, new blue and greenish yellow	1·00	1·00	☐ ☐
NI96	N **8**	(E)	black and new blue	2·50	2·50	☐ ☐

NI97	40p	black and new blue	1·75	1·75	☐ ☐
NI98	42p	black, new blue and orange-yellow	1·75	1·75	☐ ☐
	a.	black, new blue and greenish yellow	1·50	1·50	☐ ☐
NI99	44p	black, new blue and greenish yellow	1·00	1·00	☐ ☐
NI100 N **9**	68p	black, bright magenta and greenish yellow	2·75	2·75	☐ ☐
NI101	72p	black, greyish black, bright magenta and greenish yellow	2·50	2·50	☐ ☐

(b) Printed in photogravure by De La Rue

NI102 N **6**	(2nd)	bright magenta, greenish yellow, new blue and black	70	60	☐ ☐
NI103 N **7**	(1st)	greenish yellow, new blue and black	80	75	☐ ☐
NI104 N **8**	48p	olive-grey and black	1·20	1·20	☐ ☐
NI105	50p	olive-grey and black	1·20	1·20	☐ ☐
NI105a	56p	olive-grey and black	1·25	1·25	☐ ☐
NI105b	60p	olive-grey and black	1·40	1·40	☐ ☐
NI106 N **9**	78p	bright magenta, greenish yellow and black	2·00	2·00	☐ ☐
NI107	81p	bright magenta, greenish yellow and black	2·00	2·00	☐ ☐
NI107a	90p	bright magenta, greenish yellow and black	2·00	2·00	☐ ☐
NI107b	97p	bright magenta, greenish yellow and black	2·25	2·25	☐ ☐

Presentation Pack (P.O. Pack No. 66)
(Nos. NI94/6, NI100)   7·00   ☐
PHQ Cards (set of 4) (Nos. NI94/6, NI100) 2·00   10·00   ☐ ☐

Nos. NI94/6 were initially sold at 20p, 28p and 38p, the latter representing the basic European airmail rate.

No. NI98 (Walsall printing) appears bluish grey and No. NI98a (De La Rue printing) appears olive-grey.

Stamps as NI95 but self-adhesive were issued on 11 March 2008 in sheets of 20 with *se-tenant* labels. These sheets were printed in lithography by Cartor and perforated 15 × 14 without the ellipitcal holes. The labels show either Northern Ireland scenes or personal photographs.

Stamps as No. NI95 but self-adhesive were issued again on 17 March 2009 in sheets of 20 with *se-tenant* labels showing Northern Island castles. These sheets were printed in lithography by Cartor.

Stamps as Nos. EN18, NI95, S131 and W120 but self-adhesive were issued on 29 September 2008 in sheets of 20 containing five of each design with *se-tenant* labels.

N 10

Celebrating Northern Ireland

2008 (11 Mar.) Sheet 123 × 70 mm. Printed in lithography by De La Rue. Two phosphor bands. Perf 15 × 14½ (with one elliptical hole in each vertical side) (1st) or 15 × 14½ (78p)

MSNI110 (1st) Carrickfergus Castle; (1st)

Giant's Causeway; 78p. St. Patrick;		
78p. Queen's Bridge and 'Angel of		
Thanksgiving' sculpture, Belfast	6·00	6·00 ☐ ☐
First Day Cover		6·00 ☐
Presentation Pack	8·00	☐
PHQ Cards (set of 5)	4·00	17·00 ☐ ☐

The five PHQ cards depict the complete miniature sheet and the four stamps within it.

N 11

50th Anniv of the Country Definitives (1st issue)

2000 (29 Sept.) Sheet 124 × 70 mm, containing designs as Nos. NI1, NI3, NI5, S1, S3, S5, W1, W3 and W5 (regional definitives of 1958) but inscribed 1st and printed in photogravure by De La Rue on pale cream. Two phosphor bands. Perf 15 × 14 (with one elliptical hole in each vertical side)

MSNI111 N 11 (1st) As No. W1; (1st) As

No. S1; (1st) As No. W5; (1st) As No. S5;		
(1st) As No. NI1; (1st) As No. W3; (1st)		
As No. S3; (1st) As No. NI3; (1st) As No.		
NI5	8·25	8·25 ☐ ☐
First Day Cover		10·00 ☐
Presentation Pack	12·00	☐
PHQ Cards (set of 10)	6·00	18·00 ☐ ☐

The ten PHQ cards show the nine individual stamps and the complete sheet.

50th Anniv of the Country Definitives (2nd issue)

2008 (29 Sept.) As Nos. NI1, NI3 and NI5 (definitives of 1958) but inscribed 1st and printed in lithography by De La Rue. Two phosphor bands. Perf 15 × 14½ (with one elliptical hole in each vertical side)

NI112	N 1	(1st)	deep lilac	1·25	1·25 ☐ ☐

NI113	N 3	(1st)	green	1·25	1·25 ☐ ☐
NI114	N 2	(1st)	deep claret	1·25	1·25 ☐ ☐

Nos. NI112/14 come from £9.72 stamp booklets.

3 Scotland

S 1	S 2	S 3	S 4

1958–67 Wmk 179

S1	S 1	3d lilac	15	15	☐ ☐
		p. Two phosphor bands	13·00	2·75	☐ ☐
		pa. One side band	20	25	☐ ☐
		pd. One centre phosphor			
		band	15	15	☐ ☐
S2		4d blue	15	15	☐ ☐
		p. Two phosphor bands	15	15	☐ ☐
S3	S 2	6d purple	20	15	☐ ☐
		p. Two phosphor bands	20	20	☐ ☐
S4		9d bronze-green			
		(2 phosphor bands)	35	40	☐ ☐
S5	S 3	1s 3d green	40	40	☐ ☐
		p. Two phosphor bands	40	40	☐ ☐
S6		1s 6d blue (2 phosphor bands)	45	50	☐ ☐

No. S1pa exists with the phosphor band at the left or right of the stamp.

1967–70 One centre phosphor band (Nos. S7, S9/10) or two phosphor bands (others). No wmk

S7	S 1	3d lilac	10	15	☐ ☐
S8		4d blue	10	15	☐ ☐
S9		4d sepia	10	10	☐ ☐
S10		4d vermilion	10	10	☐ ☐
S11		5d blue	20	10	☐ ☐
S12	S 2	9d bronze-green	6·00	6·00	☐ ☐
S13	S 3	1s 6d blue	1·75	1·50	☐ ☐
Presentation Pack (containing Nos. S3,					
		S5p, S7, S9/13)	8·00		☐

Decimal Currency

1971–93 Type S 4. No wmk

(a) Printed in photogravure by Harrison and Sons with phosphor bands. Perf 15 × 14

S14		2½p magenta (1 centre band)	25	20	☐ ☐
S15		3p ultramarine (2 bands)	35	15	☐ ☐
S16		3p ultramarine (1 centre			
		band)	15	15	☐ ☐
S17		3½p olive-grey (2 bands)	20	25	☐ ☐
S18		3½p olive-grey (1 centre			
		band)	20	25	☐ ☐
S19		4½p grey-blue (2 bands)	30	25	☐ ☐
S20		5p violet (2 bands)	1·00	1·25	☐ ☐
S21		5½p violet (2 bands)	20	20	☐ ☐
S22		5½p violet (1 centre band)	20	25	☐ ☐
S23		6½p blue (1 centre band)	20	20	☐ ☐
S24		7p brown (1 centre band)	30	30	☐ ☐
S25		7½p chestnut (2 bands)	1·25	1·25	☐ ☐
S26		8p rosine (2 bands)	45	40	☐ ☐
S27		8½p yellow-green (2 bands)	40	40	☐ ☐
S28		9p violet (2 bands)	40	40	☐ ☐
S29		10p orange-brown (2 bands)	45	50	☐ ☐
S30		10p orange-brown			
		(1 centre band)	40	50	☐ ☐

S31	10½p	blue (2 bands)	45	50	☐	☐
S32	11p	scarlet (2 bands)	50	50	☐	☐

(b) Printed in photogravure by Harrison and Sons on phosphorised paper. Perf 15 × 14

S33	12p	yellowish green	50	50	☐	☐
S34	13½p	purple-brown	70	80	☐	☐
S35	15p	ultramarine	60	70	☐	☐

(c) Printed in lithography by John Waddington. One side phosphor band (11½p, 12p, 12½p, 13p) or phosphorised paper (others). Perf 14

S36	11½p	drab	80	80	☐	☐
S37	12p	bright emerald	2·00	2·00	☐	☐
S38	12½p	light emerald	60	70	☐	☐
S39	13p	pale chestnut	85	75	☐	☐
S40	14p	grey-blue	75	75	☐	☐
S41	15½p	pale violet	80	80	☐	☐
S42	16p	drab	80	85	☐	☐
S43	17p	grey-blue	1·50	1·50	☐	☐
S44	18p	deep violet	80	80	☐	☐
S45	19½p	olive-grey	1·75	1·75	☐	☐
S46	20½p	ultramarine	3·50	3·50	☐	☐
S47	22p	blue	1·00	1·00	☐	☐
S48	22p	yellow-green	4·25	4·25	☐	☐
S49	26p	rosine	1·25	1·25	☐	☐
S50	28p	deep violet-blue	1·25	1·25	☐	☐
S51	31p	bright purple	2·50	2·50	☐	☐

(d) Printed in lithography by Questa. Perf 15 × 14

S52	12p	bright emerald (1 side band)	2·00	2·25	☐	☐
S53	13p	pale chestnut (1 side band)	70	75	☐	☐
S54	14p	deep blue (1 centre band)	60	70	☐	☐
S55	14p	deep blue (1 side band)	80	90	☐	☐
S56	15p	bright blue (1 centre band)	70	70	☐	☐
S57	17p	grey-blue (phosphorised paper)	4·00	4·00	☐	☐
S58	17p	deep blue (1 centre band)	1·00	1·10	☐	☐
S59	18p	olive-grey (phosphorised paper)	1·10	85	☐	☐
S60	18p	bright green (1 centre band)	1·25	90	☐	☐
		a. Perf 14	1·00	1·00	☐	☐
S61	18p	bright green (1 side band)	2·75	3·00	☐	☐
S62	19p	bright orange-red (phosphorised paper)	70	70	☐	☐
S63	19p	bright orange-red (2 bands)	2·25	2·00	☐	☐
S64	20p	brownish black (phosphorised paper)	95	95	☐	☐
S65	22p	yellow-green (phosphorised paper)	1·25	1·50	☐	☐
S66	22p	bright orange-red (phosphorised paper)	1·25	90	☐	☐
S67	23p	bright green (phosphorised paper)	1·25	1·10	☐	☐
S68	23p	bright green (2 bands)	14·00	14·00	☐	☐
S69	24p	Indian red (phosphorised paper)	1·25	1·25	☐	☐
S70	24p	chestnut (phosphorised paper)	1·40	1·25	☐	☐
		a. Perf 14	6·00	6·00	☐	☐
S71	24p	chestnut (2 bands)	2·75	3·00	☐	☐

S72	26p	rosine (phosphorised paper)	3·75	4·00	☐	☐
S73	26p	drab (phosphorised paper)	1·25	1·25	☐	☐
S74	28p	deep violet-blue (phosphorised paper)	1·25	1·25	☐	☐
S75	28p	deep bluish grey (phosphorised paper)	1·25	1·50	☐	☐
		a. Perf 14	8·00	8·00	☐	☐
S76	31p	bright purple (phosphorised paper)	2·25	2·25	☐	☐
S77	32p	greenish blue (phosphorised paper)	1·75	2·00	☐	☐
S78	34p	deep bluish grey (phosphorised paper)	1·75	1·75	☐	☐
S79	37p	rosine (phosphorised paper)	2·00	2·25	☐	☐
S80	39p	bright mauve (phosphorised paper)	2·00	2·25	☐	☐
		a. Perf 14	7·00	7·00	☐	☐

Nos. S55, S61, S63, S68 and S71 were only issued in stamp booklets.

Presentation Pack (P.O. Pack No. 27) (contains 2½p (S14), 3p (S15), 5p (S20), 7½p (S25)) 3·50 ☐

Presentation Pack (P.O. Pack No. 62) (contains 3p (S16), 3½p (S17), 5½p (S21), 8p (S26), later with 4½p (S19) added) 2·50 ☐

Presentation Pack (P.O. Pack No. 85) (contains 6½p (S23), 8½p (S27), 10p (S29), 11p (S32)) 2·00 ☐

Presentation Pack (P.O. Pack No. 129b) (contains 7p (S24), 9p (S28), 10½p (S31), 11½p (S36), 12p (S33), 13½p (S34), 14p (S40), 15p (S35), 18p (S44), 22p (S47)) 9·00 ☐

Presentation Pack (P.O. Pack No. 2) (contains 10p (S30), 12½p (S38), 16p (S42), 20½p (S46), 26p (S49), 28p (S50)) 18·00 ☐

Presentation Pack (P.O. Pack No. 6) (contains 10p (S30), 13p (S39), 16p (S42), 17p (S43), 22p (S48), 26p (S49), 28p (S50), 31p (S51)) 17·00 ☐

Presentation Pack (P.O. Pack No. 10) (contains 12p (S52), 13p (S53), 17p (S57), 18p (S59), 22p (S65), 26p (S72), 28p (S74), 31p (S76)) 20·00 ☐

For combined packs containing values from all three Regions see under Northern Ireland.

1993 (7 Dec.)–**98** (a) Printed in lithography by Questa. Perf 15 × 14 (with one elliptical hole in each vertical side)

S81	S 4	19p	bistre (1 centre band)	80	70	☐	☐
S82		19p	bistre (1 side band)	3·00	3·25	☐	☐
S83		20p	bright green (1 centre band)	1·50	1·50	☐	☐
S84		25p	red (2 bands)	1·10	1·00	☐	☐
S85		26p	red-brown (2 bands)	1·75	2·00	☐	☐
S86		30p	deep olive-grey (2 bands)	1·25	1·25	☐	☐
S87		37p	bright mauve (2 bands)	2·75	3·00	☐	☐
S88		41p	grey-brown (2 bands)	1·75	2·00	☐	☐
S89		63p	light emerald (2 bands)	4·00	4·25	☐	☐

(b) Printed in photogravure by Walsall (20p, 26p (No. S91a), 63p), Harrison or Walsall (26p (No. S91), 37p). Perf 14 (No. S90a) or 15 × 14 (others) (both with one elliptical hole in each vertical side)

S90	S 4	20p	bright green	

		(1 centre band)	1·00	90	☐	☐
S90a	20p	bright green				
		(1 side band)	3·50	3·50	☐	☐
S91	26p	chestnut (2 bands)	1·20	1·20	☐	☐
	a.	Perf 14	3·50	3·50	☐	☐
S92	37p	bright mauve				
		(2 bands)	1·50	1·50	☐	☐
S93	63p	light emerald				
		(2 bands)	4·00	4·00	☐	☐

Nos. S82, S90a and S91a were only issued in stamp booklets. For combined presentation packs for all three Regions, see under Northern Ireland.

S 5 Scottish Flag   **S 6** Scottish Lion   **S 7** Thistle   **S 8** Tartan

1999 (8 June)–**2002** Printed in photogravure by De La Rue (68p), De La Rue, Questa or Walsall (2nd, 1st) or Walsall (others). One centre phosphor band (2nd) or two phosphor bands (others). Perf 15 × 14 (with one elliptical hole in each vertical side)

S94	S **5** (2nd)	new blue, blue and silver	75	75	☐	☐
S95	S **6** (1st)	greenish yellow, deep rose-red, rose-red and silver	1·00	1·00	☐	☐
S96	S **7** (E)	bright lilac, deep lilac and silver	2·00	2·00	☐	☐
S97	S **8** 64p	greenish yellow, bright magenta, new blue, grey-black and silver	9·00	9·00	☐	☐
S98	65p	greenish yellow, bright magenta, new blue, grey-black and silver	3·00	3·25	☐	☐
S99	68p	greenish yellow, bright magenta, new blue, grey-black and silver	3·25	3·25	☐	☐

Presentation Pack (P.O. Pack No. 45) (contains 2nd, 1st, E, 64p) (Nos. S94/7)	14·00		☐
Presentation Pack (P.O. Pack No. 50) (contains 65p) (No. S98))	11·00		☐
Presentation Pack (P.O. Pack No. 55) (contains 2nd, 1st, E, 65p) (Nos. S94/6, S98)	15·00		☐
PHQ Cards (Nos. S94/7)	8·00	14·00	☐ ☐

Nos. S94, S95 and S96 were initially sold at 19p, 26p and 30p, the latter representing the basic European airmail rate.

For combined presentation packs for all four Regions, see under England.

S 9

2000 (15 Feb.) Type S **4** redrawn with '1st' face value as Type S **9**. Two phosphor bands. Perf 14 (with one elliptical hole in each vertical side)

S108	S **9** (1st)	bright orange-red	3·00	3·25	☐	☐

No. S108 was only issued in stamp booklets.

2003 (14 Oct.)–**10**. As Nos. S94/6 and S99 but with white borders. One centre phosphor band (2nd) or two phosphor bands (others). Perf 15 × 14 (with one elliptical hole in each vertical side)

(a) Printed in photogravure by Walsall or De La Rue (42p) or De La Rue (others)

S109	S **5** (2nd)	new blue, blue and silver	60	60	☐	☐
S110	S **6** (1st)	rose-red, greenish yellow, deep rose-red and silver	85	85	☐	☐
S111	S **7** (E)	bright lilac, deep lilac and silver	2·50	2·50	☐	☐
S112	40p	bright lilac, deep lilac and silver	1·75	1·75	☐	☐
S113	42p	bright lilac, deep lilac and silver	1·75	1·75	☐	☐
S114	44p	bright lilac, deep lilac and silver	1·50	1·50	☐	☐
S115	48p	bright lilac, deep lilac and silver	90	90	☐	☐
S116	50p	bright lilac, deep lilac and silver	80	75	☐	☐
S116a	56p	bright lilac, deep lilac and silver	1·25	1·25	☐	☐
S116b	60p	bright lilac, deep lilac and silver	1·40	1·40	☐	☐
S117	S **8** 68p	bright magenta, greenish yellow, new blue, grey-black and silver	2·00	2·00	☐	☐
S118	72p	bright magenta, greenish yellow, new blue, grey-black and silver	1·75	1·75	☐	☐
S119	78p	bright magenta, greenish yellow, new blue, grey-black and silver	1·50	1·50	☐	☐
S120	81p	bright magenta, greenish yellow, new blue, grey-black and silver	1·40	1·30	☐	☐
S120a	90p	bright magenta, greenish yellow, new blue, grey-black and silver	2·00	2·00	☐	☐
S120b	97p	bright magenta, greenish yellow, new blue, grey-black and silver	2·25	2·25	☐	☐

(b) Printed in lithography by Enschedé

S131	S **6** (1st)	rose-red, greenish yellow, deep rose-red and silver	7·50	7·50	☐	☐

Presentation Pack (P.O. Pack No. 64) (Nos. S109/11, S117)	7·00		☐
PHQ Cards (set of 4) (Nos. S109/11, S117)	2·00	10·00	☐ ☐

Nos. S109/11 were initially sold at 20p, 28p and 38p, the latter representing the basic European airmail rate.

No. S119 was only issued in £7.66 stamp booklets. Stamps as No. S131 but self-adhesive were issued on 30 November 2007 in sheets of 20 with se-tenant labels. These sheets were printed by Cartor in lithography, and perforated 15 × 14 without the elliptical holes. The labels show either Scottish scenes or personal photographs.

Stamps as Nos. EN18, NI95, S131 and W120 but self-adhesive were issued on 29 September 2008 in sheets of 20 containing five of each design with se-tenant labels.

Opening of New Scottish Parliament Building

2004 (5 Oct.) Sheet 123 × 70 mm. Printed in photogravure by De La Rue. One centre phosphor band (2nd) or two phosphor bands (others). Perf 15 × 14 (with one elliptical hole in each vertical side)

MSS132 Nos. S109, S110 × 2 and

S112 × 2	6·00	6·00	☐	☐
First Day Cover		7·25	☐	

S **10**

Celebrating Scotland

2006 (30 Nov.) Sheet 124 × 71 mm. Printed in photogravure by De La Rue. Two phosphor bands. Perf 15 × 14 (with one elliptical hole in each vertical side) (1st) or 14 × 14 (72p)

MSS133 (1st) As No. S110; (1st) Scottish

Flag; 72p St. Andrew; 72p Edinburgh

Castle	6·00	6·00	☐	☐
First Day Cover		6·50	☐	
Presentation Pack	8·00		☐	
PHQ Cards (set of 5)	4·00	17·00	☐	☐

The five PHQ cards depict the complete miniature sheet and the four stamps within it.

Stamps as the 1st class Scottish flag stamp within **MS**S133 but self-adhesive were issued on 30 November 2009 in sheets of 20 with *se-tenant* labels showing Scottish castles. These sheets were printed in lithography by Cartor.

50th Anniv of the Country Definitives

2008 (29 Sept.) As Nos. S1, S3 and S5 (definitives of 1958) but inscribed 1st and printed in lithography by De La Rue. Two phosphor bands. Perf 15 × 14½ (with one elliptical hole in each vertical side)

S134	S **1**	(1st) deep lilac	1·25	1·25	☐ ☐
S135	S **3**	(1st) green	1·25	1·25	☐ ☐
S136	S **2**	(1st) deep claret	1·25	1·25	☐ ☐

Nos. S134/6 come from £9.72 stamp booklets.

S **11** 250th Birth Anniv of Robert Burns (Scottish poet)

2009 (22 Jan.). Sheet 145×74 mm. Printed in photogravure by Enschedé. One centre band (2nd) or two phosphor bands (others). Perf 14½ (size 34×34 mm) or 15×14 (with one elliptical hole in each vertical side) (others).

MSS137 (2nd) No. S109; (1st) 'A Man's a Man for a' that' and Burns ploughing (detail) (James Sargent Storer) (34×34 mm); (1st) No. S110; (1st) Portrait of Burns (Alexander Nasmyth) (34×34

mm); 50p No. S116; 81p No. S120	8·00	8·00	☐	☐
First Day Cover		8·50		☐
Presentation Pack	12·00		☐	
PHQ Cards (set of 3)	3·50	12·00	☐	☐

The three PHQ cards show the two 34×34 mm Robert Burns stamps and the complete miniature sheet.

4 Wales

W **1**　　　　W **2**　　　　W **3**

1958–67 Wmk 179

W1	W **1**	3d	lilac	15	15	☐ ☐
		p.	One centre phosphorband	20	15	☐ ☐
W2		4d	blue	20	15	☐ ☐
		p.	Two phosphor bands	20	15	☐ ☐
W3	W **2**	6d	purple	35	30	☐ ☐
W4		9d	bronze-green (2 phosphor bands)	40	35	☐ ☐
W5	W **3**	1s 3d	green	40	40	☐ ☐
W6		1s 6d	blue (2 phosphor bands)	40	40	☐ ☐

1967–69 One centre phosphor band (Nos. W7, W9/10) or two phosphor bands (others). No wmk

W7	W **1**	3d	lilac	10	15	☐ ☐
W8		4d	blue	10	15	☐ ☐
W9		4d	sepia	15	15	☐ ☐
W10		4d	vermilion	15	15	☐ ☐
W11		5d	blue	15	15	☐ ☐
W12	W **3**	1s 6d	blue	3·50	3·50	☐ ☐
Presentation Pack (comprises Nos. W4,						
		W6/7, W9/11)		4·00		☐

W **4** With 'p'　　　　W **5** Without 'p'

Decimal Currency

1971–92 Type W 4. No wmk

(a) Printed in photogravure with phosphor bands

W13	2½p	magenta (1 centre band)	20	20	☐ ☐
W14	3p	ultramarine (2 bands)	25	20	☐ ☐
W15	3p	ultramarine (1 centre band)	25	25	☐ ☐
W16	3½p	olive-grey (2 bands)	20	30	☐ ☐
W17	3½p	olive-grey (1 centre band)	20	30	☐ ☐
W18	4½p	grey-blue (2 bands)	30	30	☐ ☐
W19	5p	violet (2 bands)	1·25	1·25	☐ ☐
W20	5½p	violet (2 bands)	25	30	☐ ☐
W21	5½p	violet (1 centre band)	25	30	☐ ☐
W22	6½p	blue (1 centre band)	20	20	☐ ☐
W23	7p	brown (1 centre band)	25	25	☐ ☐
W24	7½p	chestnut (2 bands)	1·75	1·75	☐ ☐
W25	8p	rosine (2 bands)	30	35	☐ ☐

W26	8½p	yellow-green (2 bands)	30	35	☐	☐
W27	9p	violet (2 bands)	40	40	☐	☐
W28	10p	orange-brown (2 bands)	40	40	☐	☐
W29	10p	orange-brown (1 centre band)	40	40	☐	☐
W30	10½p	blue (2 bands)	45	45	☐	☐
W31	11p	scarlet (2 bands)	45	45	☐	☐

(b) Printed in photogravure on phosphorised paper

W32	12p	yellow-green	50	50	☐	☐
W33	13½p	purple-brown	60	70	☐	☐
W34	15p	ultramarine	60	70	☐	☐

(c) Printed in lithography. Perf 14 (11½p, 12½p, 14p (No. W39), 15½p. 16p, 18p (No. W46), 19½p, 20½p, 22p (No. W54), 26p (No. W61), 28p (No. W63)) or 15 × 14 (others)

W35	11½p	drab (1 side band)	90	80	☐	
W36	12p	bright emerald (1 side band)	2·00	2·00	☐	☐
W37	12½p	light emerald (1 side band)	70	70	☐	☐
	a.	Perf 15 × 14	4·75	4·25	☐	☐
W38	13p	pale chestnut (1 side band)	60	60	☐	☐
W39	14p	grey-blue (phosphorised paper)	70	70	☐	☐
W40	14p	deep blue (1 centre band)	75	75	☐	☐
W41	15p	bright blue (1 centre band)	80	75	☐	☐
W42	15½p	pale violet (phosphorised paper)	75	75	☐	☐
W43	16p	drab (phosphorised paper)	1·75	1·75	☐	☐
	a.	Perf 15 × 14	1·75	1·75	☐	☐
W44	17p	grey-blue (phosphorised paper)	70	80	☐	☐
W45	17p	deep blue (1 centre band)	90	80	☐	☐
W46	18p	deep violet (phosphorised paper)	1·00	95	☐	☐
W47	18p	olive-grey (phosphorised paper)	95	90	☐	☐
W48	18p	bright green (1 centre band)	75	75	☐	☐
	b.	Perf 14	7·50	7·50	☐	☐
W49	18p	bright green (1 side band)	2·00	2·00	☐	☐
W50	19p	bright orange-red (phosphorised paper)	1·00	80	☐	☐
W51	19½p	olive-grey (phosphorised paper)	1·75	2·00	☐	☐
W52	20p	brownish black (phosphorised paper)	90	90	☐	☐
W53	20½p	ultramarine (phosphorised paper)	3·75	3·75	☐	☐
W54	22p	blue (phosphorised paper)	1·10	1·10	☐	☐
W55	22p	yellow-green (phosphorised paper)	95	1·10	☐	☐
W56	22p	bright orange-red (phosphorised paper)	1·00	1·10	☐	☐
W57	23p	bright green (phosphorised paper)	1·00	1·10	☐	☐
W58	24p	Indian red (phosphorised paper)	1·25	1·25	☐	☐
W59	24p	chestnut (phosphorised paper)	75	75	☐	☐
	b.	Perf 14	7·50	7·50	☐	☐
W60	24p	chestnut (2 bands)	1·25	1·50	☐	☐
W61	26p	rosine (phosphorised paper)	1·10	1·10	☐	☐
	a.	Perf 15 × 14	5·75	6·00	☐	☐

W62	26p	drab (phosphorised paper)	1·75	1·75	☐	☐
W63	28p	deep violet-blue (phosphorised paper)	1·50	1·50	☐	☐
	a.	Perf 15 × 14	1·50	1·50	☐	☐
W64	28p	deep bluish grey (phosphorised paper)	1·50	1·50	☐	☐
W65	31p	bright purple (phosphorised paper)	1·75	1·75	☐	☐
W66	32p	greenish blue (phosphorised paper)	1·75	1·75	☐	☐
W67	34p	deep bluish grey (phosphorised paper)	1·75	1·75	☐	☐
W68	37p	rosine (phosphorised paper)	2·25	2·25	☐	☐
W69	39p	bright mauve (phosphorised paper)	2·25	2·25	☐	☐

Nos. W49 and W60 were only issued in stamp booklets. The former exists with the phosphor band at the left or right of the stamp.

Presentation Pack (P.O. Pack No. 28) (contains 2½p (W13), 3p (W14), 5p (W19), 7½p (W24)) **3·50** ☐

Presentation Pack (P.O. Pack No. 63) (contains 3p (W15), 3½p (W16), 5½p (W20), 8p (W25), later with 4½p (W18) added) **2·50** ☐

Presentation Pack (P.O. Pack No. 86) (contains 6½p (W22), 8½p (W26), 10p (W28), 11p (W31)) **2·00** ☐

Presentation Pack (P.O. Pack No. 129c) (contains 7p (W23), 9p (W27), 10½p (W30), 11½p (W35), 12p (W32), 13½p (W33), 14p (W39), 15p (W34), 18p (W46), 22p (W54)) **9·00** ☐

Presentation Pack (P.O. Pack No. 3) (contains 10p (W29), 12½p (W37), 16p (W43), 20½p (W53), 26p (W61), 28p (W63)) **20·00** ☐

Presentation Pack (P.O. Pack No. 7) (contains 10p (W29), 13p (W38), 16p (W43a), 17p (W44), 22p (W55), 26p (W61), 28p (W63), 31p (W65)) **17·00** ☐

Presentation Pack (P.O. Pack No. 11) (contains 12p (W36), 13p (W38), 17p (W44), 18p (W47), 22p (W55), 26p (W61a), 28p (W63a), 31p (W65)) **20·00** ☐

For combined packs containing values from all three Regions see under Northern Ireland.

1993 (7 Dec.)–**96** Printed in lithography by Questa. Perf 15 × 14 (with one elliptical hole on each vertical side)

W70	W **4**	19p	bistre (1 centre band)	80	70	☐	☐
W71		19p	bistre (1 side band)	3·75	4·00	☐	☐
W72		20p	bright green (1 centre band)	1·75	2·00	☐	☐
W73		25p	red (2 bands)	1·25	1·00	☐	☐
W74		26p	red-brown (2 bands)	2·00	2·25	☐	☐
W75		30p	deep olive-grey (2 bands)	1·25	1·25	☐	☐
W76		37p	bright mauve (2 bands)	2·75	3·00	☐	☐
W77		41p	grey-brown (2 bands)	2·00	2·00	☐	☐
W78		63p	light emerald (2 bands)	4·50	4·75	☐	☐

No. W71 was only issued in stamp booklets.

For combined presentation packs for all three Regions see under Northern Ireland.

1997 (1 July)–**98** Printed in photogravure by Walsall (20p, 26p (No. W80a), 63p), Harrison or Walsall (26p (No. W80), 37p) Perf 14 (No.

W79a) or 15 × 14 (both with one elliptical hole on each vertical side)

W79	W **5**	20p	bright green				
			(1 centre band)	80	80	☐	☐
W79a		20p	bright green				
			(1 side band)	3·00	3·00	☐	☐
W80		26p	chestnut (2 bands)	1·00	1·00	☐	☐
		a.	Perf 14	3·00	3·00	☐	☐
W81		37p	bright mauve (2 bands)	2·75	2·75	☐	☐
W82		63p	light emerald (2 bands)	5·00	5·00	☐	☐

Presentation Pack (P.O. Pack No. 39)
(Nos. W79 and W80/2)   17·00 ☐

Nos. W79a and W80a were only issued in stamp booklets.

W **6** Leek	W **7** Welsh Dragon	W **8** Daffodil	W **9** Prince of Wales Feathers

1999 (8 June)–**2002** Printed in photogravure by De La Rue (68p), Walsall or De La Rue (1st), (2nd), (No.W83) or Walsall (others). One phosphor band (2nd) or two phosphor bands (others). Perf 14 (No. W83a) or 15 × 14 (others) (both with one elliptical hole on each vertical side)

W83	W **6**	(2nd)	orange-brown, yellow-orange and black (1 centre band)	60	50	☐	☐
W83a		(2nd)	orange-brown, yellow-orange and black (1 side band)	4·00	4·00	☐	☐
W84	W **7**	(1st)	blue-green, greenish yellow, silver and black	1·00	1·00	☐	☐
W85	W **8**	(E)	greenish blue, deep greenish blue and grey-black	1·75	1·75	☐	☐
W86	W **9**	64p	violet, gold, silver and black	9·00	9·00	☐	☐
W87		65p	violet, gold, silver and black	3·25	3·25	☐	☐
W88		68p	violet, gold, silver and black	3·25	3·25	☐	☐

Presentation Pack (P.O. Pack No. 46)
(contains 2nd, 1st, E, 64p)
(Nos. W83, W84/6))   14·00 ☐

Presentation Pack (P.O. Pack No. 51) (contains
65p) (No. W87))   12·00 ☐

Presentation Pack (P.O. Pack No. 56) (contains
2nd, 1st, E, 65p) (Nos. W83,
W84/5, W87))   18·00 ☐

PHQ Cards (Nos. W83, W84/6)   8·00   14·00 ☐

Nos. W83, W84 and W85 were initially sold at 19p, 26p and 30p, the latter representing the basic European airmail rate.

No. W83a was only issued in stamp booklets.

For combined presentation packs for all four Regions, see under England.

W 10

2000 (15 Feb.) Type W **4** redrawn with '1af/st' face value as Type W **10**. Two phosphor bands. Perf 14 (with one elliptical

hole on each vertical side)

W97	W **10**	(1st)	bright orange-red	3·00	2·75	☐ ☐

No. W97 was only issued in stamp booklets.

2003 (14 Oct.)–**10**. As Nos. W83, W84/5 and W88, but with white borders. One centre phosphor band (2nd) or two phosphor bands (others). Perf 15 × 14 (with one elliptical hole on each vertical side)

(a) Printed in photogravure by Walsall or De La Rue (42p) or De La Rue (others)

W98	W **6**	(2nd)	orange-brown, deep orange-brown and black	80	75	☐	☐
W99	W **7**	(1st)	blue-green, greenish yellow, silver and black	80	75	☐	☐
W100	W **8**	(E)	greenish blue, deep greenish blue and grey-black	2·50	2·50	☐	☐
W101		40p	greenish blue, deep greenish blue and grey-black	1·50	1·50	☐	☐
W102		42p	greenish blue, deep greenish blue and grey-black	1·50	1·50	☐	☐
W103		44p	greenish blue, deep greenish blue and grey-black	1·50	1·50	☐	☐
W104		48p	greenish blue, deep greenish blue and grey-black	90	90	☐	☐
W105		50p	greenish blue, deep greenish blue and grey-black	1·00	1·00	☐	☐
W105a		56p	greenish blue, deep greenish blue and grey-black	1·25	1·25	☐	☐
W105b		60p	greenish blue, deep greenish blue and grey-black	1·40	1·40	☐	☐
W106	W **9**	68p	violet, gold, silver and black	2·00	2·00	☐	☐
W107		72p	violet, gold, silver and black	2·00	2·00	☐	☐
W108		78p	violet, gold, silver and black	1·40	1·30	☐	☐
W109		81p	violet, gold, silver and black	1·75	1·75	☐	☐
W109a		90p	violet, gold, silver and black	2·00	2·00	☐	☐
W109b		97p	violet, gold, silver and black	2·25	2·25	☐	☐

(b) Printed in lithography by Enschedé

W120	W **7**	(1st)	blue-green, greenish yellow, silver and black	4·25	4·25	☐	☐

Presentation Pack (P.O. Pack No. 65)
(Nos. W98/100, W106)   7·00 ☐

PHQ Cards (set of 4) (Nos. W98/100,
W106)   2·00   6·00 ☐ ☐

Nos. W98/100 were initially sold at 20p, 28p and 38p, the latter representing the basic European airmail rate.

No. W108 was only issued in £7.66 stamp booklets. Stamps as W120 but self-adhesive were issued on 1 March 2007 in sheets of 20 with *se-tenant* labels. These sheets were printed in lithography and perforated 15 × 14 without the elliptical holes. The labels show either Welsh scenes or personal photographs.

Stamps as Nos. EN18, NI95, S131 and W120 but self-adhesive were issued on 29 September 2008 in sheets of 20 containing five of each design with *se-tenant* labels.

Opening of New Welsh Assembly Building, Cardiff

2006 (1 Mar.) Sheet 123 × 70 mm. Printed in photogravure by De La Rue. One centre phosphor band (2nd) or two phosphor bands (others). Perf 15 × 14 (with one elliptical hole on each vertical side)

MSW121 Nos. W98, W99 × 2 and W106 × 2 5·00	5·00	☐ ☐
First Day Cover	6·00	☐

50th Anniv of the Country Definitives

2008 (29 Sept.) As Nos. W1, W3 and W5 (definitives of 1958) but inscribed 1st and printed in lithography by De La Rue. Two phosphor bands. Perf 15 × 14½ (with one elliptical hole on each vertical side)

W122	W **1** (1st) deep lilac	1·25	1·25	☐ ☐
W123	W **3** (1st) green	1·25	1·25	☐ ☐
W124	W **2** (1st) deep claret	1·25	1·25	☐ ☐

Nos. W122/4 come from Celebrating Wales £9.72 stamp booklets.

Celebrating Wales

W 11

2009 (26 FEB.). Sheet 123×70 mm. Printed in lithography by De La Rue. Two phosphor bands. Perf 15×14 (with one elliptical hole on each vertical side (1st) or 14½×14 (81p))

MSW125 (1st) Red dragon; (1st) No. W120; 81p St. David; 81p National Assembly for Wales, Cardiff	6 00	6·00	☐ ☐
First Day Cover	7·00	☐
Presentation Pack	8·00	☐
PHQ Cards (set of 5)	4·00	17·00	☐ ☐

The five PHQ cards show the four individual stamps and the complete miniature sheet.

Stamps as the 1st class red dragon stamp from **MS**W125 but self-adhesive were issued on 1 March 2010 in sheets of 20 with *se-tenant* labels showing Welsh castles. These sheets were printed in lithography by Cartor.

5 Isle of Man

Regional Issues

1	**2**	**3**

1958–67 Wmk 179. Perf 15 × 14

1	**1**	2½d red	50	1·25	☐ ☐

2	**2**	3d	lilac	50	20	☐ ☐
		p. One centre phosphor band		20	50	☐ ☐
3		4d	blue	1·50	1·50	☐ ☐
		p. Two phosphor bands		20	30	☐ ☐

1968–69 One centre phosphor band (Nos. 5/6) or two phosphor bands (others). No wmk

4	**2**	4d blue	25	30	☐ ☐
5		4d sepia	25	30	☐ ☐
6		4d vermilion	45	75	☐ ☐
7		5d blue	45	75	☐ ☐

Decimal Currency

1971 (7 July) One centre phosphor band (2½p) or two phosphor bands (others). No wmk

8	**3**	2½p magenta	20	15	☐ ☐
9		3p ultramarine	20	15	☐ ☐
10		5p violet	80	80	☐ ☐
11		7½p chestnut	90	90	☐ ☐
Presentation Pack			3·25		☐

For comprehensive listings of the Independent Administration issues of the Isle of Man, see Stanley Gibbons *Collect Channel Islands and Isle of Man Stamps.*

6 Channel Islands General Issue

C **1** Gathering Vraic   C **2** Islanders gathering Vraic

Third Anniversary of Liberation

1948 (10 May) Wmk Type 127. Perf 15 × 14

C1	C **1**	1d red	25	30	☐ ☐
C2	C **2**	2½d blue	25	30	☐ ☐
First Day Cover			35·00		☐

7 Guernsey

(a) War Occupation Issues

Stamps issued under British authority during the German Occupation.

1	**2**	**3**

1941–44 Rouletted. (a) White paper. No wmk

1d	**1**	½d green	4·00	2·00	☐ ☐
2		1d red	3·25	2·00	☐ ☐
3a		2½d blue	10·00	7·00	☐ ☐

(b) Bluish French bank-note paper. Wmk loops

4	**1**	½d green	30·00	22·00	☐ ☐
5		1d red	16·00	22·00	☐ ☐

(b) Regional Issues

1958–67 Wmk 179. Perf 15 × 14

6	**2**	2½d red	35	40	☐ ☐
7	**3**	3d lilac	30	30	☐ ☐
		p. One centre phosphor			

	band		15	20	☐	☐
8	4d blue		25	30	☐	☐
	p. Two phosphor bands		15	20	☐	☐

1968–69 One centre phosphor band (Nos. 10/11) or two phosphor bands (others). No wmk

9	**3**	4d blue	10	20	☐	☐
10		4d sepia	10	15	☐	☐
11		4d vermilion	20	25	☐	☐
12		5d blue	20	30	☐	☐

For comprehensive listings of the Independent Postal Administration issues of Guernsey, see Stanley Gibbons *Collect Channel Islands and Isle of Man Stamps.*

8 Jersey

(a) War Occupation Issues

Stamps issued under British authority during the German Occupation.

1

2 Old Jersey Farm   **3** Portelet Bay

4 Corbière Lighthouse   **5** Elizabeth Castle

6 Mont Orgueil Castle   **7** Gathering Vraic (seaweed)

1941–42 White paper. No wmk Perf 11

1	**1**	½d green	8·00	6·00	☐	☐
2		1d red	8·00	5·00	☐	☐

1943 No wmk Perf 13½

3	**2**	½d green	12·00	12·00	☐	☐
4	**3**	1d red	3·00	50	☐	☐
5	**4**	1½d brown	8·00	5·75	☐	☐
6	**5**	2d orange	7·50	2·00	☐	☐
7a	**6**	2½d blue	1·00	1·75	☐	☐
8	**7**	3d violet	3·00	2·75	☐	☐
Set of 6			30·00	21·00	☐	☐

(b) Regional Issues

8   **9**

1958–67 Wmk 179. Perf 15 × 14

9	**8**	2½d red	30	45	☐	☐
10	**9**	3d lilac	30	25	☐	☐
		p. One centre phosphor band	15	15	☐	☐
11		4d blue	25	30	☐	☐
		p. Two phosphor bands	15	25	☐	☐

1968–69 One centre phosphor band (4d values) or two phosphor bands (5d). No wmk

12	**9**	4d sepia	15	25	☐	☐
13		4d vermilion	15	25	☐	☐
14		5d blue	15	50	☐	☐

For comprehensive listings of the Independent Postal Adminstration issues of Jersey, see Stanley Gibbons *Collect Channel Islands and Isle of Man Stamps.*

REGIONAL FIRST DAY COVERS

PRICES for First Day Covers listed below are for stamps, as indicated, used on illustrated envelopes and postmarked with operational cancellations (before 1964) or with special First Day of Issue cancellations (1964 onwards). First Day postmarks of 8 June 1964 and 7 February 1966 were of the machine cancellation 'envelope' type.

£sd Issues
18 Aug. 1958

Guernsey 3d (No. 7)	20·00	☐
Isle of Man 3d (No. 2)	32·00	☐
Jersey 3d (No. 10)	20·00	☐
Northern Ireland 3d (No. NI1)	30·00	☐
Scotland 3d (No. S1)	17·00	☐
Wales 3d (No. W1)	12·00	☐

29 Sept. 1958

Northern Ireland 6d, 1s 3d (Nos. NI3, NI5)	35·00	☐
Scotland 6d, 1s 3d (Nos. S3, S5)	25·00	☐
Wales 6d, 1s 3d (Nos. W3, W5)	25·00	☐

8 June 1964

Guernsey 2½d (No. 6)	30·00	☐
Isle of Man 2½d (No. 1)	45·00	☐
Jersey 2½d (No. 9)	30·00	☐

7 Feb. 1966

Guernsey 4d (No. 8)	8·00	☐
Isle of Man 4d (No. 3)	15·00	☐
Jersey 4d (No. 11)	10·00	☐
Northern Ireland 4d (No. NI2)	7·00	☐
Scotland 4d (No. S2)	7·00	☐
Wales 4d (No. W2)	7·00	☐

1 March 1967

Northern Ireland 9d, 1s 6d (Nos. NI4, NI6)	4·00	☐
Scotland 9d, 1s 6d (Nos. S4, S6)	6·00	☐
Wales 9d, 1s 6d (Nos. W4, W6)	4·00	☐

4 Sept. 1968

Guernsey 4d, 5d (Nos. 10, 12)	3·00	☐
Isle of Man 4d, 5d (Nos. 5, 7)	4·00	☐
Jersey 4d, 5d (Nos. 12, 14)	3·00	☐
Northern Ireland 4d, 5d (Nos. NI8, NI10)	3·00	☐
Scotland 4d, 5d (Nos. S9, S11) .	3·00	☐
Wales 4d, 5d (Nos. W9, W11)	3·00	☐

Decimal Issues

7 July 1971

Isle of Man 2½p, 3p, 5p, 7½p (Nos. 8/11)	3·00	☐
Northern Ireland 2½p, 3p, 5p, 7½p (Nos. NI12/13, NI18, NI23) .	3·50	☐
Scotland 2½p, 3p, 5p, 7½p (Nos. S14/15, S20, S25)	3·00	☐
Wales 2½p, 3p, 5p, 7½p (Nos.W13/14, W19, W24)	3·00	☐

23 Jan. 1974

Northern Ireland 3p, 3½p, 5½p, 8p (Nos. NI14/15, NI19, NI24)	2·40	☐
Scotland 3p, 3½p, 5½p, 8p (Nos. S16/17, S21, S26)	2·50	☐
Wales 3p, 3½p, 5½p, 8p (Nos. W15/16, W20, W25)	2·50	☐

6 Nov. 1974

Northern Ireland 4½p (No. NI17)	1·50	☐
Scotland 4½p (No. S19)	1·50	☐
Wales 4½p (No. W18)	1·50	☐

14 Jan. 1976

Northern Ireland 6½p, 8½p (Nos. NI21, NI25)	1·50	☐
Scotland 6½p, 8½p (Nos. S23, S27)	1·50	☐
Wales 6½p, 8½p (Nos. W22, W26)	1·50	☐

20 Oct. 1976

Northern Ireland 10p, 11p (Nos. NI27, NI30)	1·75	☐
Scotland 10p, 11p (Nos. S29, S32)	1·50	☐
Wales 10p, 11p (Nos. W28, W31)	1·50	☐

18 Jan. 1978

Northern Ireland 7p, 9p, 10½p (Nos. NI22, NI26, NI29)	1·75	☐
Scotland 7p, 9p, 10½p (Nos. S24, S28, S31)	1·75	☐
Wales 7p, 9p, 10½p (Nos. W23, W27, W30)	1·75	☐

23 July 1980

Northern Ireland 12p, 13½p, 15p (Nos. NI31/3)	3·00	☐
Scotland 12p, 13½p, 15p (Nos. S33/5)	2·75	☐
Wales 12p, 13½p, 15p (Nos. W32/4)	3·00	☐

8 April 1981

Northern Ireland 11½p, 14p, 18p, 22p (Nos. NI34, NI38, NI45, NI53)	2·50	☐
Scotland 11½p, 14p, 18p, 22p (Nos. S36, S40, S44, S47)	2·50	☐
Wales 11½p, 14p, 18p, 22p (Nos. W35, W39, W46, W54)	2·50	☐

24 Feb. 1982

Northern Ireland 12½p, 15½p, 19½p, 26p (Nos. NI36, NI41, NI50, NI60)	4·00	☐

Scotland 12½p, 15½p, 19½p, 26p (Nos. S38, S41, S45, S49)	3·50	☐
Wales 12½p, 15½p, 19½p, 26p (Nos. W37, W42, W51, W61)	3·50	☐

27 April 1983

Northern Ireland 16p, 20½p, 28p (Nos. NI42, NI52, NI62)	4·00	☐
Scotland 16p, 20½p, 28p (Nos. S42, S46, S50)	4·00	☐
Wales 16p, 20½p, 28p (Nos. W43, W53, W63)	3·50	☐

23 Oct. 1984

Northern Ireland 13p, 17p, 22p, 31p (Nos. NI37, NI43, NI54, NI64)	4·75	☐
Scotland 13p, 17p, 22p, 31p (Nos. S39, S43, S48, S51)	4·00	☐
Wales 13p, 17p, 22p, 31p (Nos. W38, W44, W55, W65)	4·25	☐

7 Jan. 1986

Northern Ireland 12p (No. NI35)	2·00	☐
Scotland 12p (No. S37)	2·00	☐
Wales 12p (No. W36)	2·00	☐

6 Jan. 1987

Northern Ireland 18p (No. NI46)	2·00	☐
Scotland 18p (No. S59)	1·80	☐
Wales 18p (No. W47)	2·00	☐

8 Nov. 1988

Northern Ireland 14p, 19p, 23p, 32p (Nos. NI39, NI49, NI56, NI65)	4·25	☐
Scotland 14p, 19p, 23p, 32p (Nos. S54, S62, S67, S77)	4·25	☐
Wales 14p, 19p, 23p, 32p (Nos. W40, W50, W57, W66)	4·50	☐

28 Nov. 1989

Northern Ireland 15p, 20p, 24p, 34p (Nos. NI40, NI51, NI57, NI66)	5·00	☐
Scotland 15p, 20p, 24p, 34p (Nos. S56, S64, S69, S78)	5·00	☐
Wales 15p, 20p, 24p, 34p (Nos. W41, W52, W58, W67)	5·00	☐

4 Dec. 1990

Northern Ireland 17p, 22p, 26p, 37p (Nos. NI44, NI55, NI61, NI67)	5·00	☐
Scotland 17p, 22p, 26p, 37p (Nos. S58, S66, S73, S79)	5·00	☐
Wales 17p, 22p, 26p, 37p (Nos.W45, W56, W62, W68)	5·00	☐

3 Dec. 1991

Northern Ireland 18p, 24p, 28p, 39p (Nos. NI47, NI58, NI63, NI68)	5·50	☐
Scotland 18p, 24p, 28p, 39p (Nos. S60, S70, S75, S80)	5·50	☐
Wales 18p, 24p, 28p, 39p (Nos. W48, W59, W64, W69)	5·50	☐

7 Dec. 1993

Northern Ireland 19p, 25p, 30p, 41p (Nos. NI69, NI72, NI74, NI76)	6·00	☐
Scotland 19p, 25p, 30p, 41p (Nos. S81, S84, S86, S88)	6·00	☐
Wales 19p, 25p, 30p, 41p (Nos. W70, W73, W75, W77)	6·00	☐

23 July 1996

Northern Ireland 20p (1 centre band),
26p, 37p, 63p (Nos. NI71, NI73, NI75,
NI77)   8·75 ☐

Scotland 20p (1 centre band), 26p, 37p,
63p (Nos. S83, S85, S87, S89)   8·75 ☐

Wales 20p, 26p, 37p, 63p (Nos. W72,
W74, W76, W78)   7·00 ☐

1 July 1997

Wales 20p (1 centre band), 26p, 37p,
63p (Nos. W79 and W80/2)   6·00 ☐

8 June 1999

Northern Ireland 38p, 64p
(Nos. NI83, NI86)   4·00 ☐

Scotland 2nd, 1st, E, 64p (Nos S94/7) 6·00 ☐

Wales 2nd, 1st, E, 64p (Nos. W83,
W84/6)   6·00 ☐

25 Apr. 2000

Northern Ireland 1st, 40p, 65p
(Nos. NI84, NI87, NI88b)   7·00 ☐

Scotland 65p (No. S98)   3·00 ☐

Wales 65p (No. W87)   3·00 ☐

6 Mar. 2001

Northern Ireland 2nd, 1st, E, 65p
(Nos. NI89/92)   4·50 ☐

23 Apr. 2001

England 2nd, 1st, E, 65p (Nos. EN1/4) 3·25 ☐

4 July 2002

England 68p (No. EN5)   3·50 ☐
Northern Ireland 68p (No. NI93)   2·50 ☐
Scotland 68p (No. S99)   1·75 ☐
Wales 68p (No. W88)   1·75 ☐

14 Oct. 2003

England 2nd, 1st, E, 68p
(Nos. EN6/8, EN14)   3·25 ☐

Northern Ireland 2nd, 1st, E, 68p
(Nos. NI94/6, NI100)   3·25 ☐

Scotland 2nd, 1st, E, 68p
(Nos. S109/11, S117)   3·25 ☐

Wales 2nd, 1st, E, 68p
(Nos. W98/100, W106)   3·25 ☐

11 May 2004

England 40p (No. EN9)   2·75 ☐
Northern Ireland 40p (No. NI97)   2·75 ☐
Scotland 40p (No. S112)   2·75 ☐
Wales 40p (No. W101)   2·75 ☐

5 Apr. 2005

England 42p (No. EN10)   1·40 ☐
Northern Ireland 42p (No. NI98)   1·40 ☐
Scotland 42p (No. S113)   1·40 ☐
Wales 42p (No. W102)   1·40 ☐

28 Mar. 2006

England 44p, 72p (Nos. EN11, EN15)   2·75 ☐

Northern Ireland 44p, 72p
(Nos. NI99, NI101)   2·75 ☐

Scotland 44p, 72p (Nos. S114, S118)   2·75 ☐
Wales 44p, 72p (Nos. W103, W107)   2·75 ☐

27 Mar. 2007

England 48p, 78p (Nos. EN12, EN16)   4·00 ☐

Northern Ireland 48p, 78p
(Nos. NI104, NI106)   4·00 ☐

Scotland 48p, 78p (Nos. S115, S119)   4·00 ☐
Wales 48p, 78p (Nos. W104, W108)   3·50 ☐

1 Apr. 2008

England 50p, 81p
(Nos. EN13, EN17)   4·00 ☐

Northern Ireland 50p, 81p
(Nos. NI105, NI107)   4·00 ☐

Scotland 50p, 81p (Nos. S116, S120)   4·00 ☐
Wales 50p, 81p (Nos. W105, W109)   4·00 ☐

31 Mar. 2009

England 56p, 90p (Nos. EN13a,
EN17a)   4·75 ☐

Northern Ireland 56p, 90p
(Nos. NI105a, NI107a)   4·75 ☐

Scotland 56p, 90p (Nos. S116a, S120a) 4·75 ☐
Wales 56p, 90p (Nos. W105a, W109a)   4·75 ☐

31 Mar. 2010

England 60p, 97p (Nos. EN13b,
EN17b)   4·00 ☐

Northern Ireland 60p, 97p
(Nos. NI105b, NI107b)   4·00 ☐

Scotland 60p, 97p (Nos. S116b, S120b) 4·00 ☐
Wales 60p, 97p (Nos. W105b, W109b)   4·00 ☐

POSTAGE DUE STAMPS

PERFORATION. All postage due stamps to No. D101 are perf 14 × 15.

D **1**   D **2**

1914–22 Wmk Type 100 (Royal Cypher ('Simple')) sideways

D1	D **1**	½d green	50	25	☐	☐
D2		1d red	50	25	☐	☐
D3		1½d brown	48·00	20·00	☐	☐
D4		2d black	50	25	☐	☐
D5		3d violet	5·00	75	☐	☐
D6wi		4d green	40·00	5·00	☐	☐
D7		5d brown	7·00	3·50	☐	☐
D8		1s blue	40·00	5·00	☐	☐
Set of 8			£120	32·00	☐	☐

1924–31 Wmk Type 111 (Block G v R) sideways

D10	D **1**	½d green	1·25	75	☐	☐
D11		1d red	60	25	☐	☐
D12		1½d brown	47·00	22·00	☐	☐
D13		2d black	1·00	25	☐	☐
D14		3d violet	1·50	25	☐	☐
D15		4d green	15·00	4·25	☐	☐
D16		5d brown	65·00	45·00	☐	☐
D17		1s blue	8·50	50	☐	☐
D18	D **2**	2s 6d purple/yellow	85·00	1·75	☐	☐
Set of 9			£200	60·00	☐	☐

1936–37 Wmk Type 125 (E 8 R) sideways

D19	D **1**	½d green	12·00	10·50	☐	☐
D20		1d red	2·00	1·75	☐	☐
D21		2d black	12·00	12·00	☐	☐
D22		3d violet	2·00	2·00	☐	☐
D23		4d green	50·00	34·00	☐	☐
D24a		5d brown	33·00	28·00	☐	☐
D25		1s blue	16·00	8·50	☐	☐
D26	D **2**	2s 6d purple/yellow	£325	12·00	☐	☐
Set of 8			£450	90·00	☐	☐

1937–38 Wmk Type 127 (G vi R) sideways

D27	D **1**	½d green	13·00	3·75	☐	☐
D28		1d red	3·00	50	☐	☐
D29		2d black	2·75	30	☐	☐
D30		3d violet	10·50	30	☐	☐
D31		4d green	£110	10·00	☐	☐
D32		5d brown	16·50	75	☐	☐
D33		1s blue	78·00	75	☐	☐
D34	D **2**	2s 6d purple/yellow	85·00	1·25	☐	☐
Set of 8			£260	18·00	☐	☐

1951–52 Colours changed and new value (1½d) Wmk Type 127 (G vi R) sideways

D35	D **1**	½d orange	3·50	3·50	☐	☐
D36		1d blue	1·50	75	☐	☐
D37		1½d green	2·00	2·00	☐	☐
D38		4d blue	50·00	22·00	☐	☐
D39		1s brown	28·00	5·25	☐	☐
Set of 5			75·00	28·00	☐	☐

1954–55 Wmk Type 153 (Mult Tudor Crown and E 2 R) sideways

D40	D **1**	½d orange	7·00	5·25	☐	☐
D41		2d black	26·00	23·00	☐	☐
D42		3d violet	75·00	60·00	☐	☐
D43		4d blue	26·00	32·00	☐	☐
D44		5d brown	20·00	20·00	☐	☐
D45	D **2**	2s 6d purple/yellow	£150	5·75	☐	☐
Set of 6			£250	£120	☐	☐

1955–57 Wmk Type 165 (Mult St Edward's Crown and E 2 R) sideways

D46	D **1**	½d orange	2·75	3·25	☐	☐
D47		1d blue	5·00	1·50	☐	☐
D48		1½d green	8·50	7·00	☐	☐
D49		2d black	45·00	3·50	☐	☐
D50		3d violet	6·00	1·50	☐	☐
D51		4d blue	25·00	6·00	☐	☐
D52		5d brown	26·00	20·00	☐	☐
D53		1s brown	65·00	2·25	☐	☐
D54	D **2**	2s 6d purple/yellow	£200	8·25	☐	☐
D55		5s red/yellow	£150	32·00	☐	☐
Set of 10			£425	65·00	☐	☐

1959–63 Wmk Type 179 (Mult St Edward's Crown) sideways

D56	D **1**	½d orange	15	1·25	☐	☐
D57		1d blue	15	50	☐	☐
D58		1½d green	2·50	2·50	☐	☐
D59		2d black	1·10	50	☐	☐
D60		3d violet	30	30	☐	☐
D61		4d blue	30	30	☐	☐
D62		5d brown	45	60	☐	☐
D63		6d purple	50	30	☐	☐
D64		1s brown	90	30	☐	☐
D65	D **2**	2s 6d purple/yellow	3·00	50	☐	☐
D66		5s red/yellow	8·25	1·00	☐	☐
D67		10s blue/yellow	11·50	5·75	☐	☐
D68		£1 black/yellow	45·00	8·25	☐	☐
Set of 13			70·00	20·00	☐	☐

1968–69 Design size 22½ × 19 mm. No wmk

D69	D **1**	2d black	75	1·00	☐	☐
D70		3d violet	1·00	1·00	☐	☐
D71		4d blue	1·00	1·00	☐	☐
D72		5d orange-brown	8·00	11·00	☐	☐
D73		6d purple	2·25	1·75	☐	☐
D74		1s brown	4·00	2·50	☐	☐
Set of 6			17·00	20·00	☐	☐

1968–69 Design size 21½ × 17½ mm. No wmk

D75	D **1**	4d blue	7·00	6·75	☐	☐
D76		8d red	50	1·00	☐	☐

D **3**   D **4**

Decimal Currency

1970–77 No wmk

D77	D **3**	½p turquoise-blue	15	2·50	☐	☐
D78		1p reddish purple	15	15	☐	☐
D79		2p myrtle-green	20	15	☐	☐
D80		3p ultramarine	20	15	☐	☐
D81		4p yellow-brown	25	15	☐	☐
D82		5p violet	25	15	☐	☐
D83		7p red-brown	35	1·00	☐	☐

D84	D **4**	10p	red	30	30	☐ ☐
D85		11p	green	50	1·00	☐ ☐
D86		20p	brown	60	25	☐ ☐
D87		50p	ultramarine	2·00	1·25	☐ ☐
D88		£1	black	4·00	1·00	☐ ☐
D89		£5	orange-yellow			
			and black	36·00	1·50	☐ ☐
Set of 13				40·00	7·75	☐ ☐

Presentation Pack (P.O. Pack No. 36)		
(Nos. D77/82, D84, D86/8)	20·00	☐
Presentation Pack (P.O. Pack No. 93)		
(Nos. D77/88)	10·00	☐

D **5**   D **6**   D **7**

1982 No wmk

D90	D **5**	1p	lake	10	30	☐ ☐
D91		2p	bright blue	30	30	☐ ☐
D92		3p	deep mauve	15	30	☐ ☐
D93		4p	deep blue	15	25	☐ ☐
D94		5p	sepia	20	25	☐ ☐
D95	D **6**	10p	light brown	30	40	☐ ☐
D96		20p	olive-green	50	60	☐ ☐
D97		25p	deep greenish blue	80	90	☐ ☐
D98		50p	grey-black	1·75	1·75	☐ ☐
D99		£1	red	3·25	1·25	☐ ☐
D100		£2	turquoise-blue	7·00	4·25	☐ ☐
D101		£5	dull orange	14·00	2·25	☐ ☐
Set of 12				24·00	10·00	☐ ☐
Set of 12 Gutter Pairs				48·00		☐
Presentation Pack				48·00		☐

1994 (15 Feb.) Perf 15 × 14 (with one elliptical hole on each vertical side)

D102	D **7**	1p	red, yellow and black	10	75	☐ ☐
D103		2p	magenta, purple			
			and black	10	75	☐ ☐
D104		5p	yellow, red-brown			
			and black	15	50	☐ ☐
D105		10p	yellow, emerald			
			and black	30	75	☐ ☐
D106		20p	blue-green, violet			
			and black	75	1·50	☐ ☐
D107		25p	cerise, rosine			
			and black	1·50	2·00	☐ ☐
D108		£1	violet, magenta			
			and black	7·00	10·00	☐ ☐
D109		£1.20	greenish blue,			
			blue-green and black	8·00	12·00	☐ ☐
D110		£5	greenish black,			
			blue-green and black	30·00	20·00	☐ ☐
Set of 9				45·00	45·00	☐ ☐
First Day Cover					22·00	☐
Presentation Pack				60·00		☐

ROYAL MAIL POSTAGE LABELS

These imperforate labels were issued as an experiment by the Post Office. Special microprocessor-controlled machines were installed at post offices in Cambridge, London, Shirley (Southampton) and Windsor to provide an after-hours sales service to the public. The machines printed and dispensed the labels according to the coins inserted and the buttons operated by the customer. Values were initially available in ½p steps to 16p and in addition, the labels were sold at philatelic counters in two packs containing either 3 values (3½, 12½, 16p) or 32 values (½p to 16p).

From 28 August 1984 the machines were adjusted to provide values up to 17p. After 31 December 1984 labels including ½p values were withdrawn. The machines were taken out of service on 30 April 1985.

Machine postage-paid impression in red on phosphorised paper with grey-green background design. No watermark. Imperforate.

1984 (1 May–28 Aug.)

Set of 32 (½p to 16p)	15·00	22·00	☐ ☐
Set of 3 (3½p, 12½p, 16p)	2·50	3·00	☐ ☐
Set of 3 on First Day Cover (1 May)		6·50	☐
Set of 2 (16½p, 17p) (28 August)	4·00	3·00	☐ ☐

ROYAL MAIL FASTSTAMPS

Following trials of a number of self-service machines capable of dispensing postage labels, Royal Mail began installing "Post and Go" machines in larger post offices in October 2008. In addition to postage labels, the machines, manufactured by Wincor Nixdorf, dispense stamps with a pre-printed background and an inkjet printed indicator of the service required, together with a four-part code.

The first machines were sited at the Galleries post office in Bristol and came into use on 8 October 2008. They dispensed five different labels, dependent on the service; the code at the foot of the stamp referring to the branch in which the machine is sited, the machine number within the branch, and the session and transaction numbers.

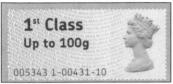

FT 1

(Gravure Walsall, inkjet printed service indicator)

2008 (8 Oct). Type FT **1**. Self-adhesive. Olive-brown background. Two phosphor bands. P 14½.

FS1	"1st Class Up to 100g"	1·25	1·40	☐	☐
FS2	"1st Large Up to 100g"	1·50	1·75	☐	☐
FS3	"Europe Up to 20g"	1·50	1·75	☐	☐
FS4	"Worldwide Up to 10g"	1·75	2·00	☐	☐
FS5	"Worldwide Up to 20g"	2·50	2·75	☐	☐
Set of 5		7·50	7·75	☐	☐
Special Pack (Nos. FS1/5) (31.3.09)		8·00		☐	

The special pack contains separate stamps. These are reproductions of the first "Post and Go" stamps printed at the Galleries Post Offices, Bristol. They differ from machine printed stamps in having the service indicator and branch code printed in gravure.

It is possible to obtain *se tenant* strips of mixed values from "Post and Go" machines but we do not list these.

FT 2 Blue Tit

Birds of Britain (1st series)

2010 (17 Sept). Multicoloured. Self-adhesive. Designs printed in photogravure by Walsall; inkjet printed service indicator. Two phosphor bands. Perf 14½.

FS6	(1st Class up to 100g)	1·00	1·00	☐	☐
FS7	(1st Large up to 100g)	1·50	1·75	☐	☐
FS8	(Europe up to 20g)	1·50	1·75	☐	☐
FS9	(Worldwide up to 10g)	1·75	2·00	☐	☐
FS10	(Worldwide up to 20g)	2·50	2·75	☐	☐
First Day Cover (No. FS6 in 6 designs)			6·00		☐
Special Pack (No. FS6 in 6 designs)		5·50		☐	

Nos. FS6/10 were each available in six different designs: Type FT **2**, goldfinch, wood pigeon, robin, house sparrow and starling.

Nos. FS6/10 were available from Post and Go terminals in 30 post offices.

Stamps from the special pack and first day cover sold by Tallents House differ from machine printed stamps in having the service indicator and branch code printed in gravure.

OFFICIAL STAMPS

Various stamps of Queen Victoria and King Edward VII overprinted in Black.

I.R.   **I. R.**   **O.W.**

OFFICIAL **OFFICIAL** **OFFICIAL**
(O 1)   (O 2)   (O 3)

ARMY   **ARMY**

GOVT
OFFICIAL **OFFICIAL** **PARCELS**
(O 4)   (O 5)   (O 7)

BOARD **R.H.** **ADMIRALTY**

OF

EDUCATION **OFFICIAL** **OFFICIAL**
(O 8)   (O 9)   (O 10)

1 Inland Revenue
Overprinted with Types O **1** or O **2** (5s, 10s, £1)

1882–1901 Queen Victoria

O 2	52	½d green		70·00	28·00	☐	☐
O 5		½d blue		70·00	24·00	☐	☐
O13	71	½d vermilion		10·00	4·00	☐	☐
O17		½d green		15·00	10·00	☐	☐
O 3	57	1d lilac (Die II)		6·00	4·00	☐	☐
O 6	64	2½d lilac		£400	£150	☐	☐
O14	74	2½d purple on blue		£120	15·00	☐	☐
O 4	43	6d grey (Plate 18)		£450	£110	☐	☐
O18	79	6d purple on red		£325	90·00	☐	☐
O 7	65	1s green		£5000	£1500	☐	☐
O15	82	1s green		£750	£250	☐	☐
O19		1s green and red		£3500	£1250	☐	☐
O 9	59	5s red		£7000	£1900	☐	☐
O10	60	10s blue		£9000	£2800	☐	☐
O11	61	£1 brown (Wmk Crowns)		£60000	£22000	☐	☐
O12		£1 brown (Wmk Orbs)	£90000	£30000		☐	☐
O16		£1 green		£10000	£2250	☐	☐

1902–04 King Edward VII

O20	83	½d blue-green	24·00	3·25	☐	☐
O21		1d red	17·00	2·25	☐	☐
O22	86	2½d blue	£900	£250	☐	☐
O23	83	6d purple	£375000	£170000	☐	☐
O24	93	1s green and red	£3500	£700	☐	☐
O25	95	5s red	£25000	£8000	☐	☐
O26	96	10s blue	£95000	£40000	☐	☐
O27	97	£1 green	£60000	£24000	☐	☐

2 Office of Works
Overprinted with Type O **3**

1896–1902 Queen Victoria

O31	71	½d vermilion	£250	£110	☐	☐
O32		½d green	£350	£160	☐	☐
O33	57	1d lilac (Die II)	£400	£110	☐	☐
O34	78	5d dull purple and blue	£2800	£1000	☐	☐
O35	81	10d dull purple and red	£4800	£1500	☐	☐

1902–03 King Edward VII

O36	83	½d blue-green	£550	£160	☐	☐
O37		1d red	£550	£160	☐	☐
O38	85	2d green and red	£1900	£400	☐	☐
O39	86	2½d blue	£3250	£600	☐	☐
O40	92	10d purple and red	£32000	£6000	☐	☐

3 Army
Overprinted with Types O **4** (½d, 1d) or O **5** (2½d, 6d)

1896–1901 Queen Victoria

O41	71	½d vermilion	5·00	2·50	☐	☐
O42		½d green	5·00	10·00	☐	☐
O43	57	1d lilac (Die II)	5·00	4·00	☐	☐
O44	74	2½d purple on blue	35·00	25·00	☐	☐
O45	79	6d purple on red	80·00	45·00	☐	☐

Overprinted with Type O **4**

1902 King Edward VII

O48	83	½d blue-green	5·50	2·25	☐	☐
O49		1d red	5·50	2·25	☐	☐
O50		6d purple	£160	75·00	☐	☐

4 Government Parcels
Overprinted with Type O **7**

1883–1900 Queen Victoria

O69	57	1d lilac (Die II)	75·00	18·00	☐	☐
O61	62	1½d lilac	£325	70·00	☐	☐
O65	72	1½d purple and green	£110	15·00	☐	☐
O70	73	2d green and red	£175	30·00	☐	☐
O71	77	4½d green and red	£275	£200	☐	☐
O62	63	6d green	£2500	£1000	☐	☐
O66	79	6d purple on red	£200	50·00	☐	☐
O63	64	9d green	£2000	£800	☐	☐
O67	80	9d purple and blue	£300	75·00	☐	☐
O64	44	1s brown (Plate 13)	£1300	£225	☐	☐
O64c		1s brown (Plate 14)	£2750	£400	☐	☐
O68	82	1s green	£550	£225	☐	☐
O72		1s green and red	£500	£200	☐	☐

1902 King Edward VII

O74	83	1d red	32·00	13·00	☐	☐
O75	85	2d green and red	£150	38·00	☐	☐
O76	83	6d purple	£250	38·00	☐	☐
O77	91	9d purple and blue	£600	£160	☐	☐
O78	93	1s green and red	£1300	£275	☐	☐

5 Board of Education
Overprinted with Type O **8**

1902 Queen Victoria

O81	**78**	5d dull purple and blue	£3500	£850	☐	☐
O82	**82**	1s green and red	£8750	£4500	☐	☐

1902–04 King Edward VII

O83	**83**	½d blue-green	£160	38·00	☐	☐
O84		1d red	£160	38·00	☐	☐
O85	**86**	2½d blue	£4000	£300	☐	☐
O86	**89**	5d purple and blue	£22000	£6000	☐	☐
O87	**93**	1s green and red	£120000		☐	

6 Royal Household
Overprinted with Type O **9**

1902 King Edward VII

O91	**83**	½d blue-green	£375	£200	☐	☐
O92		1d red	£325	£175	☐	☐

7 Admiralty
Overprinted with Type O **10**

1903 King Edward VII

O101	**83**	½d blue-green	27·00	13·00	☐	☐
O102		1d red	16·00	6·50	☐	☐
O103	**84**	1½d purple and green	£300	£140	☐	☐
O104	**85**	2d green and red	£325	£150	☐	☐
O105	**86**	2½d blue	£450	£140	☐	☐
O106	**87**	3d purple on yellow	£400	£150	☐	☐

PHILATELIC, NUMISMATIC AND PHILATELIC MEDALLIC COVERS

On 2 June 1993 Royal Mail and the Royal Mint prepared a commemorative cover to celebrate the 40th anniversary of the Coronation of Her Majesty The Queen. The cover bore the Royal Mint's Coronation Anniversary Crown and the £10 'Britannia' stamp, issued on 2 March 1993 (No. 1658).

On 1 March 1994 a similar cover was produced for the 25th Anniversary of the Investiture of HRH The Prince of Wales. The cover bore the set of five stamps issued on that date (Nos. 1810/14), showing paintings by Prince Charles, and a commemorative medal struck by the Royal Mint.

So began a series of Philatelic Numismatic Covers (PNC) and Philatelic Medallic Covers (PMC) produced by Royal Mail and the Royal Mint.

This listing comprises only those jointly produced covers sold by the Philatelic Bureau. Privately sponsored covers incorporating coins or medals including those sponsored by the Royal Mint alone, are outside its scope.

No.	Date	Issue	Stamps	Coin/Medal	Price
RMC1	2.6.93	Coronation 40th Anniv	1658	£5 Coin	28·00
RMC2	1.3.94	Prince of Wales Investiture 25th Anniv	1810/14	Medal	22·00
RMC3	27.7.94	Bank of England 300th Anniv	1666×4 +label	£2 Coin	20·00
RMC4	20.5.95	R. J. Mitchell Birth Cent	1666×4+label	Medal	20·00
RMC5	15.8.95	End of Second World War 50th Anniv	1873, 1875	£2 Coin	20·00
RMC6	29.10.95	William Wyon Birth Bicent	Y1725	Medal	20·00
RMC7	21.4.96	Queen's 70th Birthday	1666×4+label	£5 Coin	24·00
RMC8	14.5.96	European Football Championship	1925/9	£2 Coin	20·00
RMC9	1.10./3.11.96	Classic Sports Cars	1945/9	Medal	20·00
RMC10	28.1.97	King Henry VIII 450th Death Anniv	1965/71	£1 Coin	20·00
RMC11	30.6.97	Transfer of Hong Kong to Chinese Rule	1671×4+label	Hong Kong $5 Coin	20·00
RMC12	23.8.97	British Aircraft Designers	1984/8	£2 Coin	20·00
RMC13	20.11.97	Royal Golden Wedding	2011/14	£5 Coin	24·00
RMC14	24.2.98	Order of the Garter 650th Anniv	2026/30	£1 Coin	20·00
RMC15	5.7.98	NHS 50th Anniv	2046/9	50p Coin	20·00
RMC16	25.8.98	Notting Hill Carnival	2055/8	50p Coin	20·00
RMC17	14.11.98	HRH Prince of Wales 50th Birthday	1666×4+label	£5 Coin	24·00
RMC18	12.5.99	Berlin Airlift 50th Anniv	1666×4+label	Medal	20·00
RMC19	1.7.99	New Scottish Parliament Building	S94/7	£1 Coin	20·00
RMC20	1.10.99	Rugby World Cup, Wales	1664a×4+label	£2 Coin	20·00

No.	Date	Issue	Stamps	Coin/Medal	Price
RMC21	31.12.99	Millennium	**MS**2123	£5 Coin	34·00
RMC22	4.4.00	National Botanic Garden of Wales	2124×4+label	£1 Coin	20·00
RMC23	14.8.00	150 Years of Public Libraries	2116, 2121, 2100	50p Coin	20·00
RMC24	4.8.00	Queen Mother's 100th Birthday	**MS**2161	£5 Coin	24·00
RMC25	1.1.01	Archers Radio Programme 50th Anniv	2107/8, 2110	Medal	20·00
RMC26	24.5.01	RN Submarine Service Cent	2202/5	Medal	20·00
RMC27	20.6.01	Queen Victoria Death Cent	2133+label	£5 Coin	24·00
RMC28	2.10.01	Northern Ireland	NI89/92	£1 Coin	20·00
RMC29	6.02	Golden Jubilee	2253/7	£5 Coin	24·00
RMC29a	6.2.02	Golden Jubilee	2258/9	£5 Coin and £5 note	28·00
RMC30	31.5.02	World Cup Football, Japan & Korea	5×1st from **MS**2292	£1 Coin	20·00
RMC31	16.7.02	17th Commonwealth Games, Manchester	2299/303	4×£2 Coins	30·00
RMC32	11.12.02	Queen Mother Commemoration	2280/3	£5 Coin	24·00
RMC33	25.2.03	Discovery of DNA 50th Anniv	2343/7	£2 Coin	21·00
RMC34	2.6.03	Coronation 50th Anniv	2368/77	£5 Coin	24·00
RMC35	27.8.03	Extreme Endeavours	2360/5	£1 Coin	20·00
RMC36	7.10.03	British Museum 250th Anniv	2404/9	Medal	20·00
RMC37	13.1.04	Classic Locomotives	2417/22	£2 Coin	21·00
RMC38	6.4.04	Entente Cordiale Cent	2446/7 + France 50c, 75c	£5 Coin	25·00
RMC39	13.4.04	Ocean Liners	2448/53	Medal	22·00
RMC40	25.5.04	RHS Bicentenary	2456/61	Medal	21·00
RMC41	30.11.04	Scotland Definitive	S109/10, S112/13	£1 Coin	20·00
RMC42	24.2.05	Charlotte Brontë 150th Death Anniv	2518/23	50p Coin	20·00
RMC43	1.3.05	Wales Definitive	W98/9, W101/2	£1 Coin	20·00
RMC44	21.4.05	World Heritage Sites	2532/5+Australia 2×50c. & 2×$1	50p Coin + Australia 50c.	24·00
RMC45	5.7.05	End of the War 60th Anniv	**MS**2547	Medal and £2 Coin	24·00
RMC46	18.10.05	Battle of Trafalgar Bicent	2574/9	2×£5 Coins	37·00
RMC47	23.2.06	Brunel Birth Bicent	2607/12	2×£2 Coins	24·00
RMC48	17.3.06	Northern Ireland Definitive	NI94/5, NI98, NI100	£1 Coin	20·00
RMC49	21.4.06	Queen's 80th Birthday	2620/7	£5 Coin	27·00
RMC50	6.6.06	World Cup Football	2628/33	Medal	22·00
RMC51	18.7.06	National Portrait Gallery 150th Anniv	2640/9	Medal	22·00
RMC52	21.9.06	Victoria Cross 150th Anniv	2657/62	2×50p Coins	23·00
RMC53	16.1.07	Act of Union 300th Anniv	6×1st as 2570 but litho	£2 Coin	23·00
RMC54	13.2.07	'The Sky at Night' 50th Anniv	2709/14	Medal	22·00
RMC55	22.3.07	Abolition of the Slave Trade Bicent	2728/33	£2 Coin	23·00
RMC56	23.4.07	England Definitive	EN6/8, EN12, EN15	£1 Coin	20·00
RMC57	5.6.07	First Machin Stamps 40th Anniv	Type 1984	Medal	22·00
RMC58	3.7.07	British Motor Racing	2744/9	Medal	22·00
RMC59	26.7.07	Scouting centenary	2758/63	50p Coin	23·00
RMC60	20.11.07	Diamond Wedding	2780/6	£5 Coin	35·00
RMC61	1.4.08	Territorial Army Cent	2774/6	Medal	22·00
RMC62	13.5.08	St. Paul's Cathedral 300th Anniv	**MS**2847	Medal	22·00
RMC63	5.6.08	First Machin Coin 40th Anniv	Type 1984	Medal	22·00
RMC64	17.7.08	Farnborough 'A Celebration of Aviation'	2885/60	Medal	22·00
RMC65	24.7.08	1908 Olympic Games, London Cent	4×1st	£2 Coin	25·00
RMC66	29.9.08	Country Definitives 50th Anniv and £1 Coin 25th Anniv	**MS**NI111	£1 Coin	20·00
RMC67	6.11.08	Armistice 90th Anniv	2883/5	Medal	22·00
RMC68	13.1.09	Mini car 50th Anniv	2889×2	Medal	22·00
RMC69	22.1.09	Robert Burns 250th Birth Anniv	**MS**S137	£2 Coin	23·00
RMC70	12.2.09	Charles Darwin Birth Bicent	2898/903	£2 Coin	30·00
RMC71	2.3.09	First Concorde Test Flight 40th Anniv	2891×2	Medal	22·00
RMC72	23.4.09	Accession of Henry VIII 500th Anniv and Accession of Elizabeth I 450th Anniv	2925, 2929 2×£5	Coins	35·00
RMC73	19.5.09	Royal Botanic Gardens, Kew 250th Anniv	**MS**2941	50p Coin	23·00
RMC74	1.9.09	Fire and Rescue Service	2958/63	Medal	22·00
RMC75	18.9.09	Big Ben 150th Anniv	Type **1517**+label	Medal	22·00
RMC76	22.10.09	Countdown to London 2012 Olympic Games	2981/90	£5 Coin	26·00
RMC77	2.2.10	Girlguiding Cent	**MS**3025	50p Coin	23·00
RMC78	25.2.10	Royal Society 350th Anniv	3026/35	Medal	22·00
RMC79	11.3.10	Battersea Cats and Dogs Home 150th Anniv	3036/45	Medal	22·00
RMC80	21.4.10	City of London	As 1st St. George's flag stamp from **MS**EN19 but self-adhesive+label	£1 Coin	24·00
RMC81	13.5.10	Dunkirk	**MS**3086	Medal	22·00
RMC82	27.7.10	Countdown to London 2012 Olympic Games	3097/106	£5 Coin	26·00
RMC83	1.8.10	Florence Nightingale	2570+label	£2 Coin	24·00

The Archive has everything from the first edition of the Monthly Journal in 1890 to the December 2009 issue of Gibbons Stamp Monthly.

Covering all of the articles, illustrations, notes and more. If it was in the magazine, then it's on the digital archive.

Just think of all of those great articles you can rediscover or read for the first time. You will have access to over 40,000 pages.

Gibbons Stamp Monthly
exactly how *you* want it...

NEW and EXCLUSIVE

You can have every issue of GSM since 1890 at your fingertips to search, browse, print and store as you choose, when you choose, with the **Gibbons Stamp Monthly Digital Archive**

If you're passionate about collecting, you really don't want to be without it – the **GSM DIGITAL ARCHIVE**. It is the perfect complement to the hobby of kings.

You'll have private access to **a complete library of information on almost anything you can think of from the world of stamp collecting**. The Archive is an absolute treasure trove of facts, articles, images and commentary on everything from specific topics like Machins to High Value Keyplates to more general fields such as King George VI – and it spans 120 years of these riches.

In short, it is **GSM exactly how you want it** – without it taking up vast amounts of space, getting dog-eared or in the wrong order. At your leisure and at the touch of a button or click of a mouse, you'll be able to view front covers, contents lists, articles, correspondence, book reviews, illustrations, notes and jottings from 120 years of Gibbons Stamp Monthly, with **full search and full browse capabilities built in**.

You can be the editor of the world's most important stamp magazine. You will have access to over **40,000 pages worth of the most useful and interesting philatelic material available**, delivered to you in a convenient, easy to use, searchable, digital format.

This is the exclusive GSM Archive, covering all articles, features, editorial and other content right from the first issue of the Monthly Journal, Gibbons Stamp Weekly & Gibbons Stamp Monthly – from 1890 up to 2009.

Build your own library of information on any topic you can think of by saving articles to your own archive or **print them off and store them physically** if you choose.

With full unlimited printing capabilities available, you are not confined to reading the articles on your computer screen.

The NEW & EXCLUSIVE Gibbons Stamp Monthly Archive is available now.
The full 5 DVDs (+ bonus disc) are available to you for just £199.95 or, looking at it another way, just 20p per magazine! You can even pay in 3 equal instalments if that makes it easier for you.
Get *your* copy today – **JUST £199.95**
Prices correct as of November 2010 and subject to change.

 Est 1856
STANLEY GIBBONS

Call us today on FREEPHONE 0800 611 622 *(UK)*
or +44 1425 472 363 *(International)* to secure your copy
www.stanleygibbons.com | Email: orders@stanleygibbons.co.uk

AN OLD-FASHIONED ANSWER TO COLLECTORS' 21ST CENTURY PROBLEM

THE DEMISE OF STAMP APPROVALS WAS LONG ANTICIPATED – BUT SOMEHOW THE SERVICE REFUSED TO SURRENDER

Managing Director Andrew McGavin of Avon & Omniphil Approvals explains:

52 years ago in 1958 two different philatelic entrepreneurs set up in business as two different competing approvals services called Omniphil and Avon Approvals.

It was an auspicious time to start in stamps. Placing an advertisement in 'Boy's Own' was expensive – but not so expensive when 3,000 requests for stamps on approval would be received in just one week!

In those days boys could only dream of travelling to far-off places by collecting stamps, so that being able to see stamps from places they were unlikely to ever go to was exciting in itself.

Most boys and many girls would have stamp collections, and most schools would have stamp clubs. Interest was so strong that 100,000 collectors would visit international stamp exhibitions.

As the years went by more people became affluent and travelling became increasingly easier and cheaper – so that the children of the generations that collected stamps in their childhood had no interest in collecting stamps from Florida when they could simply go there ... and television and computer games competed for their interest.

Throughout those decades, week in - week out, those competing Approvals companies would send collectors all over the world selections of individually priced stamps for them to choose from, purchase and return the rest.

Stamp shops proliferated, and then started to decline against competition from Stamp Fairs and rising high street rentals and rates – so that increasing numbers of collectors purchased directly from stamp auctions, once the mysterious preserve of dealers, now made more accessible to collectors.

A little like 'Electricity' and 'Water Works' in Monopoly - those long established Approval companies consolidated to lower costs and serve fewer clients, still serving many hundreds of collectors. The stamp trade as a whole went 'underground' so that most dealers would supply from lists by post or auctions supply by post or in person...

... and then came the internet and eBay – and remarkably the stamp trade took to these new distribution channels like a duck to water – after all stamps were the instrument to carry a letter – so the letter naturally became the instrument to carry them as values rose.

Stamp business surged, prices rose ... and then a peculiar problem became ever-increasingly noticeable – it was almost easier for collectors to find more expensive stamps in auctions and on the internet – than to find the cheaper stamps that nobody could now afford to handle ... except for, you've guessed ... Avon and Omniphil Approvals – now serving well over 1,300 different collectors week in week out.

If you would like to see a selection of individually priced stamps upon approval – please tell them the country/ countries or themes that you collect and whether you collect mint and or used and they will send you a selection like the hundreds of thousands they have sent before....

Omniphil & Avon: REQUEST HOME VIEWING COUPON

⭘ Please send me a selection of stamps upon approval, my only obligation is to return those not required and pay for those selected by credit card (mastercard/visa), UK cheque or P.Order. I can cancel/resume service whenever I wish:

I collect countries / themes. Please list all countries/themes collected: ....
....
....

I collect MINT and / or USED (please circle condition collected)

Name. ....

Address: ....
....
.... Postcode:...........................

Overseas clients must provide £20 (US$30) refundable deposit.

Please provide Mastercard/Visa # (overseas clients only):

▢▢▢▢▢▢▢▢▢▢▢▢▢▢▢▢▢▢▢▢▢▢

Expiry: ▢▢ / ▢▢ CVC/SEC: ▢▢▢

POST TO: Omniphil & Avon Approvals (CBS), P.O. Box 10, Tewkesbury, Glos GL20 8YX
Tel. #: 01684 299 278 • e-mail: approvals@upastampauctions.co.uk

For **FREE** 'Stamp Tips of The Trade' visit our website…
www.upastampauctions.co.uk

Stanley Gibbons Luxury Hingeless Albums

Produced in conjunction with DAVO (Netherlands), the SG Luxury Hingeless Albums comprise dark blue padded leatherette, peg fitting binders, embossed with country crest, complete with matching slipcase. The SG Luxury Hingeless albums come with clear mounts and pages are updated annually with printed supplements.

Great Britain

Covering the stamps of Great Britain from 1840-2009, the Great Britain Luxury Hingeless album runs in line with the Stanley Gibbons Collect British Stamps catalogue. An index is provided at the front of each volume covering date of issue, brief description, SG number and the page number where the stamp can be found.

R5284	Great Britain Luxury Vol 1 Album (1840-1970)	£125.95
R5285	Great Britain Luxury Vol 2 Album (1970-1989)	£145.00
R5290	Great Britain Luxury Vol 3 Album (1990-1999)	£119.95
R5295	Great Britain Luxury Vol 4 Album (2000-2007)	£115.00
R5331	Great Britain Luxury Vol 5 Album (2008-2009)	£75.00
R5284(SO)	Great Britain Luxury Volume 1-5 Album Set	£495.00

Great Britain QEII

Covering the stamps of the reign of Queen Elizabeth II (1952-2009), the Stanley Gibbons Luxury Hingeless Great Britain QEII albums are designed to be used in conjunction with the Stanley Gibbons catalogue, Collect British Stamps. The GB QEII comes complete with an Index page as per the standard GB Luxury Hingeless.

R5546	Queen Elizabeth Luxury Vol 1 (1952-1989)	£139.95
R5581	Queen Elizabeth Luxury Vol 2 (1990-1999)	£124.95
R5583	Queen Elizabeth Luxury Vol 3 (2000-2007)	£139.95
R5618	Queen Elizabeth Luxury Vol 4 Album (2008-2009)	£75.00
R5546(SO)	Queen Elizabeth Luxury Vol 1-4 Album Set	£425.00
R5546(SC)	Queen Elizabeth SG Wide Slipcase Only	£13.25

Prices correct as of November 2010 and subject to change.

Our Luxury Hingeless range also includes albums for Jersey, Guernsey, Alderney, Isle of Man, Australia, Canada, New Zealand and Falkland Islands (including Dependencies).

For our full range of albums, visit **www.stanleygibbons.com**

Est 1856
STANLEY GIBBONS

Stanley Gibbons Publications
7 Parkside, Christchurch Road, Ringwood, Hampshire, BH24 3SH
Tel: +44 (0)1425 472 363 | Fax: +44 (0)1425 470 247
Email: orders@stanleygibbons.co.uk
www.stanleygibbons.com